Young Students
LEARNING
LIBRARY®

YOUNG STUDENTS
LEARNING LIBRARY®

SCIENCE YEARBOOK

A New England Publishing Associates Book

LARRY E. HAND ■ MARGARET HEINRICH HAND
——————— EDITORS ———————

NEWFIELD PUBLICATIONS

SHELTON, CONNECTICUT

YOUNG STUDENTS LEARNING LIBRARY
SCIENCE YEARBOOK 1994

Administrator: Susan Brainard
Copy Editor: Anne Longley
Composition: Flying Dutchman Production Studio

Special edition prepared for Newfield Publications by New England Publishing Associates, Inc.

ISBN 0-8374-9806-6

Printed in the United States of America

Table of Contents

Photo and Art Credits

The Year in Science

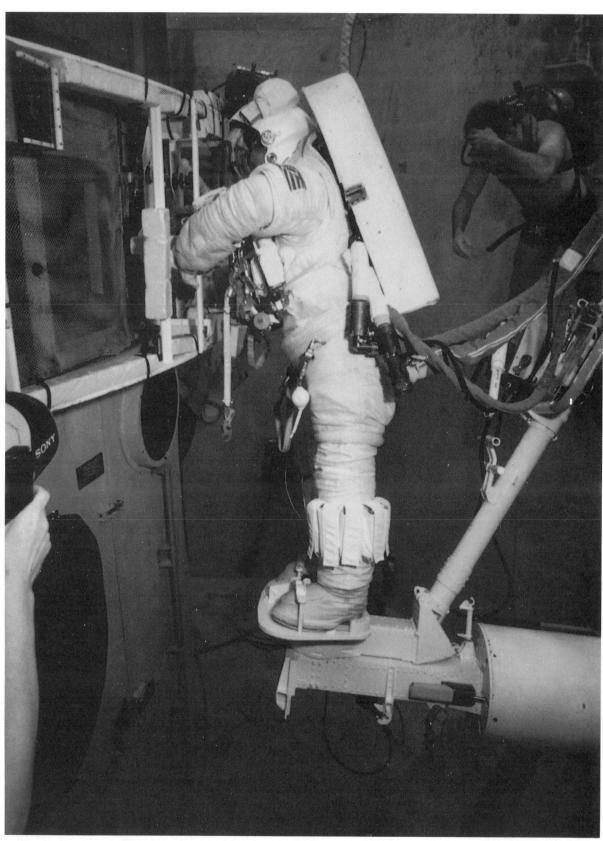

Astronaut Kathryn D. Thornton practices in an underwater tank for a special mission.

"Big Science" Takes Center Stage

"Big science" captured tremendous attention in 1993. The hot concept of post-World War II America—where the federal government liberally funds major research efforts such as space exploration and sophisticated weapons and communications development—clashed with the economic and political realities of the 1990s. The outcome left some projects with scaled-back scopes and one, the superconducting supercollider, with no further goal at all, except to shut down.

Other areas of science in the spotlight included adolescents' health, endangered animal species and their relationship with humans, the ecology of America's waterways, technological advancements along the "information superhighway," and, of course, the weather. This *Science Yearbook* covers much of the science news of 1993. However, since a publication schedule precluded waiting until the end of the year to begin writing most of the chapters, some news from the later part of 1993 is included in this section.

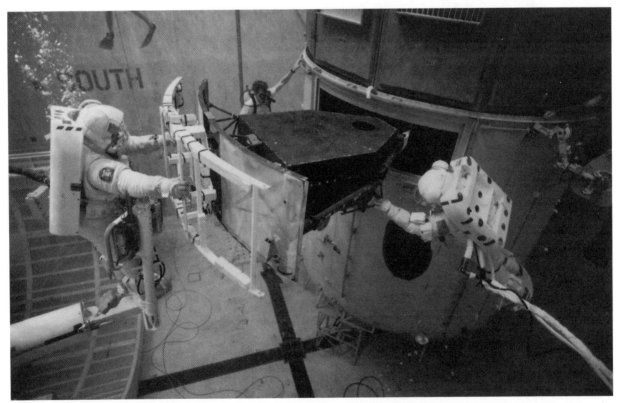

Before blasting off in the space shuttle Endeavour *to repair the Hubble space telescope, astronauts went through some of the most intense training ever for one mission, including extensive underwater sessions. Above, astronauts F. Story Musgrave and Jeffrey A. Hoffman use the pool of the Johnson Space Center's Weightless Environment Training Facility to practice replacement of the Hubble's wide field planetary camera.*

A Big Question in Space

Space exploration is among the biggest of the big science categories. And in late 1993, the National Aeronautics and Space Administration, or NASA, embarked on its most challenging mission since astronauts landed on the moon: a space shuttle trip to repair the ailing Hubble space telescope. The bus-sized telescope has been plagued with difficulties since it was launched in 1990.

First, just weeks after Hubble was in orbit, NASA discovered that a manufacturing defect in the telescope's main mirror was blurring its vision. Since then, Hubble has been hampered by three additional factors: the failure of three out of six gyroscopes that control the telescope's direction; faulty electricity-generating solar cells that cause the telescope to have jitters when passing into and out of sunlight; and the failure of some computer memory boards.

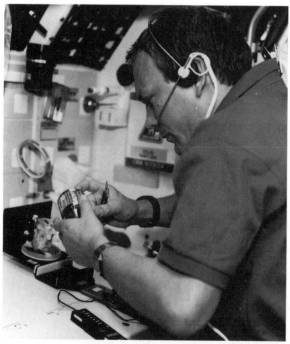

Among the highlights of NASA's space shuttle flights in 1993 were science experiments onboard. Here, Hans Schlegel works with a fungi experiment in the science module onboard the Earth-orbiting space shuttle Columbia. *Schlegel was one of two payload specialists representing the German Aerospace Research Establishment on a Spacelab mission.*

NASA officials estimated the price of the Hubble repairs at $378 million, and the space shuttle trip at $251 million, for a total mission expense of $629 million. Already, the government had spent about $3 billion on Hubble, and many scientists and interested observers feared that if this mission failed, funding for space exploration would start drying up. However, if the Hubble mission succeeded, it would be a shot in the arm for a space program that had suffered several image-tarnishing setbacks, beginning with the explosion of the space shuttle *Challenger* in 1986 and continuing through the mystifying loss in August 1993 of the *Mars Observer*. As its name implies, that spacecraft was to orbit Mars and send back information about that planet, but NASA lost contact with the *Observer*.

Seven astronauts blasted off December 2 on the space shuttle *Endeavour* with a precisely timed task list to complete during the next several days. Four of the astronauts conducted five dramatic spacewalks during the mission, one more than any previous mission. The astronauts replaced 11 Hubble parts, including corrective optics, a new power system, and upgraded computer memory. The initial assessment of the mission was positive, but it was scheduled to take NASA about two months to focus and align Hubble's instruments and determine whether its vision had been corrected.

Supercollider's Demise

Congress shut down the biggest physics experiment ever undertaken, the superconducting supercollider, in October. The death blow came after $2 billion had been spent on the project, and 10 miles—of a planned 54 miles—of tunnels had been dug beneath Waxahatchie, Texas. The superconducting supercollider, or SSC, was plagued from the start by cost overruns. It had mushroomed from an original cost estimate of $4.4 billion in 1988 to a projected $11 billion or more to complete.

The SSC was to have contained more than 10,000 superconducting magnets, fitted together inside the tunnel 30 feet underground. The tunnel and magnets were to be cooled to -452 degrees Fahrenheit by a river of liquid helium. Inside the SSC, or high-energy particle accelerator, elementary protons would be hurled around, then crashed, or collided, together

Even in its hampered state, the Hubble space telescope has already been of benefit to astronomy. This three-photo series shows the potential of Hubble. The first photo shows a ground view of the M31 galaxy, the 31st object in a catalog of nonstellar objects compiled by French astronomer Charles Messier in 1774. M31 can be seen with the naked eye from the ground in the shape of a cloud the width of a full moon. The second view of M31 is from a ground-based telescope. The center is seen as just a bulge.The third picture, from Hubble observations, reveals a double-nucleus center for M31. The two peaks are separated by five light-years, and the true center is really the dimmer component. The entire Hubble image is 40 light-years across.

with the force of 40 trillion electron volts—20 times more powerful than any existing accelerator. Such a capability would allow scientists to re-create conditions of the universe just after it came into being and, hopefully, generate knowledge about matter unattainable through current available mechanisms. The purely scientific purpose of the SSC was to provide a vehicle for understanding the nature of the universe.

In some ways, the demise of the supercollider was a sign of the economic realities of the early 1990s, with the United States trying to overcome a recession while reducing swelling tax burdens. But it also was evident that the focus of scientific research has been shifting from science for science's sake to science for practical applications. Even some scientists were pleased that the supercollider was killed, seeing the action as a sign that scarce dollars would now be spent on smaller but more numerous science projects.

Success Measured in Degrees

While another big science program, the U.S. Human Genome Project, could claim credit for a number of biomedical advancements during the year, its leaders fell just short of getting congressional approval for its requested budget for the fiscal year that began in October. The result is that new disease treatments and preventive measures beginning to flow from the project will be delayed, said Dr. Francis Collins, director of the program coordinated by the National Institutes of Health.

"This is the most powerful organized effort in science that humans have ever undertaken. This is investigating ourselves," Collins said, during an Associated Press interview at the American Society of Human Genetics annual meeting in October. In the planning for the Human Genome Project, experts agreed that it would take $3 billion over 15 years to fund such a venture. But actual funding has never met projected needs. During the first three years of the program, fiscal years 1991, 1992, and 1993, projected needs totaled $523.2 million but actual budgets totaled $471.6 million.

However, a discovery announced in December by two teams of doctors gave the field of human genetics research a major lift, and potential cancer sufferers major hope. The doctors—Bert Vogelstein and Kenneth Kinzler of Johns Hopkins University, and Richard Kolodner of Dana-Farber Cancer Institute in Boston and Richard Fishel of the University of Vermont—found in their research that a flawed gene identified as MSH2 causes about 10% of all colon cancer. And because of their research, a new screening test may be available within two years to warn people who may have this defective gene to take preventive measures against colon cancer.

About 1 in 200 people in the Western world inherit the gene, and those who do are at high risk of developing colon cancer and other forms of cancer, including uterine, stomach and ovarian cancer. One of the most common inherited diseases, colon cancer affects some 152,000 Americans, of whom more than one-third face death.

Dr. Collins, the director of the National Center for Human Genome Research, saw a broad implication in the discovery: The pending gene-screening test "seems likely to be the first DNA test that will find its way into general clinical practice and will usher in a new era of genetic medicine." DNA, or deoxyribonucleic acid, is the chemical that contains the hereditary instructions for most living organisms. *(See Chapters 1, 2, and 3.)*

Purdue University Professor Greg Martin examines a genetically transformed, disease-resistant tomato plant.

Gene Therapy Advances

Although still in a state of infancy, gene therapy claimed several advances in 1993. Among the most public therapy trials were cases involving cystic fibrosis, or CF. "A giant step forward," is how Dr. Claude L'Enfant, director of the National Heart, Lung and Blood Institute, characterized results of the first human CF gene-therapy trials.

One of the doctors involved in the trials presented initial results at the North American Cystic Fibrosis Conference in Dallas, Texas, in October. The results showed that for the first time, gene therapy can correct the underlying defect that causes CF.

In therapy trials conducted by Dr. Michael J. Welsh and colleagues at the Howard Hughes Medical Institute of the University of Iowa, healthy genes were "ferried" into the noses of volunteer patients to compensate for the mutant gene that causes CF. The process reversed the abnormality in the noses of three people, but no attempt was made to treat the patients' lungs.

"We chose to apply the genetic material to the lining of the nose because it most closely resembles the lining of the airways of the lungs, and because if adverse effects occurred, we would not put the patient at risk," Dr. Welsh said, in a statement issued by the Howard Hughes Medical Institute. "The purpose of the study was to test whether the biochemical defect in cystic fibrosis could be corrected, and not whether we could treat the disease."

Gene therapy also was being applied to other abnormalities. Duke University began its first gene-therapy trials with humans in September with a technique that was designed to treat a deadly skin cancer called metastatic melanoma. The disease affects more than 32,000 Americans a year, and is fatal to 6,000.

In the gene-therapy trials, Duke is removing cancerous melanoma cells from 20 patients, adding a gene to make the tumor cells produce a protein called human gamma interferon, and then reinjecting the altered cells into the patients. The protein prompts the immune system to fight the cancer. Since cancer cells can "appear" normal to the body's immune system, this approach offers a more positive way for the body to protect itself.

Tomatoes Under the Microscope

Genetics research in plants also showed advancements in 1993. Among the major announcements late in the year was an article in the November 26 issue of *Science,* in which scientists from Purdue and Cornell universities said they had cloned the first disease-resistant gene from a crop plant.

"Unlike other methods of creating disease-resistant plants, where a bacterial gene is moved into plants, here we have taken a gene from a disease-resistant tomato plant and moved it into a susceptible tomato plant," says Greg Martin, assistant professor of agronomy at Purdue and lead investigator. "The benefit to the general public is that disease-resistant genes already existing in plants offer the best forms of pest control for agriculture. This inherent disease resistance means fewer pesticides will be needed."

This research project was the first to apply a technique, called map-based cloning, from the Human Genome Project to crop genetics. In map-based cloning for this project, researchers identified sights of known traits on the chromosomes of disease-resistant tomatoes by "walking" along the chromosome, then developed segments of DNA that matched the chemical makeup of the known—or mapped—gene. The cloned segments were then transferred to other plants.

Paying Attention to Children

Health aspects relating to children and adolescents received a great deal of attention in 1993. Chapter 4 covers much of this, but more information follows.

In an analysis that combines statistics from many sources, psychologist Urie Bronfenbrenner, a founder of the national Head Start program for disadvantaged children, concluded that children of English-speaking countries are worse off than children of other industrialized nations—and American children are exposed to the greatest risks.

"In the absence of good support systems, external stresses have become so great that even strong families are falling apart. Hecticness, instability, and inconsistency of daily family life are rampant in all segments of our society, including the well-educated and the well-to-do," Bronfenbrenner said during a symposium in September at Cornell University.

A child's personal environment is not the only thing that has an effect on his or her well-being. A study conducted by Pennsylvania State University researchers found that violent, "reality-based" television shows may trigger behavior problems and aggressiveness in some children. "We really can't say that aggressive behavior is all from television, but we can say that television at least contributes," said Dr. Nancy Venbrux, a psychiatrist and one of the researchers at Penn State's Hershey Medical Center. The researchers, who announced their findings at the May meeting of the American Psychiatry Association in San Francisco, Calif., studied the viewing habits of 1,100 elementary school-aged children in central Pennsylvania.

Parents completed questionnaires about behaviors of the children and television shows they watched, paying close attention to shows—such as "Rescue 911," "Top Cops," "America's Most Wanted," and "Unsolved Mysteries"—that base their content on real events and people. "There's been such an increase in reality-based shows in recent years. We wanted to look at aggression in children and see if there were any correlations," Venbrux explains. "These shows are presented as reality, not something made up. I wonder if this would make it seem closer to home to the child. Maybe some kids aren't able to tell the difference between what's real and what's not."

Venbrux and her colleagues, Dr. Paul Kettl and Dr. Edward O. Bixler, discovered a connection between the number of hours children spent before television and scores on the Pediatric Behavior Scale, a standardized child behavior test, which has questions about disobedience, argumentativeness, cruelty, lying, etc. Results of the study showed that children with more behavior problems spent more time watching television, with the strongest link being in children who watch more than two hours a day.

As discussed in Chapter 4, television's effect on children has been under considerable public scrutiny lately by parents' groups, civic organizations, the U.S. Congress, and by the entertainment industry itself. The focus of this review has been partially on the limited menu of programs available to watch on commercial television, and whether warnings should be included at the beginning of violent shows.

A common complaint among many television viewers is that the choices of programs available on commercial networks are limited, due greatly to economic constraints, such as the willingness of advertisers to sponsor only programs that put their products before the largest audiences.

Tune In to Channel 459 for a Complete . . .

As information- and image-processing technology advances, the lack of channels to watch on the home television will become less of a problem. In fact, the problem could be reversed, giving viewers a choice of 500 different channels to browse. By pressing a button on an electronic remote control, a viewer could gain access to full-length movies, sports events, concerts, and many other programs at any given time of day, without regard to a network television schedule and without regard to whether the local video-rental store is out of a particular title.

Such a vision may be in the not-so-distant future, as the "information superhighway" (*See Chapter 14*) is developed.

A Record Year for Weather

Millions of Americans watched and read about record-breaking weather storms and floods in 1993. Damage from the flooding of the Mississippi River valley in the Midwest was still being assessed at the end of the year, as residents of this region tried to determine whether they should rebuild or move to higher ground. (*Chapter 8 covers the weather of the year, and Chapter 10 covers issues related to rivers and waterways overall.*)

Then, in December, the federal government helped them decide by offering $110 million to buy property in flood plains so that residents could move further away from the mighty Mississippi and other affected rivers. Federal officials expected possibly 10,000 people in nine states to apply for the money. Land purchased under this program will be set aside for parks or preserved as wetlands. The new program "provides greater assurance than perhaps any other measure that the people helped will not have to suffer such damage and disruption from flooding again," President Bill Clinton said.

A spokesman for American Rivers, an organization that monitors the health of America's waterways, called the measure an innovative approach to coping with the natural flood cycle of rivers. "Moving 200 towns is a radical departure from what we used to do with flooding," said Scott Faber.

How Many Owls in the Forest

The often-heated debate over the northern spotted owl that resides in forests in Washington, Oregon, and northern California (*See Chapter 9*) has focused attention for the past few years on one of the most sweeping laws in the country: the Endangered Species Act. The owl was declared a threatened species in 1990.

The California Forestry Association petitioned the U.S. Fish and Wildlife Service in October to remove the northern spotted as being threatened in California, claiming that the owl's population was underestimated in this state in 1990. A biologist for the association estimated that 8,500 spotted owls may be living in California alone, more than the 8,000 population estimated by the government for the entire three-state region. While acknowledging that the owl is more populated and is faring better in California than in Washington or Oregon, the government said it was premature to remove the bird from the threatened-species list.

The 20-year-old Endangered Species Act was up for Congressional reauthorization at the end of 1993, and it undoubtedly will be the subject of much debate on Capitol Hill in 1994. Not only was the law's effect on humans and property rights being studied, but the methods by which the government decides how to designate species as endangered or threatened were being reviewed.

Some conservationists are saying that instead of evaluating threats or dangers species-by-species, as has been the case, a broader ecosystemwide approach is needed to make the law more effective. Such a methodology would mean that scientists would study an entire ecosystem—even to the point of including humans—and recommend programs to stem the danger to potentially threatened species before a state of emergency exists.

The first step in research for this approach—a national biological survey—already was included in the U.S. Department of the Interior's budget for the fiscal year beginning in October 1993. The survey, if and when it is fully carried out, could provide a basic inventory of the country's biological characteristics.

Inventory's a Key

Inventory, as it turns out, was a key word in much of science in 1993. Geneticists were compiling minute details of human chromosomes. NASA was hoping the Hubble telescope can provide astronomers with a better idea of what is beyond the range of Earth-bound telescopes. And many life science professionals were taking stock of the country's future: its children and adolescents.

PART ONE

UNDER THE MICROSCOPE

Nobel Prize recipient Kary Mullis, developer of the polymerase chain reaction, next to a DNA model at Cold Spring Harbor Laboratory.

1

THE ESSENCE OF LIFE: A FOCUS ON GENES

When an individual gets frustrated attempting to assemble a toy, machine, or other device, an old saying often is uttered: If all else fails, read the directions.

But that isn't so easy when the "machine" is the human body, and the directions are written in the genetic code. Scientists researching the causes and potential cures of hereditary diseases don't have the benefit of a detailed chart, or map, of human genes—yet.

But in the future, some scientists have postulated, a person may be able to turn on a personal computer, and access not only a detailed map of downtown Chicago, but a genetic map of the human body that shows where genes predisposed to Lou Gehrig's disease, cystic fibrosis, or colon cancer are located. And by that time, gene therapy may have advanced to the point that if a person does show a predisposition for diseases, specific gene-splicing procedures could correct some situations. At the very least, in the case of colon cancer, alternative lifestyles and eating habits could be adopted, thereby delaying, easing, perhaps prohibiting, the disease.

The key to whether or how fast all of this happens can be summed up in three letters: DNA. It's the secret to life, the molecule that determines whether a person has brown hair or blond hair, and often whether a person is sick or healthy. DNA, deoxyribonucleic acid, and the genes contained within it, dominated much of the science news of 1993. Numerous announcements associated certain diseases with certain genes. Magazine articles explored the relationship between genes and behavior, genes and disease, genes and human evolution, genes and crime.

One of the big stories of the year was DNA, itself. The spring of 1993 marked the 40th birthday of the discovery of DNA's double-helix structure by scientists James Watson and Francis Crick. Watson and Crick proffered their discovery in the April and May 1953 issues of the journal *Nature*. And while science usually progresses too rapidly for reprints of 40-year-old articles to be of significant value to contemporary readers, the editors of the *Journal of the American Medical Association* felt the Watson-Crick papers important enough to reprint them on their 40th birthday.

James Watson (left) and Francis Crick stand near the model of the 1953 discovery, the double helix structure of DNA. This photo was taken in March 1993, at Cold Spring Harbor Laboratory, during the 40th anniversary celebration of their discovery.

Lay and science publications wrote of the 40th-anniversary celebration held March 1–3 at New York's Cold Spring Harbor Laboratory, with which Watson had been associated for 25 years. Crick, who had been working at the Salk Institute in La Jolla, Calif., joined his colleague for the celebration, and the two of them once again became the center of attention in the science world. A prestigious group of scientists, biotechnology executives, and friends gathered at Cold Spring Harbor. Many of those scientists—including Dr. Kary Mullis, who developed the polymerase chain reaction, a technique for amplifying DNA, and Dr. W. French Anderson, a pioneer in gene therapy—had advanced the study of genetics based on the Watson-Crick discovery.

After all, the Watson-Crick work earned them a Nobel Prize, laid the groundwork for a revolution in molecular biology, and eventually spawned the creation of today's burgeoning biotechnology industry. Since 1953, scientists have cracked the human genetic code, linked certain diseases to specific genes, and, in some cases, embarked on an ambitious course of gene therapy. Other scientists have developed tomatoes that stay ripe longer, cows that give less-fatty milk, and mice that emulate people with certain diseases—a step that can rapidly advance the treatment or possible cure of some diseases.

While scientists still do not have a comprehensive map of human genes, the effort to produce such a monumental work is well under way. Researchers worldwide are working, through a program called the Human Genome Initiative, to map the approximately 100,000 genes of the human body.

In the United States, a massive effort is being coordinated by the National Center for Human Genome Research (NCHGR) at the National Institutes of Health (NIH) in Bethesda, Md. Called the Human Genome Project, the NCHGR program is slated to spend $3 billion over a 15-year period toward mapping and sequencing, or determining the order of, human genes.

A map of the human genome will be essentially a "blueprint" that contains the sum total of human genes. When all genes are placed in the order in which they appear in DNA, the final "blueprint" is expected to be the equivalent of 1 million printed pages. However, the information will be computerized in data bases that will be accessible to scientists conducting research.

What Is DNA?

DNA is a molecule that forms the basic unit of heredity for most living organisms. Practically every cell in the human body contains a ribbon of DNA

DNA luminaries listen to a speaker at the Cold Spring Harbor celebration in March 1993. From left, are Bentley Glass, Norton Zinder, Francis Crick, and Jan Witkowski.

roughly equivalent in length to a 6-ft. stepladder. DNA is nucleic acid, composed of two strands of nucleotides, or bases, called adenine, cytosine, guanine, and thymine. The bases are generally referred to as A, for adenine; C, for cytosine; G, for guanine; and T, for thymine.

A ribbon of DNA—a double-helix structure as outlined by Watson and Crick in 1953—consists of two strands that coil around each other like a spiral staircase. The bases chemically progress up the stairs in pairs, two bases per step, holding the strands together by hydrogen bonds. C always pairs with G, and A always pairs with T. *(See illustration, this page.)* There are about 3 billion "base pairs" within the human genome.

A specific sequence of pairings—such as CG, GC, TA, CG, GC, TA—contained within one section of a DNA ribbon, constitutes a gene. Scientists estimate that humans have 50,000–100,000 genes in each cell of the body. The sequence is equivalent to a set of instructions for building the protein that is essential to life. Genes vary in size, containing anywhere from 2,000 to 2 million base pairs each.

DNA and genes reside within chromosomes. Each cell of the human body has 46 chromosomes, or 23 pairs. One set of 23 chromosomes is inherited from the mother and one from the father. The matched chromosome pairs are identified by numbers 1–22, then by X or Y for the 23rd, or sex, pair. The sex chromosomes determine whether an organism is male or female. A father contributes either an X or Y chromosome. A mother contributes an X chromosome. An offspring who inherits two X chromosomes will be a female, and an offspring who inherits an X and a Y chromosome will be a male.

How DNA Communicates

For DNA to determine what is inherited from one generation to the next, it has to communicate. The conventionally accepted method is that it does this through a messenger. The double-stranded DNA untwists, or unzips itself, exposing two sides of base pairs. The base sequence—or set of instructions—from an exposed strand of DNA becomes a template for connection to bases contained in "messenger RNA" (mRNA). (RNA, or ribonucleic acid, is a nucleic acid, but it is only single-stranded and the

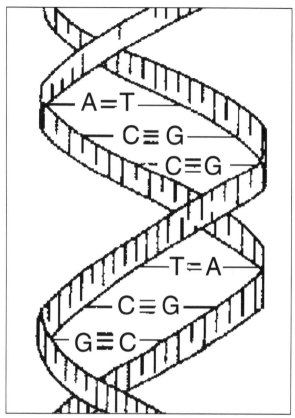

DNA has a double-helix structure. A ribbon of DNA consists of two strands that wind around each other. Bases of the strands are made up of the chemicals adenine (A), cytosine (C), guanine (G), and thymine (T). The order of paired bases determines hereditary characteristics.

thymine base is replaced by a uracil base.) Messenger RNA carries DNA's message to a ribosome, the cell component in which the synthesis into protein begins. At that point, "transfer RNA" translates the DNA into amino acids, which, in turn, build protein.

This is nature's way of building an organism, so to speak, from the cell up. DNA in the original cell prescribes the makeup of the next cell, and the progression continues. However, when a mistake occurs in nature's duplicating process—such as when a particular sequence of base pairs, or a gene's set of instructions—is interrupted in some way, a "mutation" is said to occur. Such mutations cause abnormal development of the organism and, depending on the type of mutation and its location on a specific chromosome, can be the cause of certain diseases.

Another way DNA communicates is through "jumping genes," first explored by geneticist Barbara McClintock in the late 1940s. Her research revealed that genes can sometimes "jump" from one chromosome to another, or from one spot to another on a chromosome. Scientists now call those genes transposons, and recent research has even centered on the possibility of genes jumping from one species to another. However, most of the mapping and other genetics research today focuses on the conventional method of communication for DNA.

Historical Markers

The study of heredity is not a new science. The 19th-century Austrian monk Gregor Mendel wrote of hereditary "factors" passing traits from each parent—much like a deck of cards is shuffled and dealt—to a child. Within the initial cell of the child, the traits do not blend, but one dominates the other, thereby determining the makeup of the child. Mendel's Laws, which he wrote based on the study of pea plants, later became the laws of heredity.

The factors are now called "alleles," of which two—one from each parent—reside within most genes. Popularly referred to as dominant and recessive genes, one allele can be dominant, the other recessive, or they both can be dominant or recessive. A recessive allele is inactive when a dominant allele is present. Together they illustrate the combination of genes inherited from the mother and father.

Frederick Miescher, another 19th-century scientist, from Switzerland, discovered DNA itself. He isolated it from pus contained in surgical bandages and Rhine River trout semen. He called the chemical material "nuclein" at the time.

Chromosomes were discovered in the late 1800s through the independent work of two German scientists. And just after the turn of the century, scientists started realizing that Mendel's "factors" had ties with chromosomes. Geneticist Wilhelm Johannsen, in 1909, renamed Mendel's factors "genes."

The road to the modern study of genetics was paved by many scientists and is littered with a string of Nobel Prizes.

Much of the early genetics research in the United States centered on the fruit fly. Thomas Hunt Morgan of Columbia University earned a Nobel Prize in 1933 for his work cross-breeding numerous fruit flies. He showed that genes were located on chromosomes, but they were too small to study at that time, so their structure remained elusive.

However, Herman Miller, who had worked with Morgan, later developed the first gene map that showed locations on chromosomes of the fly genes that control such traits as eye color and wing size. He was awarded the Nobel Prize in 1946.

As debate raged in the scientific community over what actually constituted a gene—since chromosomes contain DNA and protein—George Beadle and Edward Tatum proved that genes dictate the formation of enzymes. They won a 1958 Nobel Prize.

Then the scientists were directed back to Miescher's discovery when Oswald T. Avery showed that the basis of heredity is deoxyribonucleic acid, the substance Miescher described as nuclein. Once it was determined what constituted DNA, the focus shifted to how DNA was structured.

The Watson-Crick Legacy

Since the 1953 Watson-Crick papers in *Nature* defining the double-helix, a number of scientists have used that basic DNA structure to create significant landmarks in science. Watson, Crick, and their colleague, Maurice Wilkins, were awarded their Nobel Prize in 1962. Among the landmarks since 1953 are:

1957: Arthur Kornberg and Severo Ochoa develop a way of synthesizing DNA in the laboratory using the molecule's own polymerase, an enzyme that catalyzes the duplication of DNA.

1960: Messenger RNA is discovered as the chemical agent that reads DNA's instructions and carries them to the cell's component that begins the manufacturing of protein.

1961–66: The genetic code—the recipe of how the sequences of DNA bases correspond to amino acids in proteins—is deciphered.

1967: DNA ligase is discovered. This enzyme welds molecules, which is a necessary step in genetic engineering.

1970: Restriction enzymes are discovered. These substances cut DNA at specific points, making it possible to later match up base pairs from two different strands. The University of Geneva's Werner Arber and Johns Hopkins University's Hamilton Smith and Daniel Nathans were awarded the Nobel Prize for this in 1978.

1972: Paul Berg of Stanford University splices the first hybrid DNA molecules that were artificially combined in the laboratory. That became known as "recombinant DNA."

1975–77: Rapid sequencing of DNA base pairs becomes possible due to technology developed by scientists at Cambridge University and Harvard University.

1976: University of California/San Francisco scientists Michael Bishop and Harold Varmus demonstrate that one cancer-causing gene is just a modified normal gene. Their Nobel came in 1989.

1977: Bacteria are engineered to make human hormone. This later resulted in the ability to make human insulin and growth hormone.

1982–83: Genetic engineering takes off when scientists inject a foreign gene into mouse eggs, which in turn produce big mice. Other scientists introduce foreign genes into plant species.

1983: James Gussella of Massachusetts General Hospital and his colleagues isolate a "marker" on the road to finding the gene that causes Huntington's disease. That gene was pinpointed in 1993.

1983: Kary Mullis develops the polymerase chain reaction, a technique for amplifying a DNA section to the point where millions of copies of DNA can be made and studied.

1988: Harvard University is awarded the first patent for a genetically engineered animal. The "onco-mouse" was engineered as a cancer research tool. It carries human cancer-causing

cells that scientists monitor as the mouse grows.

1988: Through the Humane Genome Organization, scientists enthusiastically gather in Switzerland to discuss the massive effort of mapping and sequencing the entire human genome.

1989: At a joint meeting between the U.S. Department of Energy, the National Institutes of Health, and a contingent of scientists from various institutions, the charter for the Human Genome Project is drafted.

When the genome project was forming, James Watson was again at the center of attention. He was

Dr. Francis S. Collins, while at the University of Michigan, was co-discoverer of the gene that causes cystic fibrosis. He now heads the most ambitious science project ever: the U S. Human Genome Project.

instrumental in shaping its initial program efforts, and he became its first director.

"No, James Watson did not singlehandedly launch the human genome program, but, probably more than anyone else could, the 64-year-old Nobelist gave it instant credibility—both among scientists and the public," wrote Joseph Palca, in a May 15, 1992 *Science* article titled "The Genome Project: Life After Watson." Palca continued, "Watson's fans say that, as head [of NCHGR], he played a critical role in holding together an often fractious amalgamation of researchers, bureaucrats, politicians, and foreign partners that made the project go."

Watson resigned, however, in 1992 after what was reported in various news accounts as a dispute between him and NIH Director Bernadine Healy. But, as reported by Leslie Roberts, in another May 15 *Science* article titled "A Standing Ovation From the Troops," Watson's fervor for the program didn't wane. Watson, speaking to the Cold Spring Harbor group that gathered in March 1993, advised his successor to fight for funding for the project, Roberts reported. Watson was quoted as saying: "All science isn't equally interesting. Getting the human genes and the other genomes is the most important thing in biology."

Earlier in 1993, a noted "gene hunter," Dr. Francis Collins, was appointed director of the NCHGR. The 42-year-old Collins, who had been chief of Medical Genetics at the University of Michigan since 1987, was co-discoverer of the gene that causes cystic fibrosis, and the gene that causes neurofibromatosis.

Taking Inventory

One of the first goals of the U.S. Human Genome Project essentially is to take inventory of the 24 chromosomes, defined as chromosomes 1–22, X, and Y. That involves "mapping" genes according to the chromosomes in which they reside.

Understanding Our Genetic Inheritance. The Human Genome Project: The First Five Years, FY 1991–1995, published jointly by the U.S. Department of Health and Human Services and the U.S. Department of Energy—the two federal agencies responsible for the project—lists the project's five-year goals as:

- Mapping and sequencing the human genome
- Mapping and sequencing the DNA of model organisms
- Collecting and distributing data
- Addressing ethical, legal, and social considerations
- Conducting research training
- Developing technology
- Transferring technology

Multipoint Research Effort

Large-scale mapping projects are under way at a number of academic and scientific institutions around the country under the auspices and funding of the NCHGR. Major research programs involving mapping and developing technology to be used in sequencing genes are taking place at 11 institutions.

The locations for those large-scale mapping projects are: Whitehead Institute for Biomedical Research, Cambridge, Mass.; Washington University, St. Louis, Mo.; Stanford University, Stanford, Calif.; Salk Institute, La Jolla, Calif.; Children's Hospital of Philadelphia, Pa.; University of California at Berkeley; University of Texas Health Sciences Center, San Antonio; University of Iowa, Iowa City; University of Michigan Medical Center, Ann Arbor; Baylor College of Medicine, Houston, Texas; and University of Utah, Salt Lake City. *(See illustration, Page 25.)*

As of mid-July 1993, the NCHGR had 136 grants in force around the country, including the 11 major projects above, totaling more than $60.3 million in funding. The grants ranged from small, educational projects of a few thousand dollars to huge efforts such as the $8.3 million genome mapping project at Whitehead Institute. Also among the grants were projects aimed at solving legal and ethical considerations, such as one $236,000 study entitled "Genome Mapping: Implication for Health and Life Insurance," at the University of Southern California in Los Angeles.

The recent grant to the Whitehead Institute is just an extension of research work in progress there. At the Whitehead/MIT Center for Genome Research, scientists from several institutions, under the leadership of Dr. Eric Lander, have developed maps of the mouse genome and come up with new strategies for

Dr. Eric S. Lander, as director of the Center for Genome Research at Whitehead Institute for Biomedical Research in Cambridge, Mass., heads one of the most comprehensive genome projects in the country.

manipulating, marking, and identifying DNA. In disease-specific research, the center's scientists have, among other things, zeroed in on a gene that slows the onset of colon cancer in a mouse model. Using the expertise and emerging technology, the center will use the latest grant to develop low-resolution physical maps of the human genome.

One relatively new program, the Cooperative Human Linkage Center, headed by Dr. Jeffrey C. Murray, was established at the University of Iowa in late 1992. As in most other genome research programs, however, scientists connected with the center are based at a number of different institutions. The Iowa program was designed to generate a high-reso-

The Whitehead Institute has a number of genetics research projects under way. Researchers include Dr. Ruth Lehmann (right), who is studying the embryonic structure of the fruit fly Drosophila melangaster; *Richard C. Mulligan (top right), who has developed vectors for transferring genes into an organism; and Terry L. Orr-Weaver (above), who is studying the chromosomal structure of the fruit fly* D. melanogaster.

lution genetic map of the human genome and to carry out research into ethical, legal, and social implications of genetics research. An education program for high-school teachers also is planned.

On Campus, Too

While the NCHGR was initially farming out most of the research to laboratories around the country and awarding grants for specific research activities in its "extramural" program, the genome project added a dimension in 1993. In February, the NCHGR created an "intramural" program at the NIH campus in Maryland.

The intramural program is focusing on applying genome technology to hunting disease genes and developing DNA-based diagnostic ability and gene therapies. The program, with a $10 million first-year budget and an anticipated $25 million second-year budget, is serving as a hub for various NIH scientists in search of specific genes.

The intramural program has four basic research laboratories:

- A **Laboratory of Cancer Genetics** concentrates not only on inherited predispositions to some cancers, but also on cancers that may result from genetic changes throughout life.

- A **Laboratory of Genetic Disease Research** concentrates on identifying causes of human genetic diseases and trying to identify common disease genes.

- A **Laboratory of Human Gene Therapy** concentrates on gene therapy techniques. Technologies

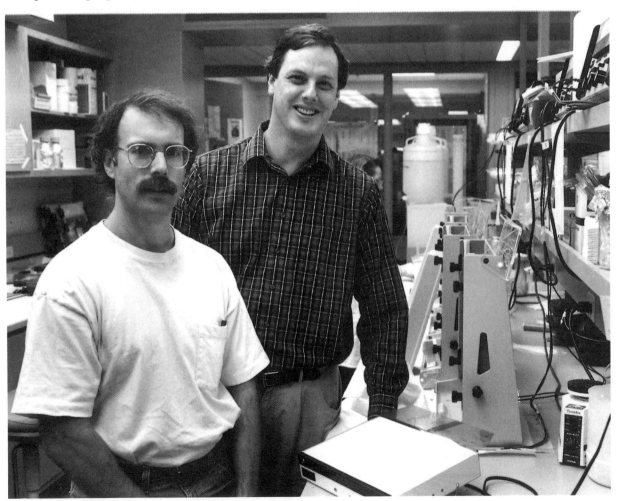

Drs. Jeff Murray (left) and Val Sheffield are heading up the genome project at the University of Iowa.

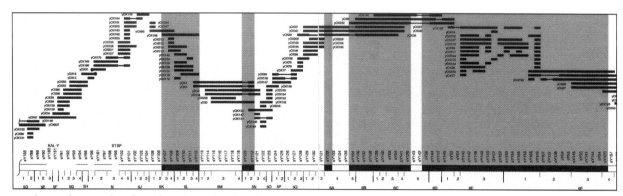

A physical map, developed at the Whitehead Institute, shows this Y chromosome consisting of 196 overlapping recombinant DNA clones.

will be developed to inject cloned genes and DNA into cells to correct inherited diseases or DNA mutations that lead to diseases.

- **Core Laboratories** concentrate on providing support for a range of research, including mapping and therapy, and serve as a focal point for collaboration among NIH researchers.

To help implement and make use of the research in those laboratories, the NCHGR intramural program has set up three clinical entities:

- A **Diagnostic Development Branch** will concentrate on advancing the efforts of the Laboratory of Genetic Disease Research by clinically applying novel diagnostic tools to predict a predisposition to inheritable diseases.
- A **Medical Genetics Branch** is home to investigators who examine patients and families with inherited diseases. The unit is planned to be a focal point for training physicians in medical genetics.
- A **Clinical Gene Therapy Branch** will actually apply new developments to the treatment of human disease, then monitor and evaluate patients who receive experimental therapies.

What Is Mapping?

"Mapping," as defined for the project, is "the process of determining the position and spacing of genes, or other genetic landmarks, on the chromosomes." A "map" can be either a genetic linkage map or a physical map.

Genetic linkage maps form the main basis for making physical maps of the genome. Genetic maps, which identify genes associated with genetic diseases, show the frequency of genetic "markers." These can be physical traits, medical syndromes, or detectable DNA sequences that can be inherited together, as a group, without being separated when a cell divides. The closer the genes are on a chromosome, the greater the chance they will be passed on together. Scientists have studied family histories to help devise genetic linkage maps.

Just as the distance between two cities is measured in miles, genes in genetic linkage maps are measured in centimorgans, named after geneticist Thomas Hunt Morgan. In humans, on average, a centimorgan equals 1 million base pairs. But to express the measurement precisely, it has to be stated in terms of percentages: a centimorgan equals a 1% chance that a genetic marker will be separated from its neighbor genetic marker as one generation inherits a combination of genes from the mother and father. The markers could be separated from each other during the process of recombination, or the rearrangement of genes as reproductive cells are formed. In that process, an offspring inherits a combination of genes from both parents. The child's genes will not be exactly like either parent's, but a unique combination.

Genetic linkage maps offer scientists a way to analyze chromosomes and genes without cloning, or directly copying, genes in the laboratory. Using family histories, scientists can plot the frequency of inheritance of diseases and traits over a number of generations and hone in on the location and order of genes on a chromosome. In one method, DNA from white blood cells taken from families with a certain disease can be analyzed for curious variations in the sequence of the DNA bases. When these variations are discovered, they are recorded as restriction-fragment-length-polymorphisms, or RFLPs. Each RFLP is unique to a certain spot on a specific chromosome, and it becomes a reference point for pinpointing damaged genes.

Genetic linkage maps, in short, point out markers along the road of life, much as a roadmap would show landmarks between two cities, but without a specified mileage distance between landmarks.

Physical maps, on the other hand, are well suited to laboratory research on the genome. For physical maps, the distance between markers is measured in actual physical lengths, typically the number of base pairs, without regard to the *chance* for inheriting groups of genes.

To construct a physical map of a chromosome, scientists essentially break a chromosome apart and put it back together again. They can cut a chromosome into large fragments of DNA, clone the DNA sequences, and then reassemble the sections by matching up the overlapping pieces. Scientists call the matching pieces "contigs," because they are from contiguous pieces. A physical map can consist of part or all of a chromosome, depending on the size of the various pieces that were cut up and cloned.

One complicating factor in the mapping of genes is their makeup. A gene can consist of several "regions," each with a different purpose. *(See illustration, this page.)* The coding region, or exon, contains the base pairs to supply the sequence, or blueprint, for instructions in making protein. The regulatory region is a kind of switch that turns the gene on when nature programs it to be turned on. Then there is a noncoding region, or intron, that, according to research so far, does little or nothing toward the function of the cells.

Scientists estimate that the coding regions of genes make up only 2%–5% of the entire human genome. The remaining 95%–98% has been referred to as "junk" DNA, but researchers are investigating its role in regulating gene activity. Animal studies have shown that how genes are organized within a chromosome influences their work.

In a report in the June 22, 1993 issue of *Biochemistry,* chemists at the California Institute of Technology in Pasadena reported that they had discovered a landmark that apparently "flags" introns. Their conclusion coincides with a theory that "introns act as spacers where breaks for genetic recombination occur," wrote K.F. Schmidt in a story titled "A DNA structure that tags genetic junk?" in the July 10 issue of *Science News.*

Animal models have been a major focus in the human genome project. Analysis of smaller genomes can provide scientists with a guide as to how a gene's structure relates to its function. While the mouse genome is much smaller, many regions of it are very similar to the human genome.

Baseline Map Published

Prior to 1990, gene mapping was a fragmented process taking place in various laboratories around the world, and an overall "view" of the genome was not possible. But that year, gene mappers agreed to pool their efforts and devise a standard baseline map of the human genome. The first major result of that effort was the October 2, 1992 publication in the journal *Science* of "A Comprehensive Genetic Linkage Map of the Human Genome."

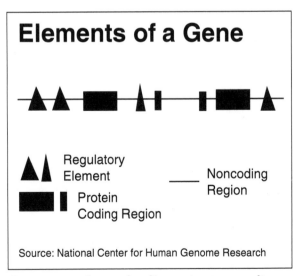

Genes are made up of coding regions, noncoding regions, and regulatory elements.

The map lists 1,416 genetic markers, including 279 genes and expressed base sequences, and represents more than 90 percent of the human genome. Creation of the map was coordinated by the NCHGR and the Centre d'Etude du Polymorphisme Humain in France. More than 70 laboratories from around the world contributed.

According to the NCHGR's *Progress Report* for fiscal years 1991 and 1992, "The map will be a starting point for the continued collection and placement of new and better-quality DNA markers, and it will provide a useful tool for scientists engaged in mapping and identifying genes." The map will be maintained and updated through a genome research program at the University of Iowa Medical Center, one of a number of institutions around the country to work with the Human Genome Project under NCHGR coordination.

As published, the comprehensive map is not in a traditional map form that could be compared to a system of highways and streets illustrated in a road atlas. The genetic linkage map is a collection of data, organized in textual and tabular form, about chromosomes 1–22 and X.

In its March 1993 *Human Genome Report Card,* the NCGHR presented graphic maps of chromosomes 1–22, X, and Y. The report summarized the progress of the genome mapping project as of that time and illustrated the enormity of the remainder of the project: 3,837 genes mapped to chromosomes, or 3.8% of the goal for finding and mapping genes. As for base sequences, only 0.7% had been completed.

Genome Data Base

Johns Hopkins University in Baltimore, Md., with a three-year grant of up to $15.9 million awarded in 1991, was charged with keeping the books on the human genome project. Through the Genome Data Base (GDB)—the largest public research data base of its kind—Hopkins will be the primary depository for genetic research conducted around the world.

"The GDB will be a centerpiece of human genome research around the world. It will open doors to international collaborations, which are so important to the success of the [human genome] project," said James Watson, who was head of the NCHGR at the time the grant was announced.

Dr. Michael E. Johns, dean of the Hopkins School of Medicine, said, "We are on the threshold of assembling the library of genes that combine to create human life. The GDB will bring together information from around the globe, thus becoming a journal of who we are. . . . The convergence of the work of the world's genetic scientists into a single electronic database will greatly facilitate their work and increase the overall efficiency of the human genome project, which holds great promise for the future of mankind."

And a comment by David J. Galas, head of the DOE Office of Health and Environmental Research, got to the heart of how geneticists will be conducting

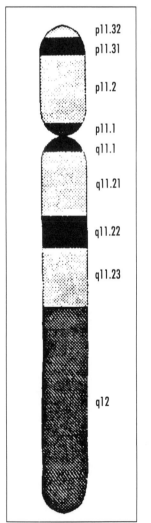

A map of the Y chromosome shows where genetic markers have been located.

p11.32
p11.31

p11.2

p11.1
q11.1

q11.21

q11.22

q11.23

q12

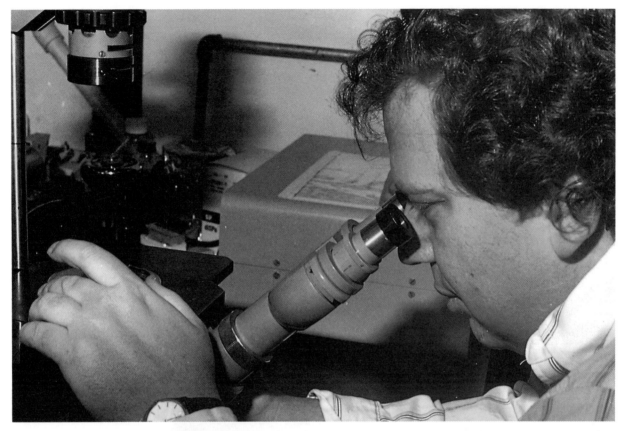

At Cold Spring Harbor Laboratory, scientists Nikolai Lisitsyn (right) and Mike Wigler (above), working on a segment of the human genome project, have developed a kind of DNA spell-checker to help identify DNA sequences. They compare one piece of DNA with a known sequence with another piece of DNA whose sequence has not been determined. The two samples are heated, then cooled, and the double-helix strands are separated. When they re-entwine with each other, unique target sequences pair up.

Glen Evans, at the Salk Institute in La Jolla, Calif., has been active in developing technology to advance human genome research.

their research well into the future. "Someday soon," Galas said, "scientists will seek information about the functioning of living things from their computer terminals before they approach the laboratory bench."

The database hold the following categories of information:

- Map objects—genes and markers—that can be used to locate or identify genes on specific chromosomes.
- The location of those map objects on chromosomes.
- Molecular descriptions of disease genes and descriptions of their chromosome locations.
- Cross references for further information in scientific literature.

Social and Ethical Issues

As progress is made in the Human Genome Project, and as scientists close in on the causes of hereditary diseases, a number of social and ethical issues have surfaced: How will all this information be used? Will employers demand a genetics test to screen out propective employees who may, at some point in the future, develop a hereditary disorder? Will insurance companies require a genetics test—much like the blood test many use today to screen for AIDS— to decide whether to sell an insurance policy to a person or family? If an individual submits to a genetics test for personal reasons, how private are the results?

Concern of genetic ethics has brewed actively since the early 1970s, when gene-splicing techniques were being developed and some people feared they would lead to the generation of dangerous organisms. As early as 1975, at an international meeting of geneticists in California, scientists urged adoption of guidelines for regulating recombinant DNA research. The federal government issued its first guidelines for human experiments in 1985, but the debate over the potential of such rapidly escalating science rages on.

Even the program's director, Francis Collins, expressed concerns when he was appointed to his position in 1993. According to a February 1, 1993 *Boston Globe* article titled "'Superstar' takes over the helm," by Richard Saltus, Collins said, "Are we going to end up with some kind of homemade eugenics?" Then, referring to efforts to develop ethical and legal standards simultaneously with scientific results, Saltus quoted Collins as saying, "This is the first technology that's ever been developed in concert with research into its impact on society."

The Human Genome Project institutionalized these concerns when it established its Ethical, Legal, and Social Implications Branch, referred to as ELSI.

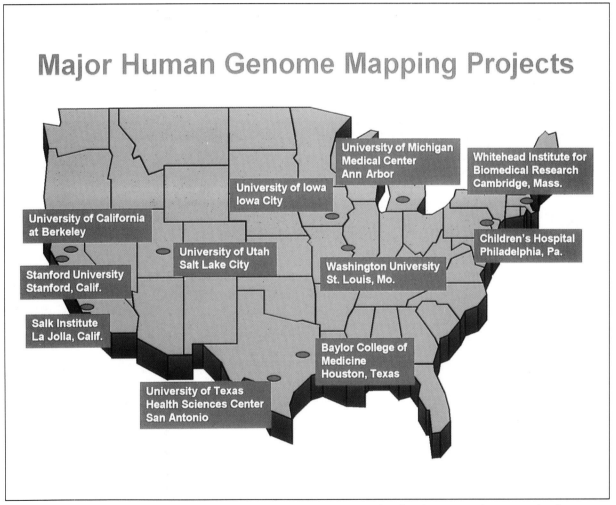

The Human Genome Project's 11 major mapping centers are: 1. Whitehead Institute for Biomedical Research, Cambridge, Mass.; 2. Washington University, St. Louis, Mo.; 3. Stanford University, Stanford, Calif.; 4. Salk Institute, La Jolla, Calif.; 5. Children's Hospital of Philadelphia, Philadelphia, Pa.; 6. University of California at Berkeley; 7. University of Texas Health Sciences Center, San Antonio; 8. University of Iowa, Iowa City; 9. University of Michigan Medical Center, Ann Arbor; 10. Baylor College of Medicine, Houston, Texas; and 11. University of Utah, Salt Lake City.

About 5% of the extramural research funding in 1991 and 1992 went toward various projects, conferences, and workshops around the country to identify current and potential problems. Those issues fell mostly into three major categories: safe and effective clinical practices, access to and use of personal genetic information, and public and professional perceptions of genetics.

As scientists embark on a new program, they follow well-defined, strict procedures so that the results of their work can be compared apple-for-apple with results of other scientists' work. A set of procedures is referred to as a protocol. And while genetics research has increased rapidly in the past few years, it still is in relative infancy in terms of everyday clinical practice. Naturally, development of protocols became one of the top priorities in the category of clinical practices. Also, basic research

guidelines are being developed and reviewed; criteria are being set up to determine the efficacy of genetic testing and counseling from the patient's frame of reference; and quality-control mechanisms are being put in force at laboratories performing genetic tests.

While the genome project will someday result in a comprehensive map of the human genome, such a map will be a composite of the human genetic makeup rather than any one individual's "blueprint." However, because of the active level of clinical testing in hereditary disease research, and due to advancements in technology available for genetic testing, a vast storehouse of genetic information is being built up of individuals and families. To date, no comprehensive policies and procedures exist to safeguard the privacy of that information, other than normal doctor-patient privileges and laws that govern medical information in general. A number of

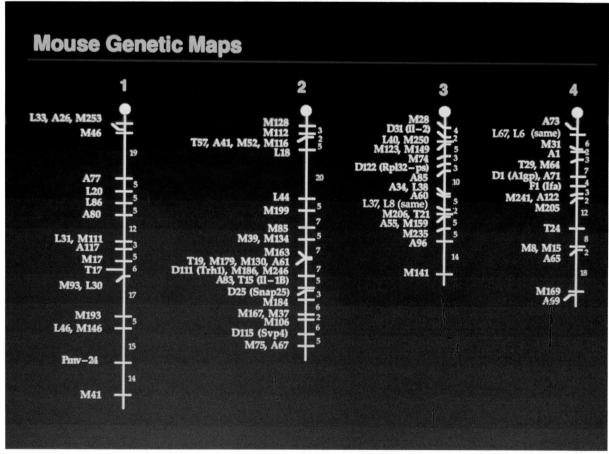

A genetic linkage map, developed at the Whitehead Institute for Biomedical Research, shows the layout of four chromosomes of the mouse genome.

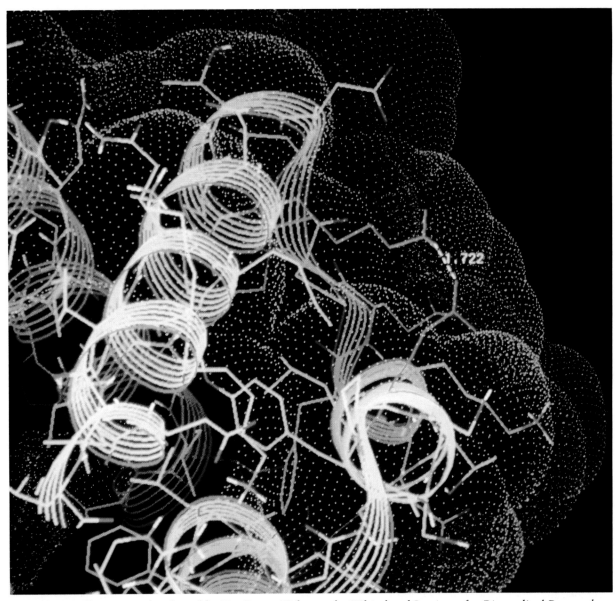

A computer illustration developed by Dr. Bruce Tidor at the Whitehead Institute for Biomedical Research shows how scientists are able to use computers to conduct research in genetics.

research projects have been initiated through the genome project to develop such policies.

A rapidly accelerating use of DNA technology is in the science of forensics, where genetic tests have been used to convict and acquit individuals of crimes. However, the scientific efficacy of some DNA forensic methods has been questioned, and a lively debate is ongoing in and out of court. *(See a discussion of DNA and other forensic science methods in Chapter 6.)*

A Matter of Timing

While gene-mapping projects proceed at a steady pace, the sequencing of DNA bases pairs—the second major goal of the human genome project—lags at the speed of technology development for sequencing methods. Until technology is developed to reduce laborious tasks of sequencing—and, as a result of the amount of work involved, the cost of sequencing—this phase of the project is hampered.

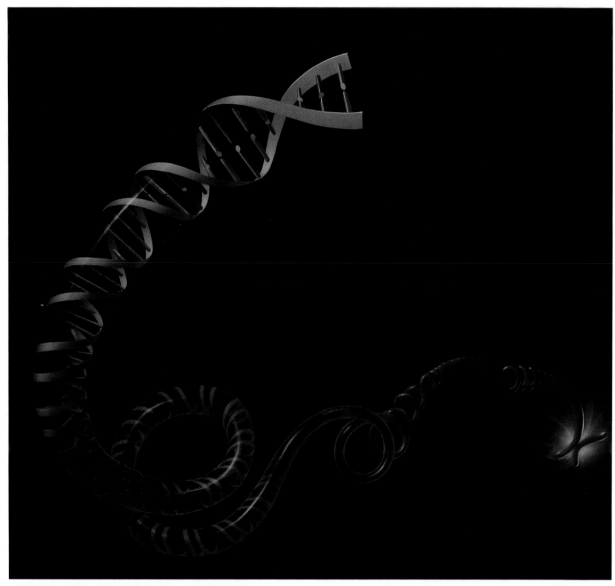

A DNA molecule unfolds into a double helix.

As of 1990, the cost of sequencing genes was estimated at $3–$5 per base pair. Since the human genome contains an estimated 3 billion base pairs, that cost prohibits proceeding at a fast rate. At just $3 per base pair, the hypothetical cost of sequencing alone would soar to $9 billion, or almost two-thirds of the entire human genome project's planned budget over 15 years. The human genome project's goal is to reduce, through technology development, the cost to 50 cents per base pair.

Sequencing has been taking place in laboratories since the early 1970s, when scientists started using enzymes to cut strips of DNA into recognizable, manageable pieces. The process of sequencing can be described in 10 steps:

1. A fragment of DNA is cloned.
2. Smaller fragments of that original fragment are cloned.
3. DNA templates are prepared.
4. Sequencing reactions are performed.
5. The products of the sequencing reactions are resolved.
6. The sequence ladder is then read.

7. The data is entered into a computer.
8. The sequence is then assembled using the computer.
9. Discrepancies are analyzed.
10. Possible coding regions are analyzed.

With existing technology, molecular biologists have been able to sequence segments of DNA that contain up to several thousand base pairs. Typically, though, step six, reading the sequence of the ladder, involves a strip of DNA that is 200–500 bases long. To assemble an entire genome, researchers must amass an enormous number of these small segments—manually reading and matching the ends of each one—into one major document that, again, could be 3 billion base pairs long. Research is well under way into technologies such as robotics, which will automate the many tedious functions.

Not Just for the Present and Future

The human genome initiative has been fruitful to more scientists than just the ones who work on present and future needs. Other scientists, such as archaeologists and anthropologists are escalating their use of DNA research to trace the distant past. And other scientists, such as geneticist Mary-Claire King of the University of California at Berkeley, are conducting mitochondrial DNA (mtDNA) research to find clues to the not-so-distant past. King helped develop techniques of analyzing mtDNA, extracted from bones, which were used by forensic scientists to identify remains of children kidnapped by military police during Argentina's "Dirty War" against political dissidents from 1976–1983.

But King also is heavily involved in the worldwide program called the Human Genome Diversity Project. Through that effort, researchers will study genetic material from human populations around the world to try to learn more about human evolution and the origins of the various populations.

One of the most controversial questions in anthropology has been: "Who were the first Americans?" Researchers trying to answer the questions have analyzed stone tools and fire pits in sites such as Clovis, N.M., where some say the first Americans settled after crossing a land bridge from Asia to Alaska some 11,000 years ago.

But population geneticists, who have analyzed genes from living people and from remains of paleoindians, claim that the first Americans arrived in Alaska from Asia much earlier than that.

In Summary, . . .

Just perhaps, when the whole of the data from the wide-ranging efforts of scientists all over the world is entered into a giant computer, that computer can print out a giant encyclopedia that contains the instruction manual on human beings. The hope is, however, that the giant instruction book will be understood when it is printed in a minuscule alphabet that contains only four letters: T, A, C, and G.

In this photo of chrysanthemums, a gene suppresses the color of the flower.

2

HARNESSING THE MOLECULE

As the world population has increased, the area of land used to produce food has shrunk. Only through efficiency and technology can enough food products be grown to feed the people of the future. Some companies, encouraged by the U.S. government, are betting that genetically engineered foods can help to provide the world with a safe, predictable, even better-tasting array of fruits and vegetables.

Companies such as Monsanto Co., St. Louis, Mo., DNA Plant Technology Corp., Cinnaminson, N.J., and Calgene Fresh, Evanston, Ill., have been growing and testing genetically altered plants for years. And as the greenery of the summer of 1993 began to fade into the browns and yellows of fall, Calgene Fresh and DNA Plant were seeing red—as in the color of the long-anticipated, first two commercial varieties of genetically engineered tomatoes.

Genetic engineering, popularly and commercially called biotechnology, is a science devoted to refinement. Refinement can be manifest in many forms. In the case of tomatoes, it can mean a longer shelf life, a richer taste, a bolder color. But in a laboratory mouse, refinement can mean one mouse suitable for testing for causes and cures of cystic fibrosis, and another mouse suitable for testing for causes and cures of one of the many forms of cancer.

For tomatoes—or corn, or potatoes—a more stable product produced through genetic engineering means less spoilage, or throwaway. That, in theory at least, leads to a more stable food supply. And for a mouse, with certain traits removed or other traits imbedded, it's possible to zero in on the effects of certain diseases without extra variables interfering. That, in theory, speeds the process of finding therapeutic drugs and cures.

It is not a new phenomenon in the agricultural world to cross-breed plants and animals. One recent example of traditional cross-breeding was the introduction of the vegetable broccoflower, a cross between broccoli and cauliflower. Biotechnology, however, allows for more precise, trait-by-trait breeding, through its use of recombinant DNA. Scientists can literally pick the gene they want to insert into a host plant, rather than cross-breeding groups of genes that possibly contain some undesirable traits.

The Government's Policy

The U.S. Food and Drug Administration made its position on biotechnology plain when it announced its safety policy toward genetically engineered foods in May 1992: "These new technologies will benefit all Americans by providing foods that are tastier, more varied, more wholesome, and that can be produced more efficiently. The policy we are announcing today will ensure the safety of these foods while facilitating their availability as quickly as possible," said Louis H. Sullivan, secretary of health and human services at that time.

He continued, "Fruits, vegetables, and grains developed through biotechnology mark an evolutionary step in the production of new varieties. They will give producers new tools through which to introduce improved traits in crops to benefit growers, processors, and consumers."

Amid criticism and alarm from some public sectors over potential dangers of humans eating genetically engineered foods, the FDA announced a safety policy based on confidence in biotechnology and consistency with the way it handles all food additives. The policy boils down to two basic lines of thought. If the "host," or recipient plant involved in a gene transfer is "generally recognized as safe," and the "donor," or source of the gene being transplanted into the host is "generally recognized as safe," then there is no need for widespread government safety testing prior to a product's entry into the commercial food business. But if the genetic engineering involves a substantive change in a product, such as removing vitamin C from a tomato, then the very least that is required is a label advising consumers that the tomato has been altered through scientific processes.

The FDA basically left the safety question up to the biotech companies to decide for themselves whether their foods are safe, using a list of questions as a standard of reference:

- Has the concentration of any naturally occurring toxicants in the plant been increased?
- Has an allergen not commonly found in the plant been introduced?
- Have the levels of important nutrients changed?
- Have new substances that raise safety questions been introduced into food?

- What are the environmental effects?
- Have the genetic material and it "expression products" been well characterized?
- Have accepted, established scientific practices been followed?

Biotech's Goals

Much of the effort going into biotechnology in plants focuses on resistance to the types of problems that farmers have always battled: pests, viruses, drought, and blight. However, some of the effort also is going into producing vegetables, fruits, or oils that meet modern needs, such as products that have lower saturated fats. Still others are aimed at the market as it is today. A year-round demand exists for fresh produce, and biotechnology can help produce varieties that better withstand the transportation from warm growing regions such as Florida and California to the colder sections of the country in winter time.

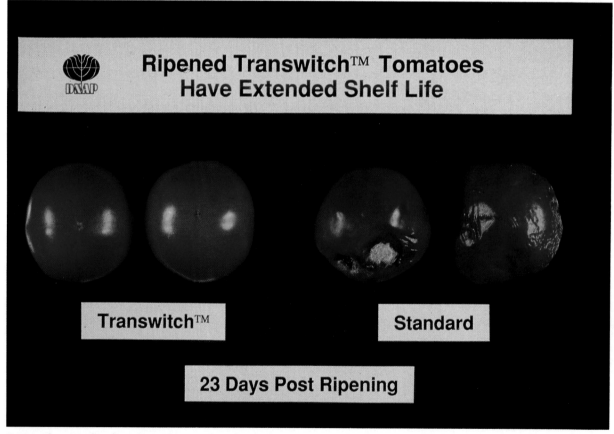

DNA Plant Technology has a patented method for prolonging tomatoes' shelf life.

Bringing the FLAVR SAVR™ tomato to consumers

1. Begin by isolating the gene in tomatoes which causes them to soften.

2. Copy that gene and put the copy into the tomato plant – backwards. This slows down the natural softening process.

3. Plant FLAVR SAVR™ seeds and grow FLAVR SAVR™ tomato plants just like other fresh tomato plants.

4. Allow FLAVR SAVR™ tomatoes to spend more days on the vine for extra flavor and a desirable texture.

5. Pick by hand and deliver to the store. FLAVR SAVR™ tomatoes retain their peak flavor.

A Calgene Fresh illustration shows a simplified view of how a "Flavr Savr" tomato goes to market.

As for tomatoes, the commercial method of growing and shipping has been to pick them green and spray them with an ethylene gas that ripens them during the several days it sometimes takes them to make it from farm to supermarket. The tomatoes also have to be firm enough to resist bruising during shipping. But the artificial ripening also produces an artificial, sometimes nonexistent, taste. Still, consumers spend an estimated $4 billion nationwide to buy 2.8 billion pounds of fresh tomatoes every year.

Biotechnology companies seek essentially to slow the ripening process, or give it more time on the vine, rather than speed the process up after the tomato is picked.

Calgene has developed its tomato, dubbed commercially as the "Flavr Savr," expected to be in supermarkets in the fall of 1993, using "antisense" genetic engineering. Using patented methods (although the legal ownership of the patent has been in legal limbo), scientists inject a gene that prevents a tomato from making its usual amount of poly-

After they're in the store (right), soybeans may look the same. But in the field, they're different.

(Below) The soybean plants on the right, implanted with a gene to combat herbicides, thrive against the soybean plants on the left.

(Top) Cotton bolls can be modified (left) to protect themselves against the cotton bollworm.

(Bottom) A closeup of corn stalks shows one damaged by insects and one, injected with the bacillus thuringiensis gene, that has protected itself from insects.

galacturonase (PG), an enzyme that softens the fruit at maturity. The antisense technique allows the tomato to stay on the vine longer and mature flavor-wise, without increasing the risk of bruising during shipping.

Commercially, the extra time on the vine was expected to amount to about a week. However, as reported in the November 28, 1992 issue of *Science News,* at the U.S. Department of Agriculture's Plant Gene Expression Center in Albany, Calif., tomatoes with antisense genes stayed "on the vine for as long as five months, ripening only to a pale orange." The antisense gene effectively reduced the tomato's production of the ripening hormone, ethylene. Many

(Above) You'd never know by looking at them, but these cows have had supplements of BST to make them more efficient milk producers.

(Opposite) Scientists at Monsanto's Life Sciences Center near St. Louis have plenty of greenhouse space to develop their plants.

plants produce their own ethylene, which controls the biochemical processes involved in ripening.

While Calgene has been concentrating on slowing the softening of the tomato with antisense genetics, DNA Plant has been developing its own patented method of prolonging the tomato's life. Called Transwitch™, the DNA Plant method effectively suppresses the gene that produces ethylene.

The difference in the two technologies is this: an antisense gene instructs messenger RNA, the substance that carries out DNA's instructions, to make a reverse copy of itself. That "antisense" copy then attaches itself to regular mRNA and prevents it from relaying its message for the tomato to continue ripening. DNA Plant's Transwitch™ method uses a different gene to instruct the mRNA to make a positive, or "sense" copy itself, and, apparently, the two positives cancel each other out.

In addition to tomatoes, DNA Plant has been using the technology to sweeten and improve the texture of items such as peppers, cherry tomatoes, and snap peas. The company also recently received a patent using the technology to control the color of petunias.

An industrywide, comprehensive chart showing the type of genetic engineering for plants, the crop to which it applies, and the anticipated benefit appears on page 41. The information, supplied by the International Food Information Council in Washington, D.C., illustrates the vast range of possibilities plant engineering has for food.

Animal Engineering

Genetic engineering offers a range of possibilities when it comes to animals, also. In addition to the traditional concept of engineering mice for medical laboratory research, scientists can now inject genes into farm animals to cause them to produce healthier food products.

At Monsanto, a number of research projects are under way, including ones to make cows give more milk and pigs to grow more, but leaner pork. Those two projects center on the use of hormones. For the cow, the focus is *bovine somatotropin* (BST). The cow produces this protein hormone, which is necessary in the production of milk, naturally in its pituitary gland. For the pig, the focus is on porcine somatotropin (PST), a protein hormone the pig naturally manufactures in its pituitary gland. Both the cow and pig research projects are still in the trial stages, and not producing commercial results.

In a report entitled "Biotechnology and the American Agricultural Industry," published in the March

This mouse is a knockout. From Jackson Laboratory in Bar Harbor, Maine, it has been genetically engineered to "knock out" the gene that prevents cystic fibrosis, so that scientists can study the progress of the disease.

20, 1991 *Journal of the American Medical Association,* the AMA's council on scientific affairs wrote that while animal engineering had not progressed as rapidly as plant technology, the potential was great: "For the consumer, these improvements will translate into nutritionally improved meats and other animal byproducts, decreases in food prices through better farm management and decreased animal disease, and a secure food supply for the future."

Among the advances in livestock sciences the AMA council evaluated were:

- Recombinant DNA-based animal vaccines.
- DNA-based methods for early detection of disease in farm animals.
- Genetically altered feed crops for farm animals.
- Recombinant DNA-based protein supplements to increase a cow's milk production and a pig's meat production.
- Creation of transgenic farm animals for improving the output of livestock herds.

The comparatively recent genetic technology of being able to create genes—or recombine DNA molecules—in the laboratory has made it possible to do what scientists have known for many years. It was apparent that if a cow was issued a supplement of BST, its milk production would increase. But producing that BST supplement was expensive, because it involved extracting substances in small quantities, and at a painstaking pace, from the cows themselves. Now, scientists insert BST-coding genes into *Escherichia coli* bacteria, which then produce recombinant BST (rBST) in large quantities.

The creation of recombinant hormones is a parallel research effort to the development of transgenic animals, which are created in much the same way as genetically engineered plants. A gene that is known to produce a desirable trait is spliced into a section of DNA and then the recombinant DNA is transferred to a host animal. And transgenic animals are created not only for food uses, but for medical purposes as well.

Mice Widely Used

The most common transgenic animal is the mouse, and it has been getting even more attention as the science of genetics has progressed over the past few years. Harvard University received the first patent on a transgenic mouse in 1988. That mouse was altered to be used in cancer research. Its genes were realigned so that it would be predisposed to cancer. Dr. Philip Leder, one of the two scientists who developed that mouse, has since obtained, with his colleague, William J. Muller, another mouse patent. The second one was engineered to develop a large prostate gland, a virtual living laboratory for research into common problems of older men.

Other mouse patents that have been issued include one for a mouse engineered for research into the AIDS virus and another for a mouse that will be used to evaluate developments in combatting diseases that affect agricultural livestock. A patent would cover specific gene sequences contained in the engineered animal that do not exist in a natural animal. The sequence, of course, determines the identifiable traits of the engineered animal and, depending on developments over the next few months, possibly the pharmaceutical characteristics the animals may produce.

Some of the wide range of possibilities for genetic engineering of mice and other animals were explored in a February 3, 1993 *New York Times* article titled "U.S. Resumes Granting Patents On Genetically Altered Animals": "Scientists expect to see such developments as laboratory mice made genetically suited for research on AIDS and other human diseases; genetically altered pigs that produce human hemoglobin for use in blood substitutes, and bioengineered cows that produce milk with the proteins found in human mother's milk."

According to that article, "most experts believe a big wave of animal patents is imminent in the United States." Biotech companies said they need the protection of patents to deter someone from just buying the animals and breeding as many others as they like themselves, after the original developers spent years on the engineering.

One controversial effort mentioned in the article was the plan by one company to transplant human genes into pigs in hopes of the pigs eventually producing organs, such as livers, hearts, and kidneys, that could be used for transplanting into humans. DNX Corp. of Princeton, N.J., already has produced a pig that makes human hemoglobin.

Yeast and Mice

To help produce genetically engineered mice on a medically efficient scale, scientists are using a recently developed technology called yeast artificial chromosomes, popularly called YACs. One of the problems with working with mice in the past was that scientists did not have a way to transfer a large-enough sample of DNA into mice to adequately provide a research basis for some diseases. But YACs, which are yeast molecules that efficiently make multiple copies of synthetic DNA, proved to be the vehicle needed. The YAC was discovered by geneticists Maynard V. Olson and David Burke in 1987 at Washington University in St. Louis, Mo.

"Not until this spring have molecular geneticists used YACs for moving big genes into other organisms and shown that those genes pass on to succeeding generations," wrote Elizabeth Pennisi in a June 5, 1993 article titled "Mouse of a Different YAC," in *Science News*.

Formerly, transgenic mice were limited to carrying foreign genes with 50,000 base pairs or less. But the genetic origins of many diseases often span as many as 1 million base pairs. While no such transfers of that magnitude had been completed as of mid-1993, the technology was being developed to do so.

The *Science News* article further explained the importance of YACs to research: "With most gene-mapping strategies, molecular biologists can narrow the site of a gene to a section of chromosome, but then they must work incredibly hard to pinpoint its location to within less than a million base pairs. With YACs, they can now use some of the hundreds of mutant mouse strains to identify the exact genes responsible for these defects."

Sharing the Wealth of Research

No technology is fully useful unless it can be applied cost-effectively across a broad spectrum.

In July, a number of health organizations combined resources to award a $1.5 million grant to the Jackson Laboratory in Bar Harbor, Maine, for establishment of an international clearinghouse for distribution of genet-

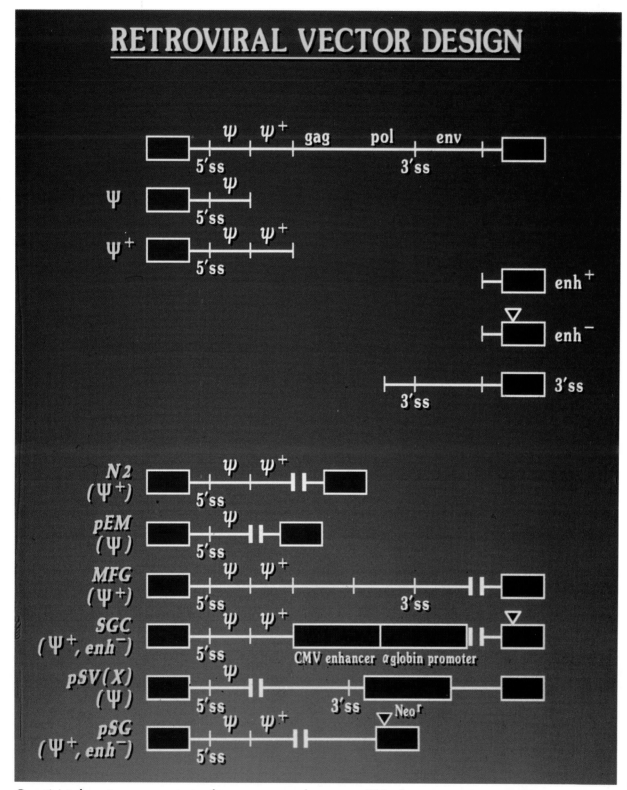

Geneticists have to use some type of vector to transplant genes. This shows one type, a retrovirus, developed by Richard Mulligan at the Whitehead Institute for Biomedical Research.

ically engineered mice to be used as human disease models. Participating in the award were the American Cancer Society, American Heart Association, Cystic Fibrosis Foundation, Howard Hughes Medical Institute, March of Dimes, and Multiple Sclerosis Society.

"Many scientists want us to serve as the central resource, providing these invaluable models that are kept virus-free and distributed in such a way as to optimize these new biomedical research resources that are difficult and expensive for them to maintain," said Dr. Kenneth Paigen, director of the Jackson Laboratory.

"The mice will be distributed to researchers worldwide at the lowest feasible cost and without restriction on their uses for research. It is only through a cooperative effort that these laboratory models can be developed," Paigen said.

A nonprofit research institution, the Jackson Laboratory has 60 years of experience researching mammalian genetics, developing and distributing inbred strains and mutant stocks, and educating geneticists on mice in biomedical research. "Currently, most of these new mutant stocks are available only in limited quantities and at high prices, because they are maintained in small research colonies with a high daily cost for animal care," Paigen said. But the grant is expected to lower the cost charged to other research institutions by defraying some of the costs.

As of July 1993, there were 50 mouse "models" available for distribution, including one, called "CFTR Knockout," engineered especially for cystic fibrosis research. Scientists hope that by "knocking out" the CFTR gene in the mouse, the mutant will provide a living laboratory to help develop therapies for CF.

WHAT BIOTECH COMPANIES HAVE IN MIND
Biotechnology companies have a wide range of goals in mind when it comes to genetically engineered plants.

Type of Modification	Plants under research	Expected benefit
Controlled Ripening	Tomato, pea, pepper, tropical fruits	Vine ripening, improved shelf life, improved food processing quality
High solids content	Tomato, potato	Improved food processing
Insect resistance	Cotton, corn, potatoes, tomatoes	Reduce pesticides
Fungal resistance	Pepper, tomato	Reduce fungicides
Viral resistance	Potato, tomato, cantaloupe, squash, alfalfa, corn, oilseed rape, soybeans, grapes	Increase viral resistance, reduce pesticides
Herbicide tolerance	Corn, cotton, soybeans, tomato, oilseed rape	Less herbicide, reduced groundwater contamination
Improved nutrition	Corn, sunflowers, soybeans	Increase amino acids in host crop
Improved nutrition	Oilseed rape	Increase amount of unsaturated oils in plant
Freezing tolerance	Tomato, fruits, vegetables	Improved texture
Heat stability	Oilseed rape, peanut	Improved food processing, new uses of healthier oils
Low caffeine content	Coffee	Naturally decaffeinated coffee
Controlled starch buildup	Corn, peas	Retain sweetness
Various	Vegetables	Reduce risk of human disease

Source: International Food Information Council

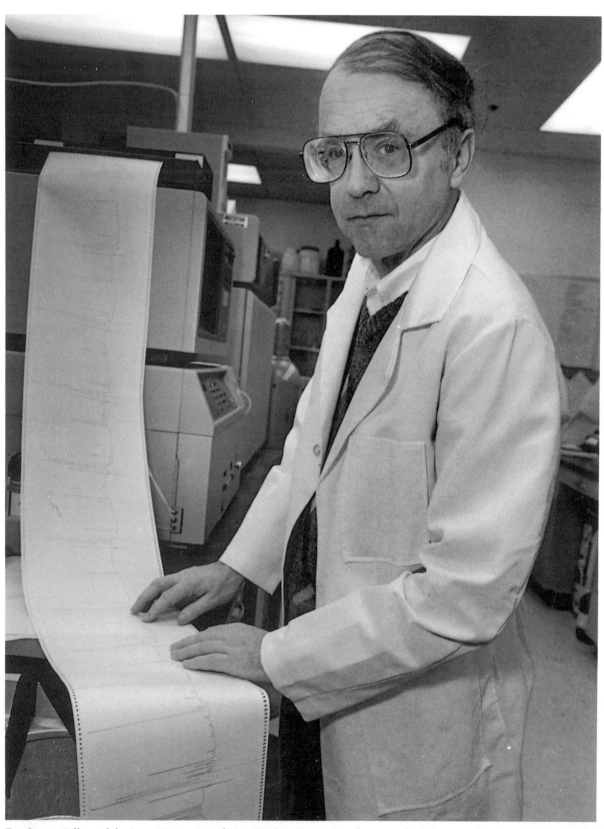

Dr. Simon Pilkis, of the State University of New York at Stony Brook, researched the gene that is now associated with Type II diabetes.

3

Mastering the Molecule

Breakthroughs in the science of genetics came at breakneck speed in 1993. Some doctors announced discoveries of genes linked with major diseases. Other doctors embarked on ambitious gene-therapy trials in efforts to cure such ailments as cystic fibrosis. And a universal feeling was that more news is on the immediate horizon.

In March alone, two major announcements were made. One was the discovery of the defective gene that causes Huntington's disease, and the other was discovery of the gene for Lou Gehrig's disease. In May, a team of scientists from the University of Helsinki and Johns Hopkins University announced that they had discovered a genetic link for colon cancer. Then in July, scientists announced that they had found what turned out to be one of the most controversial topics of the year: a genetic link to homosexuality. This chapter contains a summary of those and other events of 1993.

Cystic Fibrosis

Researchers' experience with cystic fibrosis is one of the most publicized examples of the recent pace in genetics and genetic therapy. Cystic fibrosis (CF) is an inherited disease that afflicts 20,000 babies a year in the United States and is the most common lethal inherited disease. Few of those babies live to the age of 30, because the disease clogs the lungs and digestive tracts with sticky mucus. Typically, recurrent pneumonia breaks down the lungs and kills the person. For years, scientists had known that CF was caused by a recessive gene, meaning a child had to inherit two defective genes, or one from each parent, to acquire the disease. Then, in 1989, the gene itself was found.

Dr. Francis Collins, then of the University of Michigan, and Dr. Lap-Chee Tsui and Dr. Michael Riordan, both of the Hospital for Sick Children in Toronto, Canada, discovered the cystic fibrosis gene after an exhaustive search. They identified the gene as a fragment of DNA, 250,000 base pairs long, on chromosome 7 that codes for a 1,480-amino acid protein now called the cystic fibrosis transmembrane conductance regulator (CFTR). In most CF patients studied, a defective CFTR protein appeared to be unable to transport chloride ions across cell membranes properly, which causes a reduction in extracellular water and a thickening of mucus secretions. The doctors published their findings in the September 8, 1989 issue of *Science*.

Less than four years later, the first gene therapy clinical trial for CF victims was under way. On April 17, 1993, Dr. Ronald G. Crystal began administering a CF gene-therapy treatment to a 23-year-old man. In the first step, the man inhaled through his nasal passages a "modified adenovirus," which was a cold virus rendered harmless and injected with a healthy copy of the CF gene. The next day, the man received droplets of the virus "drizzled for seven minutes down his trachea and into the lower lobe of his left lung," according to a story titled "Gene Therapy Begins For Fatal Lung Disease," in the April 20 *New York Times*.

"This pioneering research marks the first use of gene therapy for a common genetic disorder. It is also the first use in humans of a cold virus as a vehicle for gene transport," said Dr. Claude Lenfant, director of the National Heart, Lung, and Blood Institute (NHLBI), in announcing the treatment.

Dr. Crystal and his colleagues designed the therapy study to determine whether the transfer of a

Dr. Ronald G. Crystal performed the gene therapy trial on cystic fibrosis patients.

Huntington's Disease

A 10-year search for a Huntington's disease gene ended in March when researchers announced that they had located it where a curious mutation occurs on chromosome 4. The Huntington's disease gene contains a three-letter sequence that repeats over and over in a sort of "genetic stutter."

The search for this gene took not only 10 years, but also a collaboration of 58 individuals in five institutions: Massachusetts General Hospital, the University of California/Irvine, Massachusetts Institute of Technology, the Imperial Research Fund in England, and the University of Wales. Although the gene was known in 1983 to reside somewhere on chromosome 4, its exact location was clouded by a dense concentration of genes within a section of the chromosome. The researchers published their findings in the March 24, 1993 issue of the journal *Cell*.

"This is a great day. This was the big fish that keeps getting away," said Dr. Francis Collins, at that time a geneticist at the University of Michigan but later director of the National Center for Human Genome Research. He was quoted in a March 24 story in the *Boston Globe,* which also quoted one of the primary researchers in the search, Dr. James Gusella of Massachusetts General Hospital, as saying, "The problem was much tougher than any of us could have imagined."

In the same article, geneticist David Housman of the Massachusetts Institute of Technology, said the discovery was possible "only because of the unusual collaboration among scores of scientists in the United States and Europe who overcame the normal competitive temptations and shared their results freely."

In the identified gene, the mutation that causes Huntington's disease repeats a three-letter base sequence, CAG, numerous times. In a person not predisposed to Huntington's disease, this sequence could repeat as many as 34 times, scientists said. But in 75 families studied, in which the mutant gene was found, the sequence was repeated at least 42 times. The more repetitions, it seemed, the earlier the onset of the disease.

Huntington's disease afflicts about 30,000 Americans, but an estimated 150,000 people are at risk. The disease attacks body and mind, killing brain cells and causing involuntary, jerky movements. It also impairs thought and leads to dementia. The disease

normal CFTR gene to airway cells will enable the cells to produce a normal, functional CFTR protein. They also want to know how long such an effect will last, whether the patient's lung function improves, and whether symptoms, such as abnormal mucus, improve.

According to the NHLBI, the institute responsible for administering the therapy, nine more patients aged 21 or older who have mild to moderate symptoms of CF were to be involved in a series of clinical trials. The patients, ironically, probably will not benefit tremendously from the experiment, since they can only receive the treatment once, according to the initial clinical trials protocol approved by the National Institutes of Health's Recombinant DNA Advisory Committee.

"What we hope to learn from this initial study is whether this new approach works. If it does, we're on the way to a cure," Dr. Crystal said.

usually strikes people between the ages of 20 and 60, but more often in the 30s. One of the most famous victims of Huntington's disease was folk singer Woody Guthrie, who was struck with the disease in 1952.

Children of people who have Huntington's disease have a 50% chance of inheriting the mutant gene that causes it, and the children who do inherit are virtually certain to contract the disease if they live long enough. After the pinpointing of the gene on chromosome 4, scientists can test individuals to determine whether they have that mutant gene, and even predict the age at which the disease will strike. Although a cure still did not exist in 1993, the gene discovery was viewed as a major step toward the development of new therapies and a potential cure.

Lou Gehrig's Disease

Scientists announced in the March 4, 1993 edition of the journal *Nature* that they had pinpointed a defective gene involved in one form of the inherited disease called amyotrophic lateral sclerosis (ALS), more popularly known as Lou Gehrig's disease, after the baseball player who died from the mysterious ailment in 1941. The disease results in muscle deterioration, paralysis, and, eventually, death.

Scientists in the United States, Canada, Belgium, and Australia researched dozens of families with the familial form of ALS, focusing on chromosome 21. Led by Dr. Robert H. Brown, Jr., at Massachusetts General Hospital, and Dr. Teepu Siddique, of Northwestern University, the researchers found that in 13 families, 11 different mutations occurred in the gene that produces an enzyme called superoxide dismutase (SOD).

That enzyme is one of the body's most powerful defense mechanisms and is present in all tissues. SOD prevents damage to cells by particles known as free radicals, which are created as the cell burns energy and breaks down oxygen. The effects of radiation, toxic chemicals, and other environmental factors also create free radicals. Antioxidants such as SOD, or vitamins A, C, and E, keep the free radicals from destroying genes and cells.

Discovery of the gene, dubbed SOD-1, was expected to lead quickly to genetic tests for families at risk of developing ALS. If the defective gene is found in such tests, scientists would hope to be able intervene early enough to prevent symptoms.

"This is no cure, but it brings hope where before there was no hope," said Siddique, when he and Brown announced the gene's discovery. Siddique also saw hope for other neurological disorders when the professional community absorbs the results of such a cooperative effort among the scientists involved: 32 physicians or scientists at 13 institutions.

In another research effort, announced in the January 1 *Proceedings of the National Academy of Sciences,* a team led by James O. McNamara, of the Duke University Medical Center in Durham, N.C., announced that they had identified another gene, also on chromosome 21, that may cause a form of ALS. This gene, they said, generates the code for a key nerve-cell receptor which, when defective, allows too much calcium to enter and damage a cell.

At Johns Hopkins University School of Medicine, scientists announced in July that they had developed the first "test-tube" model of a biochemical defect that may cause ALS, and that the testing of potentially therapeutic drugs could now be done more easily and quickly than before. Clinical trials were set to begin later in the year.

Colon Cancer

Another international team of scientists announced in May that they had established a genetic basis for a widespread form of colon cancer, the most common inherited disease among humans. Researchers investigated a series of families with a number of colon-cancer cases and narrowed their search down to a gene on chromosome 2, where a mutation, or marker, occurred in all the related individuals with cancer but did not occur in the relatives who did not have cancer. Now that the researchers have located the marker at which mutations occur in the gene, research will continue on isolation of the gene itself.

"A single gene is responsible for the predisposition in these families," said Dr. Bert Vogelstein, in an announcement from Johns Hopkins University Medical School, where he works. "This is the first time a single gene has been linked to a common form of colon cancer. If someone has a mutant form of the gene, he or she will get this cancer."

However, now that the gene has been found, scientists theorized that a diagnostic blood test could be available within two years, improving the chances of preventing deaths. A simpler blood test, to predict who is or is not predisposed to cancer if they have a strong family history of it, was expected to be available within a matter of months, Vogelstein said.

Colon cancer is the world's second most common cancer, next to lung cancer. About 600,000 new cases of colon cancer are diagnosed every year, and 300,000 deaths occur worldwide each year as a result of colon cancer. It kills 55,000 Americans each year, but when detected early enough it has a 90% cure rate.

"This genetic defect causes about one in every seven colon cancers," said University of Helsinki geneticist Albert de la Chapelle, also a leader in the gene search. "Screening for it could potentially prevent thousands of cancer deaths a year."

"If tests show you have inherited the gene, you will be watched very carefully, and chances are the tumor will be discovered early enough to cure. Catching it early makes all the difference," Vogelstein said.

The scientists' research, published in the May 7, 1993 issue of *Science,* pinpoints genetic defects responsible for cancers of the uterus, stomach, ovary, small intestine, gall bladder, kidney, and ureter, in addition to the colon and rectum.

Of major significance in their findings is the scientific link between genetics and colon cancer in light of much debate over environmental and lifestyle effects on susceptibility to cancer. As they wrote in the *Science* article: "One problem in establishing such proof is that colon cancers are so common in the general population that it is difficult to rule out chance clustering and other nonhereditary factors. Moreover, the environment, notably diet, has been shown to play a substantial role. . . . Members of an individual family are likely to share similar environments, further complicating definitive analysis."

Bubble Boy Disease

A 6-pound, 12-ounce boy named Andrew Gobea became the first newborn baby to receive gene therapy in May, when doctors infused a teaspoonful of genes into him as he slept at Children's Hospital in Los Angeles, Calif. Andrew was born with an immune disorder popularly known as bubble boy disease. The name derives from a case where a boy named David, who suffered from severe combined immunodeficiency (SCID), lived for 12 years in a germ-free plastic bubble. He died in 1984 when a treatment failed.

About 100 children are born each year with SCID, which is caused by the absence of an enzyme that is necessary to maintain the body's immune system. White blood cells that lack the enzyme, adenosine deaminase, cannot fight infections of any kind.

For Andrew and another baby, Zachary Riggens, born at the University of California at San Francisco Medical Center, doctors extracted a small amount of blood from the umbilical cords just cut from the babies. The blood contained stem cells with the gene that codes the enzyme SCID children lack. The children inherit the defective gene if both parents contribute defective copies of it.

Diabetes Type II

The Stony Brook Health Sciences Center of the State University of New York announced in February that scientists had discovered a genetic cause for a form of Type II diabetes. Researchers led by Dr. Simon Pilkis at Stony Brook identified and characterized more than 15 mutations that can prevent the glucokinase gene from ordering the proper production and secretion of insulin.

"This is the first clear definition of a genetic cause of Type II diabetes," said Dr. Pilkis, in announcing the results of his and his colleagues' research. "Moreover, it may be one of the largest single-gene disorders described to date." The scientists' study results were published in the March 1, 1993 *Proceedings of the National Academy of Sciences.*

"This is the tip of the iceberg for learning more about diabetes and what causes it in Type II," Pilkis said. Type II refers to non-insulin-dependent diabetes mellitus. Of the 11 million Americans—nearly one in 20—who have diabetes, Pilkis estimates that 400,000–500,000 have a genetically caused form.

This discovery, as in others for other diseases, may lead to better treatments or possibly a cure. One approach in diabetes is to stimulate the glucokinase gene to produce glucose adequately. Beyond that, a goal would be to replace defective glucokinase genes with good ones.

Pilkis said other genes are likely to be associated with diabetes, and research is under way to locate them. "It is only a matter of time before other genes implicated in Type II diabetes are identified. We will be able to screen different diabetic populations or the general population for these mutations, which will tell us whether someone has a predisposition to diabetes and what category they fall into."

Leukemia

Researchers at the University of New Mexico and at Osaka University in Japan published separate reports in February that they had linked adult leukemia to paired genes on chromosome 5. In one report, Dr. Cheryl L. Willman of New Mexico's School of Medicine and her colleagues said that half of a normal pair of IRF-1 genes were missing in 13 leukemia and pre-leukemia patients they studied. Willman's and a companion study were published in the February 12, 1993 issue of *Science*.

"Our hypothesis is that if you lose a single allele [half of a gene, which can be dominant or recessive], it can lead to unrestrained cell growth," Willman said. When

Mary-Claire King, of the University of California at Berkeley, has been active in many phases of genetics and is among the best-known scientists in the nation for this field. Much of her work has been directed toward establishing the genetic link to breast cancer.

cells multiply rapidly, the rate of mutation also goes up. If the mutation rate increases enough, it "can cause a promotion to full-blown leukemia."

The other report stated that tumors quickly develop in laboratory mice if a mouse has a surplus of the IRF-2 or a shortage of the IRF-1 protein. IRF stands for interferon regulatory factor. IRF-1 instructs cells to secrete protein that *regulates* cell division, and IRF-2 tells cells to *promote* cell division. If the two proteins are out of balance, the setting is right for cancer.

"It does support the idea that a disruption in the interferon system may lead to cancer," said Dr. Sidney Pestka, an interferon specialist at the University of Medicine and Dentistry of New Jersey. Pestka was quoted in a story titled "Gene Clues to Changes That Precede Leukemia," in the February 23, 1993 *New York Times*.

Willman, according to the *New York Times* article, and her team were working on developing a test that could identify adults whose IRF genes may be out of balance, causing them to be vulnerable to leukemia.

High Hopes

Indicative of the enthusiasm among genetics researchers was a comment by well-known scientist Mary-Claire King in April. "Geneticists are very close to cloning the gene responsible for most inherited breast cancers—it could happen any day," she declared when she and two colleagues, Sarah Rowell and Dr. Susan M. Love, recommended that a national registry be established of women found to be at high risk for breast cancer.

King and her colleagues identified the gene, now referred to as BRCA1, linking early-onset familial breast cancer to chromosome 17.

But another comment by King in that same statement was indicative of the current state of genetics. The potential is great. The genes that *cause* diseases are being discovered, but sometimes the knowledge that a person has a genetic defect that may someday cause a serious disorder can be a hard pill to swallow unless science has also developed some solutions to go along with the knowledge.

"With the gene in hand, we will be able to identify those women at high risk of developing breast cancer," King said, "but once they are identified, none of their options are great—the choices can be disfiguring, devastating, or both. We need to know what will work."

About 1 in 200 women among the general world population—600,000 women in the United States—are at high risk of contracting breast cancer. They have an inherited susceptibility to the disease, and their chance of developing breast cancer by age 50 is almost 50%. Their chance for developing breast cancer by age 65 is about 80%. Coupled with the risk for breast cancer is an approximately 10% chance that they will develop ovarian cancer by age 60.

Presently, the options for such women are limited. Certainly, regular breast examinations are imperative. Hopefully, any sign of developing cancer will be detected soon enough to take effective measures. But King pointed out two other options. One radical alternative is for the woman who knows she is in the high-risk category to have her breasts and/or ovaries removed as a preventive measure. Another, experimental alternative is to enlist in a clinical trial of the anti-cancer drug Tamoxifen, which has uncertain benefits and can have side effects.

Until the specific cancer-causing gene is pinpointed on a chromosome, scientists have only one way of determining whether a woman is in the high-risk category, according to King. That way is to conduct a thorough genetic analysis of the woman's family, searching for any genetic marker that may be linked to cancer. Such a process takes considerable time and involves a number of family members. With the gene in hand, testing the one woman to see if she possesses it is all that would be required, and no family study would be necessary.

For the women who have been found to be at high risk, King and her colleagues recommended that a registry be established to track their histories. In a summary paper published in the April 21, 1993 issue of the *Journal of the American Medical Association,* the scientists wrote: "Knowing the biology of the first steps of tumor development could permit us to reverse these steps, either by replacing the products of the genes, or replacing the aberrant genes themselves in the breast ductal cells. The goal is that the next generation of women not face death from breast cancer."

A study released later in the year by researchers at the Harvard School of Public Health and Brigham and Women's Hospital, indicated that daughters and sisters of women who have had breast cancer are at lesser risk of developing it than may have previously been thought, a story called "Family Breast Cancer Risk Found Smaller," in the July 21 edition of the *Boston Globe,* reported.

While previous studies indicated that a woman whose mother or sister was a victim of breast cancer was two to three times more likely than other women to get the disease, the new study revealed that those whose mothers had breast cancer had only an 80% greater chance, and those whose sisters had the cancer had only a 130% greater chance. The study's authors said that although those odds sound high, they actually represent "moderate" risk.

Hyperactivity

Children who suffer from attention deficit disorder—hyperactivity—may have a genetic flaw in the thyroid gland, according to a study published in the April 8, 1993 *New England Journal of Medicine.* Researchers, who studied 104 members of 18 families, found that hyperactivity was common among family members who had a condition known as thyroid hormone resistance.

The researchers said that a defective gene could fail to properly code the thyroid's hormone receptor to allow enough hormone to enter. When that happens, the genes that regulate chemical messengers to the brain are not stimulated enough, and the symptoms of attention deficit can occur.

RECENT GENETIC FINDINGS

A number of findings have been announced recently that show linkages between genes and certain disorders. This table gives a sample of the linkages between disorders and genes on certain chromosomes:

Chromosome	Disorder
Chromosome 2	Colon Cancer
Chromosome 4	Huntington's Disease
Chromosome 5	Colon Cancer
Chromosome 7	Diabetes Type II
Chromosome 17	Breast Cancer
Chromosome 19	Myotonic Dystrophy
Chromosome 21	Lou Gehrig's Disease
X Chromosome	Fragile X Syndrome
X Chromosome	Lowe's Syndrome
X Chromosome	Kallman Syndrome

Genes and Sexual Preference

Scientists announced in July that they had discovered a link between a gene from the X chromosome, inherited by men from their mothers, to homosexuality among men. The report, published in the July 16, 1993 issue of *Science,* touched off a storm of controversy.

The scientists, led by National Cancer Institute geneticist Dean Hamer, said the gene is compressed among possible hundreds other genes in a small region of the chromosome. "We haven't identified the gene yet, and any theory of how it works is speculative," Hamer said, as quoted in the July 17, 1993 issue of *Science News.*

However, critics of the announcement were not so tentative. One of their biggest complaints was that now that a gene had been associated with male homosexuality, was the next step genetic tests to determine if a fetus possessed the gene, and the next step after that, abortion?

Hamer and his colleagues used traditional scientific methods to produce the study's hypothesis. They recruited 76 homosexual men, traced their genetic heritage, and determined what prior relatives were homosexual.

"When we collected the family histories, we saw more gay relatives on the maternal side than on the paternal side," Hamer said in a *Science* news story that appeared in the same issue as the study. Homosexuality was more prevalent among maternal uncles of gay men and among cousins who were sons of maternal aunts than among males of the general population. This was an implication that female members of the family passed the trait along. The X chromosome, the only one exclusively passed on by the mother, was the obvious starting point.

Hamer and his colleagues then recruited 40 pairs of homosexual brothers, extracted DNA samples, and developed genetic linkage analysis. They found that of the 40 pairs of brothers, 33 shared five markers on a stretch of DNA on the long end of the X chromosome. The linkage, by one measure, has a 99.5% certainty that a gene in this region predisposes a male to homosexuality.

But Hamer cautioned that seven of the pairs of brothers did not share this strip of DNA with the others, so it is likely that genetics is only one cause of homosexuality, with a variety of other factors also figuring in.

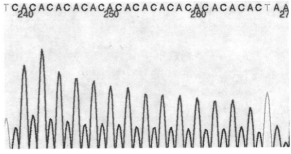

The sequences of base pairs in genes often give scientists a clue as to mutations that cause disease. This particular sequence, a printout from a section of mouse DNA, illustrates how some sequences are repeated. In humans, when triplets—a three-base combination such as CAG—repeat wildly, or stutter, a disease often results.

An Infant in Science

In cases where no cures have been found for hereditary diseases, of course, the results of genetic tests are strictly for informative purposes. Depending on the particular disease for which a person is predisposed, there may be little or no action that can be taken to avoid it. But in some cases, where environmental and lifestyle factors figure into whether the disease strikes, having such information in hand can help a person avoid a deathly illness.

Gene therapy is still in its infancy. It was only about three years ago that Dr. W. French Anderson, then of the National Institutes of Health, successfully transferred a healthy gene into a 5-year-old girl whose immune system was not functioning properly due to a faulty gene. Anderson spoke at a March meeting celebrating the 40th anniversary of the discovery of the structure of DNA at the Cold Spring Harbor Laboratory in New York. According to an article in the March 15, 1993 *Time* magazine, Anderson said, "Short term, I think that gene therapy will be applied to a broader and broader range of diseases, with more and clever approaches." But in the long term, he said, he envisions a time when "any physician can take a vial off a shelf and inject an appropriate gene into a patient."

The potential for gene therapy is immense. Thousands of diseases are rooted in hereditary origins. Other, non-hereditary diseases could perhaps be cured through genetic means. But to attain such lofty goals, the genes first have to be identified, mapped, and their data entered into a central source for all to analyze.

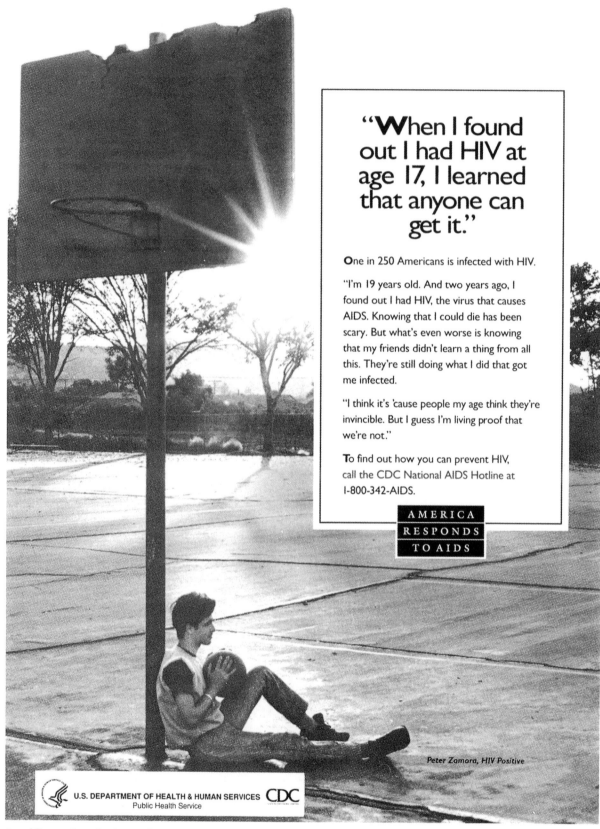

"When I found out I had HIV at age 17, I learned that anyone can get it."

One in 250 Americans is infected with HIV.

"I'm 19 years old. And two years ago, I found out I had HIV, the virus that causes AIDS. Knowing that I could die has been scary. But what's even worse is knowing that my friends didn't learn a thing from all this. They're still doing what I did that got me infected.

"I think it's 'cause people my age think they're invincible. But I guess I'm living proof that we're not."

To find out how you can prevent HIV, call the CDC National AIDS Hotline at 1-800-342-AIDS.

AMERICA
RESPONDS
TO AIDS

Peter Zamora, HIV Positive

U.S. DEPARTMENT OF HEALTH & HUMAN SERVICES CDC
Public Health Service

A public service ad advises that AIDS is not just an adult problem.

4

ADOLESCENTS AND THEIR HEALTH

The carefree days of growing up with a hometown lifestyle such as the one portrayed in the television show "Leave it to Beaver" do not exist. AIDS, substance abuse, violence, and the stress in today's world are factors that shape today's teenagers, and often not for the best.

Health and education experts came together to try to deal with problems facing today's adolescents at a conference in April 1992, in Washington, D.C., organized by the Carnegie Corporation. Called *Crossroads: Critical Choices for the Development of Healthy Adolescents,* the conference found that:

- The number of single-parent households had risen
- More teens are now engaging in sexual intercourse
- Births to unwed teenage mothers had more than doubled in 20 years
- Sexually transmitted diseases had increased 400% in less than 30 years in 10–14-year-olds
- Alcohol and drugs were now the rule and not the exception among teens
- American teens were 15 times more likely to be a victim of homicide than English teens
- More teens die as a result of automobile accidents and drunk driving than of diseases and illnesses

More attention was focused on teenagers and younger children in 1993, as health professionals and others attempted to get a grip of a segment of society particularly vulnerable to a wide range of factors. In one major announcement of the year, a committee of the Institute of Medicine called for major reform in the emergency medical services arena, to better equip medical personnel for special needs of children and teenagers.

"Widespread changes are needed to improve the emergency care that children receive in the United States," said the committee in a report, *Emergency Medical Services for Children,* released in July. According to the report, the needs of adult trauma and cardiac patients have taken precedence over the development of emergency medical services for children.

"What we do know is that some 21,000 children and young people under age 20 died in 1988 alone as a result of injury," said committee chair Donald N. Medearis, Jr., chief of children's services at Massachusetts General Hospital in Boston.

This chapter deals with these and other problems facing adolescents today, and some of the remedies that are being tried as solutions.

Drugs, alcohol, and tobacco

As middle and high schools try more and more to curb the use of tobacco in the schools, more and more teens are picking up the habit. Each year 400,000 Americans die as a direct result of smoking. According to the Department of Health and Human Services in its report *Healthy People 2000,* about 17% of the deaths in the United States occur due to the use of tobacco. An estimated 55 million Americans regularly smoke, including 29% of teens age 14-16. Overall, teen smokers now number 7 million strong—that's one in four, or 25%.

Smoking, as with most risky behaviors, is not an inner city problem. More adolescents who smoke, drink, and use drugs are white, and girls are nearly as likely to smoke as their male counterparts. Three times as many whites as blacks smoke, according to an article in the July 1993 issue of *Pediatrics* magazine.

Tobacco use through cigarettes is not the only form of tobacco that is cause for alarm today. A 1993

ALCOHOL LAWS IN THE U.S.

The 50 U.S. states, plus the District of Columbia, have wide-ranging laws when it comes to alcohol and underage use. While all states require that the sale of alcohol be limited to people at least 21 years old, the table below shows how many states back up that requirement with other laws relating to minors and alcohol.

Issue Relating to Alcohol	State Law	No State Law
Sale must be to people 21 & Over	51	0
Illegal for minors to buy alcohol	45	6
Illegal for minors to possess alcohol	49	2
Illegal for minors to consume alcohol	30	21
Illegal for minors to misrepresent age	35	16
Illegal for minors to use fake I.D.	32	19

report released by the federal Centers for Disease Control and Prevention said that chewing tobacco is used by one out of every five males in high school today. For white males, the number is one in four, and for Native Americans the figure jumps to a whopping 50%. The average age that they say they picked up the habit was nine.

While today's youth rarely see someone smoking on T.V. shows made since the 1970s, the drinking of alcohol is another thing. The way "soap opera" characters handle their problems is with a drink. Although smoking is viewed as a vice, drinking is condoned as the acceptable adult way to handle one's problems. The result of that misconception is that of the 20.7 million teens in middle through high school grades, 8–10 million "drink alcohol monthly, and 454,000 have five or more consecutive drinks at least once a week," according to U.S. Surgeon General Antonia Novello.

Using alcohol "as a tool to help them cope with troubled feelings and tense situations," 31% of American teenagers who drink alcohol said that they would drink by themselves, 25% said they would have a drink when they were bored, and 41% said they used alcohol when they were upset about something, writes Fred Hersinger in *Fateful Choices: Healthy Youth for the 21st Century* (Carnegie Corp., 1992). In a survey published in the July 1993 *Pediatrics* magazine, 65% of all 14–16-year-old teens (52.5% black and 70% white) answered "yes" to drinking alcohol.

Not Just Boys

What used to be viewed as a "boys will be boys" problem now knows no gender lines. Students in junior and senior high schools consume 35% of all wine coolers and 1.1 billion cans of beer sold in the United States each year. "Of those who engage in binge drinking, 59% are male and 41% are female. The average "binger" is 16 years old and was 12 years old when he or she took the first drink," according to *Fateful Choices*.

In a U.S. Department of Health and Human Services report, *Youth and Alcohol: Do They Know What They're Drinking?* a study found that there seems to be a great deal of confusion among today's adolescents as to which "over the counter" drinks contain alcohol. Seventy-three percent of teens aged 15 and under did not know the differences in wine coolers, mixed-drink coolers, fortified wines and even fruit-flavored mineral waters. Eighty percent of the teens interviewed were uncertain how much alcohol was in a "shot" of liquor or a can of beer.

According to another report from the Office of the Inspector General, *Youth and Alcohol: Drinking Habits, Access, Attitudes, and Knowledge,* youths under 21, and as young as 12, had little difficulty in purchasing alcohol in stores. Many students did not know that an overdose of alcohol can kill.

Alcohol can be traced as the primary cause of at least 50% of all motor vehicle accidents with an adolescent driver. In a survey of eighth-grade students, conducted by the Office of the Inspector General, 32% reported that they had been passengers in cars driven by an adolescent who had been drinking—even though 92% said that no person who had been drinking should drive. While the law to purchase alcoholic beverages in the United States states that a person must be at least 21, the laws involving a teen's attempt to purchase it or the use of a fake I.D. vary from state to state. (See chart, page 52.)

Marijuana is still the "drug" of choice among teens. A study by the University of Michigan's Institute of Social Research, based on responses by 73,000 high school seniors, showed that more than 40% of white males and 29.8% of black males had smoked marijuana during a one-year period, compared to 36% of white females and 18.4% of black females. The figures for cocaine use among the teens in this study were drastically lower: 12% for white males; 6.1% for black males; 9.3% for white females; and 2.6% for black females.

Kevin Zeese, vice president for the Drug Policy Foundation is quoted in *Fateful Choices:* "Black communities are faced with open drug dealing in their streets; they see crime and the horror associated with drugs." This, he felt, was the reason many black adolescents shy away from the use of drugs.

Music, it seems, is an indication of whether an adolescent is at high or low risk of becoming involved with not only drugs, alcohol, and tobacco, but also of cheating in class, cutting classes, engaging in sex, or driving without permission.

According to the American Academy of Pediatrics survey, heavy-metal bands were the favorite of white high-risk males, with 33% of them preferring it over all other types of music. Rock music was the favorite choice of all white females and low risk white males, but 18% of the high-risk females did prefer the heavy metal music. Music preference did not play a part in determining high or low risk black teens with both males and females choosing rap and soul music. Adolescents of both races listed gospel or Christian music more as their level of risk decreased.

Violence Intensifies

Violence seems to have become more and more a part of our everyday lives. Drive-by shootings are no longer front page news, and are watched with the same indifference that we watch the weather report on the evening news. For some families, however, violence has become a way of life. One woman in Bridgeport, Conn., according to news reports, buried her third and last son, a victim of that city's violence, in 1993. According to her, all had died as a result of random violence—being in the wrong place at the wrong time.

Unfortunately, hers is not a unique situation. According to a National Adolescent Health Survey, 41% of all boys and 24% of all girls could obtain a gun if they wanted it. In a Florida school study, 86% of all guns taken from the students had come from the homes of those students. Toy guns and real ones look so much alike to youths 14 and under that in reviewing 88 cases of youths that fatally shot other children or themselves, most happened because of loaded guns that had been found by the youths. "[B]lack males are five to six times as likely to die as a result of homicide as white males, and black girls are two to three times as likely to become homicide victims as white girls," according to *Fateful Choices.*

When a research team from the University of Maryland School of Medicine questioned 168 teens at an inner city clinic about their experiences with violence, "24% said they had witnessed a murder; 72% knew somebody who had been shot."

Such experiences can have devastating effects on today's adolescents. Lawrence Gary, director of the Institute for Urban Affairs and Research at Howard University said that even with the level of violence in the United States, this teen violence is a "new phenomenon in America." In 1988, 1,000 black children were victims of homicide, a 50% increase over 1985, and the figure just keeps rising, according to *Fateful Choices.*

The Forum on Youth Violence in Minority Communities states that having a gun in New York City is simply part of growing up among high-risk adolescents. In Washington, D.C., "serious injuries, especially from handguns, among youngsters seen at Children's Hospital have increased 1500% since 1986," reported *Fateful Choices.* Trauma centers also show an increase of shotgun wounds to teens under 18 years of age.

The Education Development Center in Massachusetts states: "Increasingly, the analogy is being drawn between life in America's poor urban neighborhoods and the battle zones of such countries as Lebanon, Northern Ireland, Afganistan, and Burma." What all this means, reported *Fateful Choices*, is that every 36 minutes a child is killed or hurt by a gun. That is more than 14,000 children each year. And while it is easy to say that those things only happen in the city, they don't.

Violence is increasing in surburbia, small towns and rural areas. And one result is that approximately 100,000 adolescents are in correctional institutions each day.

Risk factors were identified in August 1993 by an American Psychological Association panel consisting of 10 psychologists, one lawyer, and a former Washington, D.C. police chief. The panel felt that the risk factors for becoming a victim of violence included: dropping out of school, being unmarried, having a low income, or not owning a home. While three of the factors are not within the control of the teen, one is. Schools also recognize the problems associated with dropping out of school, and the need to prepare students for the time when they do graduate from school and are on their own.

The teaching of life skills, formerly the responsibility of family, school, and church, seem more and more to be handled by the school. "Its purpose is to teach adolescents how to form relationships, how to use social systems, how to develop healthy behavior, and how to allow their intellectual curiosity a wide range." No longer living in an extended family, and with the majority of homes now being run either by a single parent or with both parents working outside of the home, adolescents need "information from authorities they can trust," especially on matters relating to their personal "development and long-term health."

Debate Over TV

Television, the panel felt, "should be used to promote 'prosocial' attitudes and reduce violence." Ted Turner, a cable television executive, advised the House Energy and Commerce telecommunications subcommittee at a hearing in June "not to let up its campaign against T.V. violence." According to news reports, Turner urged the subcommittee to continue to monitor the amount of violence allowed to filter into daily programming.

The television industry announced in June that beginning with the Fall 1993 television season,

shows of questionable acceptance for children will carry a warning at the beginning of the show. The warning is: "Due to some violent content, parental discretion is advised."

While Representative Edward J. Markey (D.-Mass.) felt that this was a start, he said that he would push for legislation that would "require electronic devices to allow a parent to block shows from their home sets," according to an article in the July 1, 1993 *Hartford (CT) Courant*.

While warnings at the beginnings of shows, called the Advance Parental Advisory Plan, would have little effect on the millions of latchkey kids at home every day after school, a new technology called VideoFreedom announced in August that it had developed "cost effective technology" that would allow movie theaters and individual households alike the freedom to control what is viewed on their screens. The technology is available today on present-day televisions. All programs are broadcast at the "G" rating. Scenes depicting either violence, nudity, inappropriate language, or adult-only scenes are being "blurred." Such scenes can be "de-blurred" by a special decoding device that for now must be purchased, but in the future would be part of the standard T.V. equipment.

The blurring would not look like the blurry faces some present-day shows use to hide the identity of an "informant." Rather, a person and his neighbor would be watching different versions of the same show.

An example of how this would work would be: "An extremely graphic depiction of a man being slain by a gunshot, for example, can be selectively obscured at each level of VideoFreedom self-censoring. Level one would obscure the entire part of the frame showing the slain man, and the sounds from the victim would be indistinct. Level two would obscure all bloody portions of the victim. Level three would obscure the impact point of the bullet, and level four would involve no blurring. In addition, most viewers would not be unduly disturbed by the aesthetic effects of blurring. Blurring is applied only to selected portions of the screen or soundtrack. Color and brightness are retained in the blurring process so that there are no demarcations of blurred and unaltered material," according to VideoFreedom.

Teens watch an average of 30 hours of T.V. a week, many shows with a violent and/or sexual theme. *TV Guide* states that each year the American viewer can see "9,230 scenes of suggested sexual intercourse or innuendo, and fully 94% of the sex on soap operas involves people not married to each other." Also, it is rare in romantic scenes shown in movies, videocassettes, and rock videos that anyone seems concerned about the prevention of pregnancy. The Children's Television Act of 1990 was supposed to improve the quality of children's shows but, according to Rep. Markey, "children's television on commercial broadcast television today remains the video equivalent of a Twinkie."

The law limits advertising on these shows and requires the networks to offer more "educational and informative programs." A television station's license renewal rests, in part, on compliance with the law. PBS has always been the frontrunner in the area of educational shows for children. But, with the exception of ABC Afterschool Special, the four major networks—ABC, CBS, NBC, and Fox—have failed to produce the acceptable programming that will meet the educational needs of children.

Aside from there being few educational shows for children, Congress now says that there is far too much violence on the programs that are accessible to children. The "Parental Empowerment and Television Violence Reduction Act of 1993" introduced by Representatives Markey and Jack Fields (R.-Texas), "calls for all television sets sold in the United States to be equipped with technology to give parents the ability to block out unacceptable levels of violence."

Focus on Relationships and Behavior

The Carnegie Council on Adolescent Development sponsored a life skills training program in 1990, originally to deal with substance abuse. It soon became apparent that they needed to expand "to include adolescents' relationships with peers and their capacity to resist pressures from their peers who rationalize behavior with the excuse that 'everybody does it.'"

Another skill identified by the council as lacking in teens was assertiveness. While most adults, especially parents, feel that teens are assertive enough, the council felt that most teens needed specific training in how to go about finding out what was available

to them in the form of community services, and programs offered by health and social agencies. They also needed to be assertive in dealing with the intimidation of peer pressures, and how to resolve conflicts in a nonviolent manner. "Schools should teach problem-solving skills and 'anger management' so that children are better able to cope with crises," the American Psychological Association panel said.

Such a program, highlighted in *Fateful Choices*, has existed for more than a decade under the leadership of Robert Weisberg and his colleagues at Yale University. Since 1983, they have worked with New Haven schools to establish the Yale-New Haven Social Competence Promotion Program for middle-school students. The program deals with developing ways of dealing with potentially destructive behavior in an acceptable manner. "It proposes the following steps of behavior: 1, stop, calm down, and think before you act; 2, analyze the problem and your feelings about it; 3, set yourself a goal for action; 4, think of a variety of solutions; 5, consider the consequences of the various options; and 6, go ahead and explore what you think is the best plan, and if that plan does not work, try another."

This program has worked well in the New Haven schools. The teachers, who participated in a summer workshop conducted by the Yale faculty and veteran teachers of the program, felt "the youngsters showed improvement in controlling their impulses," and the students felt that they didn't get in as much trouble for misbehaving at school. "Both teachers and students found the program effective."

Between Schools and Health Centers

More and more attention is being centered on "school-based or school-related clinics," as 14% of adolescents have no health insurance with many of them receiving no regular health care, according to *Fateful Choices*. Less than 200,000 adolescents have school-based clinics available to them. That's less than 1% of the approximately 35 million people aged 10 to 19 in the United States. At present, there are less than 400 centers in use. While not all adolescents are in need of school-based health centers, those that do use them are almost 100% without access to any other services. Thirty-eight percent of the clients using one center said that they would not have gone somewhere else for treatment had the center not been available. Twenty-six of those that use the school-related center said that before the school center, the only form of health care had been trips to the emergency room.

Thomas H. Kean, former governor of New Jersey and presently the president of Drew University, said that New Jersey's school-based clinics give teenagers "one-stop shopping," which is important to those with the least time, money, and education to use to deal with the frustrating system of bureaucratic health care. School-related clinics have all services under one roof where adolescents can deal with all facets of their health—illnesses and preventive measures alike, according to the Fall 1992 *Carnegie Quarterly* Magazine.

A small minority of critics originally opposed school-related clinics, feeling that the availability of reproductive health information would encourage teens to increase their sexual activity. This has proven to be false. Sexual activity does not seem to have increased, and the number of teenage pregnancies has decreased.

At the Pinelands Regional District in rural New Jersey, Kean reported in 1990-91, "school suspensions declined from 322 to 73, dropouts decreased from 78 to 24 and teen pregnancies, from 20 to 13, with only one occurring in 1991–92." In Hackensack, N.J., a conflict resolution program organized by a school-based youth center reduced students' fights from 172 to 32 in a three-year period.

I'm Too Fat!

Girls are obsessed with being thin. Examples of the "right" way to look are everywhere: movie and T.V. stars, super models in magazines, even models doing ads for diet products and health centers. Ever see an overweight person in the health club ads? Girls as young as 8 years old talk of being on a diet so they can grow up to look like this or that model. While more of today's kids are fighting the battle of the bulge than did kids a generation ago, weight loss nowadays has become an obsession. In a study done in South Carolina involving 3,000 elementary school children, only 20% were overweight. However, 40% the students, in judging themselves, felt that they were fat and needed to lose weight. Of them, 15% admitted they had either fasted or vomited as a

method of weight loss, according to an article published in the March 3, 1993 *Stamford (CT) Advocate.*

Youth professionals say that they are starting to see more and more elementary school children involved in weight loss psychological disorders: bulimia and anorexia nervosa. In a study involving 500 fourth-grade girls that was published in the March 1993 issue of *3-2-1 Contact* magazine, 400 said that they had dieted when only 100 were in need of losing weight. Unfortunately, these previously were considered illnesses of older teenagers and young adults.

Adolescents Shorted on Medical Care

The health needs of the adolescent are unique. During no other time in a life will a person come in contact with such an array of potentially deadly scenarios. The threat of AIDS, pregnancy, drug and alcohol abuse, and violence are paramount in the life of the adolescent. With the Carnegie Corporation calling preventive care for our adolescents "an investment in the nation's future," the American Medical Association (AMA) is recommending annual check-ups for teens.

The American Academy of Pediatrics, in cooperation with Bright Futures, which is funded by the Maternal and Child Health Bureau of the Public Health Service, also are writing new guidelines as to acceptable health care requirements for the adolescent. All of this is in preparation for the emergence in 1994 of a new subspeciality of pediatrics called Adolescent Medicine.

The leading causes of death among adolescents are no longer illnesses and diseases; they are motor vehicle accidents, homicide, and suicide. Teens need a physician trained to understand and recognize teens in distress. What adolescents need is "a one-to-one relationship with the doctor trained in child development and sensitive to the concerns of this sensitive age group," said Dr. Esterann M. Grace, senior associate in adolescent medicine at Children's Hospital, Boston, in the March 15, 1993 *Boston Globe*. Privacy between adolescent and the doctor is the only way for the teen to feel that he or she can open up and candidly discuss problems.

Another important function of doctors in adolescent medicine is being able to steer young patients in the right direction—getting the message to teens that they must take responsibility for their own actions, and that what they eat and drink, how and if they exercise, and what risks they take in life will ultimately determine their quality of life and their future. With teens being able to discuss not only pimples and cramps, but also depression and sexuality, and a safe way to lose weight, this generation of teens will have the most up-to-date information available for living a long and healthy life to the maximum.

Accidents

The number one killer of children in the United States is nothing anyone did to them on purpose; the number one killer of children is accidents, and saying "sorry" doesn't make things better.

According to the National Safe Kids Campaign, approximately 8,000 children aged 1–14 will die from preventable injuries in 1993. That is more than all the combined deaths from childhood diseases. A frightening figure of 50,000 kids will be injured seriously enough to cause permanently disabling in-

The National Safe Kids Campaign's top spokesman is C. Everett Koop, former U.S. Surgeon General.

jury, and 25% of all children will be injured seriously enough to spend time in the emergency room of the hospital. That accounts for more than 35,000 children each day.

The leading cause of injury and death to children aged 10–14 is as passengers in motor vehicles. Next comes pedestrian injuries (being hit by a car), drownings, moped and motorcycle injuries, firearm injuries, and bicycle injuries.

Every year approximately 1,700 children ages 0–14 are killed riding in motor vehicles. Of those, 400 were under the age of 4, and of those 336, or 84%, were not restrained in child safety seats. Most of the fatalities occur on Fridays and Saturdays and during the summer months.

The second leading cause of death among children is fire: 1,200 children—that's 25 a week—are killed by home fires. Ninety percent of those deaths occured in homes without working smoke detectors. Nearly 10 times that number, 11,000, are injured.

Smoke detectors are for sale for as little as $10 each, and some towns have free smoke detectors available for all who request them. A local fire department is usually the place to check. Firefighters can instruct as to the best places in the home to place them. Smoke detectors need to be tested once a month and the batteries need to be replaced once a year. It has been suggested that a date of importance to the family—Christmas, a birthday, ground hog day, etc.—be picked by the family members as the day to change the batteries.

Ever see a movie where a house is on fire and the people are moving through the rooms to escape but the viewer can see everyone moving around? Well, that's not the way it happens. Smoke in a fire is thick and so black and people cannot see their way to the door to get out. Two different escape routes should be chosen and fire drills practiced so that a family knows how to get out in case of a fire. Smoke and heat rise, so sometimes it is necessary to crawl out. And a family should designate a place to meet outside the house, so that firefighters can be advised if a family member is still inside.

Every day 100 children are scalded by hot liquids. They are burned in bathwater too hot for their tender skin. They are burned when their curiousity gets the best of them and they pull the pots off the stove when

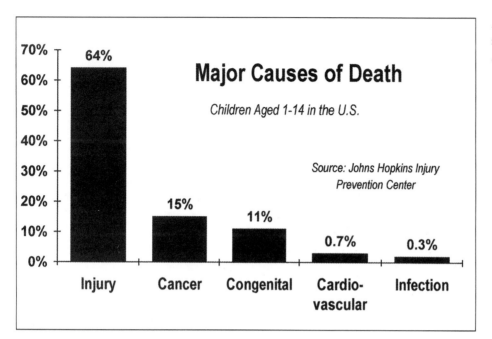

Major Causes of Death

Children Aged 1-14 in the U.S.

Source: Johns Hopkins Injury Prevention Center

Injuries cause most deaths among children.

the handles are left sticking out. Every day children under the age of 14 are burned and scalded badly enough to require hospital care. While the trip to the emergency room takes only a few hours, the scars and pain will be with the child for a lifetime.

The National Safe Kids Campaign reports that each year 37,000 children aged 0–14 have scald burns severe enough to require a trip to the emergency room. Hot-water scalds (usually from the bathwater) are three times as likely to require a hospital stay for the child, with an average stay of 17 days. Most of these burns are received by children under the age of 5. Hot water burns are more likely to happen when the child is left in the bath tub while the person bathing him leaves to answer the door, phone, etc., and the child turns on the hot water faucet.

Drowning is the third cause of unintentional injury-related deaths among children under the age of 14. Each year 1,200 children under the age of 14 die in drownings. The greatest majority of drownings take place in swimming pools, with 70% of the preschoolers being watched by at least one of their parents at the time the drowning occurs. 3,600 to 4,600 children aged 0–14 are admitted to hospitals and another 14,000 to 16,000 are treated in emergency rooms and released each year because of near-drowning experiences, according to the National Safe Kids Campaign.

The more popular bicycling has become, the higher the incidence of accidents and injuries has risen. Each year 400 children die in bicycle accidents with nearly all (360) involving a motor vehicle. In 1990, nearly 1,000 times as many children, (383,459) had to be brought to the emergency room because of bicycle accidents, according to statistics released by the National Safe Kids Campaign. Clearly, the worst injury a child can receive in an accident is one that involves trauma to the head. While only 1 in 7 children involved in bike accidents sustain head injuries, as the below-14 age group becomes older teenagers and young adults, the number of cyclists' deaths caused by head injuries jumps to 75% with all hospitalized cyclist injuries being head trauma jumping to 70%.

Bicycle helmets, once looking like football helmets have taken on a new and sophisticated look now that they have not only become a fashion statement, but also can reduce head injury by 85% and brain injury by as much as 90%. Sadly, only 5% of all children wear helmets. Many states now have bicycle helmet laws either on the books or in the works for children under the age of 14.

Motor vehicle accidents are clearly the major cause of death of youngsters under the age of 14 and also a major cause of death from 15–19; for black teens, however, between the ages of 15–19 the major cause of death is homicide.

Emergency Medical Services

Among the recommendations put forth in 1993 to improve the odds for adolescents and children, the Institute of Medicine, in its report *Emergency Medical Services for Children,* recommended the following improvements in the way emergency medical services are handled in the United States:

"Better communication networks including access to 9-1-1 emergency systems in every community nationwide; better resources for providing good care including equipping ambulances and emergency departments with instruments and medications appropriate for use in treating children; and better training for emergency care professionals who often must care for children."

The committee further emphasized that "children cannot be regarded simply as 'little adults'; children are smaller and proportioned differently. There must be different and special equipment, different-sized instruments, different doses of different drugs, and different approaches to the psychological support and medical care to be given to the ill or injured child."

The following changes were recommended at the federal level. "Congress [should] direct the U.S. Department of Health and Human Services to establish a federal center to conduct, oversee, and coordinate activities related to planning and evaluation, research, and technical assistance in emergency medical services for children." The committee also would like to see the creation of a national advisory council with its members coming from "federal agencies, state, and local governments, the health care community, and the general public," according to a report released in July 1993 by the Institute of Medicine.

Congress, the committee felt, should appropriate $30 million a year for a period of five years to allow federal and state agencies to make the necessary changes.

"The 9-1-1 system must be universally accessible and effectively linked to the emergency medical services system," the committee said. As of 1993, not all states are at 100% assessibility to the 9-1-1 system. In some states, the percentage is less than 50%. The committee also would like to see "enhanced 9-1-1 capabilities," meaning a computerized system that "automatically identifies the telephone number and location of the caller," which would tell the dispatcher exactly from where the call came even if the caller could not respond. In other words, a parent could teach a child how to dial 9-1-1 in an emergency, even if the child were unable to tell the dispatcher about the emergency.

The committee also felt that there was a need for emergency information lines, such as poison control centers, that could give emergency treatment information over the telephone and, if necessary, dispatch an ambulance. While many emergency departments offer information over the telephone, "appropriate training, clear protocols, careful documentation, and routine monitoring" was strongly recommended.

Communication, the committee felt, is important if all possible agencies are to work together in an emergency. "Public education and training programs in prevention and safety, first aid, cardiopulmonary resuscitation, and the appropriate use of emergency medical services," were programs that the committee felt should be available to the general public. Parents, day care workers, teachers, and coaches were mentioned by the committee as high priority recipients of training programs.

Emergency equipment also needs to be of a size appropriate for use on a child. An example of inappropriately sized equipment would be a cervical collar used for neck injuries. Inappropriate equipment "leads to children being placed in collars that are too large, often obscuring their faces and even impairing ventilation," the committee said.

Furthermore, the committee felt that better training in pediatric emergency care was necessary as training up to now has not devoted a lot of attention to this area. It would like to see an "accrediting organization . . . ensure that other training programs include essential elements of pediatric emergency care."

While the committee noted that "progress has been made in recent years to improve emergency care for children, [it] acknowledged that much work remains to be done. Public policies and programs for children are often too fragmented. It called such fragmentation 'unacceptable' for emergency medical services for children."

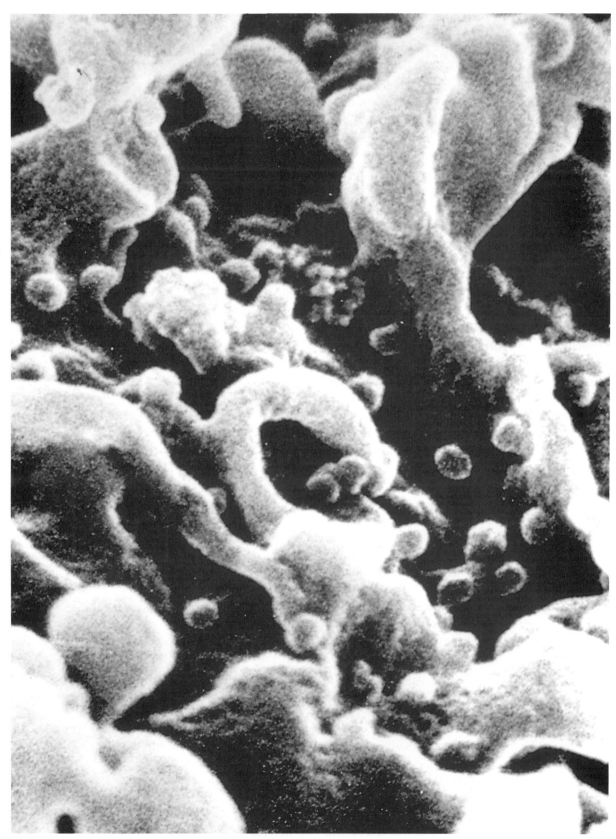

A T-4 lymphocyte infected with HIV-1.

5

FOR AIDS, A LONGER ROSTER OF VICTIMS

"The human immunodeficiency virus (HIV) has profoundly changed life on our planet. America has not done well in acknowledging this fact or in mobilizing its vast resources to address it appropriately."

Those words, written by Drs. June E. Osborn and David E. Rogers, as leaders of the the National Commission on Acquired Immune Deficiency Syndrome (AIDS), summed up the mood of many health care professionals in 1993 toward the AIDS epidemic.

"We end our four years' work hoping for a new era," Osborn and Rogers wrote in the preface to *AIDS: An Expanding Tragedy: The Final Report of the National Commission on AIDS.* The commission was chartered by federal law to promote the development of a national consensus policy on AIDS, but no such policy existed when the commission's work formally expired September 3, 1993.

In its final report, the commission made two recommendations:

- "Leaders at all levels must speak out about AIDS to their constituencies," and
- "We must develop a clear, well-articulated national plan for confronting AIDS."

Who Has Aids

According to the Centers for Disease Control and Prevention, while more men have AIDS, the number of reported cases in women in 1992 were recorded at a rate of four times that of men. Of these cases, 50% were the result of heterosexual contact. However, 57% of the heterosexual contact was with men who were IV drug users. And 44% of the women's cases were due to the women themselves using IV drugs.

Dr. June E. Osborn, dean of the School of Public Health at the University of Michigan in Ann Arbor was quoted by *Science News* as saying: "The trends are all in the direction of a heterosexually transmitted disease," The CDC reported 47,095 new cases of AIDS in 1992, an increase of 3.5% over 1991.

Arthur Ashe, 49, died February 6, 1993 of AIDS-related pneumonia in New York. Mr. Ashe, tennis champion of both the Wimbledon and U.S. Open was the only black man ever to win the titles. He became infected with the HIV virus through a blood transfusion he received for heart by-pass surgery in 1983. His illness became known to him in 1988. Although he treasured his privacy, he went public with his illness, becoming an activist against the disease, founding a fund-raising organization, and joining the boards of both Harvard and UCLA's AIDS Institutes. Today, blood is tested before transfusions are given. Unfortunately, this was not always the case.

AIDS is a killer without a conscience. An 11-year-old girl in Illinois is among 90 children in the United States that have AIDS with no clues as to how she, or the other 89 contracted the disease. She does not fall into any of the high-risk categories of AIDS, and all members of her family have tested negative.

While medical experts have theorized what might have happened, the mystery remains. She was to travel to the National Cancer Institute in Bethesda, Md., for treatment in 1993, where an experimental

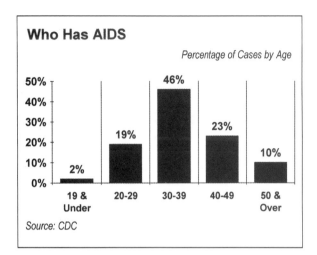

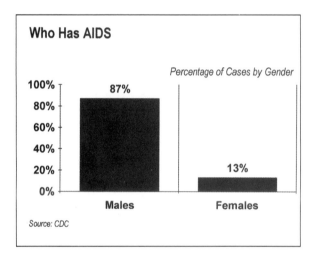

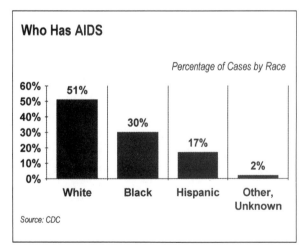

Statistics from the Centers for Disease Control and Prevention illustrated the diversity of people affected by the AIDS epidemic.

drug, rifabutin, recently approved by the Food and Drug Administration, hopefully, will work to stop the disease.

According to the Centers for Disease Control and Prevention, AIDS and its related illnesses has become the leading cause of death for young men in five states: New York, New Jersey, California, Florida, and Massachusetts. The diseases also are responsible for 61% of the deaths of young men in San Francisco, and more than half the deaths in Elizabeth, N.J., and Fort Lauderdale, Fla. AIDS and its related illnesses were responsible for more deaths of young women in the cities of New Haven and Stamford, Conn., Miami and Fort Lauderdale, Fla., Baltimore, Md., Jersey City, Newark, and Paterson, N.J., and New York City.

The AIDS epidemic, according to the CDC, is now claiming more heterosexuals, blacks, and teenagers. Among 13–19 year olds, the ratio of HIV, the virus that causes AIDS, to AIDS is running 10 to 1. There is a gap of 10 years between HIV and full-blown AIDS. The ratio, though, for teenaged girls is running 22 to 1. According to the CDC, this is a result for more infection through heterosexual relations. It also indicates a more serious problem in the future.

President Bill Clinton named Kristine Gebbie the nation's first AIDS czar in 1993. It will be her task to coordinate all government AIDS programs in the United States. She backs a needle program, wants a more open approach to AIDS education, and wants to get different government agencies talking to each other. "Anyone who is sexually active should have ready access to means of protection which includes condoms," Gebbie was quoted as saying in the June 30, 1993 *New York Times*.

Historical Perspective

A decade ago, a man in Australia needed blood during surgery. He received a blood transfusion that had been donated by a gay man who had unknowingly contracted the AIDS virus. Five people received his blood before the virus was detected. Today, the first blood recipient is alive and well and in his 80s; the other people who received the tainted blood are alive and well; and the donor is alive and well.

Dr. Brett Tindall, an AIDS researcher at the University of New South Wales, was intrigued. Were these six still alive and well because of diet, vitamins, an unknown gene that they had in common?

What the doctor may have stumbled on could be "the viral equivalent of a fossil, a clue to the origin, evolution and future of the AIDS epidemic," the March 22, 1993 *Newsweek* reported. This may not be at all the new disease that has terrorized the world for the past 10 years, but rather a disease that has been around, possibly for hundreds, or even thousands of years.

Paul Ewald, an evolutionary biologist, is a believer that HIV, the virus that causes AIDS (acquired immunodeficiency syndrome), has always been around and has infected people all along. Before, HIV had only its host body on which to rely for nourishment. Kill the host and kill itself. It was not until the lifestyles of the 1960s and '70s did HIV have the opportunity to move as quickly from being to being, allowing it to grow and become more and more aggressive.

In the scientific community, it is common knowledge that parasites—and a virus is a parasite—evolve by natural selection, that is, they are able to change, adapting to fit their particular environment. Scientists are trying to use the virus' ability to change—to mutate—so much in fighting off the drugs to control it that it will mutate itself right out of existence, or at least out of danger. A medical student, Yung-Kang Chow, has done just that in test tubes at Massachusetts General Hospital in Boston.

The drug treatment is one way of, hopefully, controlling the virus. Prevention might be another. According to *Newsweek,* "If rapid spread is what turned HIV into a killer, then condoms and clean needles may ultimately do more than prevent new infections. Used widely enough, they might drive the AIDS virus toward the benign form sighted in Australia."

All forms of life have evolved from earlier forms, and the HIV-1 and HIV-2 viruses are no exception. "When you see HIV-2, you may not be looking at a human virus but at a mangabey [an ash-colored monkey] virus in a human," said Gerald Myers, head of the HIV database project at the Los Alamos National Labratory, as reported in the March 22 edition of *Newsweek*, from which part of this historical information is adapted.

Both are "genetically similar to viruses found in African primates, the so-called SIVs [simian viruses].

The HIVs have more in common with the simian viruses than they do with each other. HIV-2, found mainly in West Africa, is so similar to the SIV that infects the sooty mangabey—from the same region—that it doesn't really qualify as a separate viral species," *Newsweek* reported. While HIV-1 is not similar to HIV-2 or to SIV, it does resemble SIVcpz, a virus found in a wild chimpanzee in Gabon, a country located in West Africa. HIV-1 is responsible for most of the world's AIDS cases.

While it is possible that HIVs and SIVs evolved separately, the most widely accepted theory is that humans were originally infected from direct contact with primates, and, while it is also possible that primates were infected by humans, the reverse is more generally accepted. There are several reasons for this line of thinking: First, SIVs, more varied than the HIVs, apparently have been evolving longer. Second, the primate-to-human senario just makes more sense. People have been touching primates for years. They have hunted them and, in the process, been scratched or bitten by the primates. Also, primates were used as food years ago and, in the butchering process, bodily fluids could have passed through cuts and sores on the humans' hands.

The Centers for Disease Control and Prevention recently reported that of two lab workers—one

Kristine Gebbie became the U.S.'s first AIDS czar in 1993.

jabbed with a needle used on an infected macaque, and one who handled monkey tissue with open sores on her hands—the latter has been SIV positive now for two years. In the first case, the lab technician was not infected, but did develop antibodies to SIV. The antibodies, however, only lasted a few months. It is still uncertain as to whether or not the SIV-infected lab worker will eventually develop AIDS.

It is still unclear as to when humans first picked up the SIV virus—possibly thousands of years ago, since people have been in direct contact with primates. Others feel that the development of AIDS began in the 1950s with the mass vaccination of Africans against polio. In Africa, the vaccine was "produced in kidney cells from African green monkeys." However, the SIVs found in African green monkeys does not resemble HIV-1. "In order to link HIV-1 to those early lots of polio vaccine, someone would have to show that they contained a monkey virus never yet found in actual monkeys."

Then, going back to the idea that HIVs are very old viruses, this theory is just as hard to prove. According to *Newsweek*, Dr. Jay Levy, an AIDS researcher at the University of California, San Franscisco, said, "We know that all these other primates harbor lentiviruses [the class that includes the SIVs and HIVs]. Why should humans be any exception?" In other words, it doesn't matter where they came from, only whether or not they caused the disease. If the HIV virus had always been the cause of the disease AIDS, then, the HIVs and AIDS should be historically paralleled. But they're not.

Dr. James Curran (left) is head of the Centers for Disease Control and Prevention, and Dr. John Ward (right) heads one of the CDC's AIDS programs.

"Antibodies to HIV have been detected in rare blood samples dating back to 1959, yet the first African AIDS cases were described in the early 1980s, when the disease started decimating the cities of Rwanda, Zaire, Zambia, and Uganda." Dr. Robert Bigger, a National Cancer Institute epidemiologist looked for AIDS-like illnesses at the African hospitals, none could be found. While it's possible that the doctor simply missed the AIDS symptoms, it is highly unlikely. Another scenario is more probable.

As mentioned earlier, when a virus—a parasite—lives within a host, the virus needs to make sure the host remains healthy enough to stay alive. A dead host means a dead virus. Most microbes travel through our social contact. Our "cold and flu" symptoms—coughing and sneezing—allow the viruses a mode of transportation from one human to another. For them to stay alive, the host needs to stay alive.

Bacteria, on the other hand, don't need their host to stay alive. They can become airborne, and stay like that for weeks, months, or even longer until another host comes along, as is the case with the bacteria that cause tuberculosis or diphtheria. The bacteria can afford to be aggressive and attack with a vengeance because the host does not need to stay alive for them to live.

HIVs affect human white blood cells. During sex or the exchange of body fluids the infected cells, or new viruses, are passed from one person to another. Now, if the people with the HIVs were an isolated group, it would not be wise for the virus to become aggressive, but as populations have become more mobile and people in more social contact with each other, the viruses have been able to move into more of the world's population.

Once the viruses were better able to move through the world's people, the more aggressively they could attack and kill their host, as there would be so many more hosts with which to live. While all of this could just be a coincidence, the circumstantial evidence is astounding: "Starting in the 1960s, war, tourism, and commercial trucking forced the outside world on Africa's once isolated villages," reported *Newsweek*.

At the same time drought and industrialization prompted mass migrations from the countryside into newly teeming cities, urbanization shattered social structures that had long constrained sexual behavior.

Prostitution exploded, and venereal disease flourished. Hypodermic needles came into wide use during the same period, creating yet another mode of infection.

For Ewald's theory to hold true, the strongest, deadliest HIVs should be in populations where it moves the quickest from host to host. And that is exactly what is happening. The people that were infected with the HIV-1 cause 90% of all the AIDS cases, and HIV- 2 is responsible for the other, milder form that affects the other 10%.

"Maybe everyone infected with HIV-2 will progress to AIDS after 40 or 50 years, but that's still in the realm of reduced virulence," said Harvard University AIDS specialist Max Essex. According to Ewald, that makes sense. West Africa, home of HIV-2 escaped the majority of the war, urbanization, and drought that affected the eastern and central areas of Africa.

"HIV-2 appears to be adapted for slow transmission in areas with lower sexual contact, and HIV-1 for more rapid transmission in areas with higher sexual contact," said Ewald. His theory can be seen in the way the HIVs affect the different populations. The people of Senegal, are affected with the HIV-2, which "appears mild in the stable and isolated West African nation."

Laboratory testing done at the University of Alabama, using Senegalese HIV-2 did not kill white blood cells in the test tube. However, on the Ivory Coast of Africa, a more urban and less traditional lifestyle than is found in Senegal, the U.S. Centers for Disease Control and Prevention found HIV-2 to be as much a killer as the HIV-1. It is not as clear-cut with the HIV-1 strain.

Intravenous (IV) drug users are, perhaps, contracting a deadlier strain than gay men since the IV users rates have remained high since the early 1980s. In two studies cited in *Newsweek,* "a 1990 study of infected gay men fewer than 8% of those not receiving early treatment developed AIDS each year. In a more recent study of IV users, the proportion of untreated carriers developing AIDS each year was more than 17%."

During tests in laboratories, when the virus has had many cells to infect, it basically goes wild, killing the cells. However, when the viruses were confined to individual cells, they became benign, so as to keep their host alive.

The Cure

HIV, much to the dismay of the scientists trying to eradicate it, mutates easily. This means that while one drug may work for a while to control it, the HIVs seem to have a way of protecting themselves and mutating.

AZT, a popular drug for AIDS a couple of years back, turned out to only be effective for a short period of time. After a while, AIDS victims' bodies became resistant to the drug, causing it to no longer work to control the AIDS.

While clean needles and condom use have begun to turn the tables on HIV, there are still 12 million people walking around with the HIV time bomb. Scientists are trying to outsmart the virus that can change or mutate almost at will.

Yung-Kang Chow, the medical student at Massachusetts General Hospital, has come up with a way of hopefully fooling the HIV out of existence. A scientific team, headed by Yung-Kang Chow, is using three drugs simultaneously. The first is AZT; the second is ddI, and the third drug is pyridinone. All three of these drugs mutate the HIVs. The hypothesis is that AZT mutates some, ddI a little more, and pyridinone a little more so that the a virus becomes too deformed to function.

Treatments

Because of the AIDS epidemic facing babies born to AIDS-infected mothers, an unproven vaccine will be used on newborns of mothers that were HIV positive in 1993. This will be a pilot program using less than 100 babies at major hospital centers. If the tests prove safe, the study will be expanded to about 800 infants. Babies are infected in one of two ways: in the womb, and passing through the birth canal.

Dr. John Sullivan, of the University of Massachusetts Medical School of Medicine in Worcester, said that "at least half of the infants are infected as they pass through the birth canal." He also said that approximately 1,500 babies are born each year in the United States with the HIV virus, according to a report in the February 12, 1993 New York *Newsday.*

WHO, the World Health Organization, now estimates that the majority of people worldwide that are now contracting AIDS are getting it through heterosexual contact. And, while that is true on a world-

Dr. Anthony S. Fauci is director of the National Institute of Allergy and Infectious Diseases, at the National Institutes of Health.

wide scale, the majority of people contracting AIDS in Hartford, Conn., is due to IV drug use. Because of this and the success of nearby New Haven's needle exchange program, Hartford began an official needle-exchange program.

New Haven expects a 30 to 35% drop in people infected with HIV because of the exchange program, according to Edward H. Kaplan, an associate professor at Yale University School of Medicine.

The program in Hartford will be a one for one exchange with a maxium of five needles per day exchanged. Drug users also will be offered AIDS testing, counseling, and the opportunity to sign up for a drug treatment program.

Beth Weinstein, the chief of the AIDS division of the state department of Health Services in Connecticut said that the New Haven needle-exchange program did not promote drug use, according to a March 23, 1993 story that appeared in the *Hartford Courant*. Connecticut legalized a needle exchange after it became one of only three states in which homosexuality had been replaced by IV drug use as the way the majority of people contracted AIDS.

WHO is recommending a live, though weakened, form of the HIV virus as a treatment. Reaction,

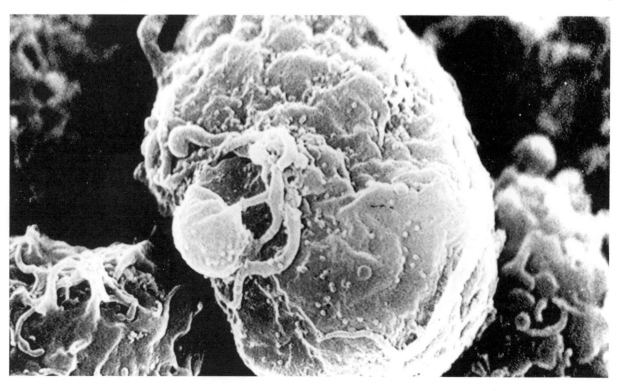

although mixed, tended to lean toward an unfavorable response. Most researchers have rejected the idea, stating that using a live virus would be taking too much of a risk. Dr. Robert C. Gallo said, "This is an extremely hazardous proposition, in my mind. I feel I have to speak out against it. . . . The risk is astronomical." Dr. Gallo is a co- discoverer of HIV.

Anthony Fauci, a scientist who also is the top AIDS official at the U.S. National Institutes of Health, said although the U.S. is not against live virus research, genetically engineered vaccine research is probably a safer way to go. A live virus vaccine would be cheaper to produce than the genetically engineered version.

WHO is concerned with getting a vaccine to the developing countries of Thailand, Uganda, Rwanda, and Brazil because of their high percentage of infected people. Some, however, feel that the Third World nations would be used as guinea pigs and the safer, genetically engineered version of the vaccine would be saved for testing in the United States.

A drug used unsuccessfully in the 1950s outside the United States to control morning sickness in pregnant women and subsequently caused serious birth defects now has a new use. Thalidomide hinders the growth of the TNF-alpha (tumor necrosis factor-alpha). "TNF-alpha is known to be probably the most important physiological activator of HIV. There is evidence that if you can inhibit TNF-alpha, then you can inhibit HIV," said Gilla Kaplan, a Rockefeller University immunologist, according to news reports.

In laboratory tests involving HIV positive blood in test tubes, the reproduction of the virus was curtailed. Additionally, thalidomide also may have some good side effects. Preliminary tests show that thalidomide helps reverse the "body wasting" that is so common in people infected with AIDS. "They start gaining weight at an unimaginable rate until they get back to normal body weight," said Kaplan.

Jonas Salk, the polio vaccine pioneer of the 1950s has been working on an AIDS vaccine. The Salk Immunogen is a "therapeutic vaccine." It is designed to work to improve the immune system of a person already infected. Others are working on vaccines to prevent infection with a genetic engineering technique. Salk is relying on the same method he used in the 1950s with polio. He is using a killed form of the virus. His critics feel that HIV is too sophistated a virus for Salk's method to be successful. Salk has

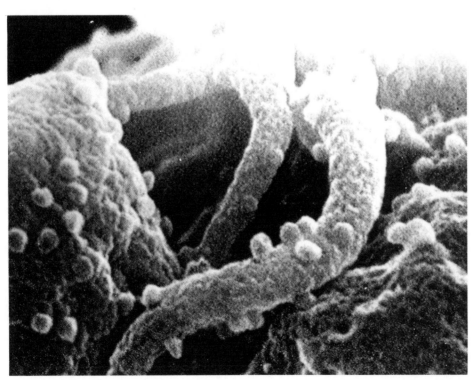

(Opposite) A scanning electron micrograph shows HIV-1 infected T-4 lymphocytes. The virus is budding from the plasma membrane of the lymphocytes.

(Left) A greater magnification of the micrograph.

tested his vaccine and it has been proven to be safe. It is still too soon to tell if the vaccine is effective.

A spherical carbon molecule, commonly referred to as a "buckyball," could be just what the scientists have been looking for. As reported in the August 3, 1993 *New York Times,* "the 'buckyball,' also called 'buckminsterfullerene,' is a spherical cage made entirely of carbon atoms—60 of them, in the most common form of the molecule. The existence of this molecule was discovered in 1985." The molecule was named after the late architect and engineer R. Buckminster Fuller. Chemists at the University of California campuses at San Franscisco and Santa Barbara said they designed a computer model of the buckyball and in tests it "inhibited the action of an enzyme needed by the virus to reproduce.

Scientists say that this is not a drug, but a chemical. "We are not claiming that this is a drug," said George L. Kenyon of the department of pharmaceutical chemistry at the San Francisco campus, "But we think it's a pretty exciting lead that could be modified later by different chemistry to make it into a drug."

The buckyball is part of a new branch of chemistry that deals with a new group of compounds known as fullerenes. They are carbon molecules that, when combined, resemble geometric domes. Dr. Kenyon said, "[that] the buckyball's success in interfering with the reproductive system of HIV, which causes AIDS, apparently results from the buckyball's size and unusual spherical shape."

HIV reproduces by growing a long protein chain, a polypeptide, which must be cut by the virus itself. HIV protease, an enzyme that works as a catalyst, is a larger molecule that has a hollow area in it called an "active site." This is where the chain must cut itself to be able to reproduce. An anti-AIDS strategy is to hinder the "active site."

Simon Friedman, one of Dr. Kaplan's graduate students, noticed "that the size of the protease active site just about matched that of the buckyball, and he began to wonder if a buckyball would fit inside it, stick, and block the site," Dr. Kenyon said. "The buckyball completely inhibited the action of the enzyme. We believe that the buckyball fits tightly inside the active site, thereby plugging the hole and barring it to the HIV polypeptide chain. Without the protease's active site, the chain cannot break up into

its reproductively essential components," said Dr. Kenyon. Hopefully, he added, this may turn out to be a tool against the problem of AIDS.

As mentioned earlier, a medical student at Massachusetts General Hospital may have come up with the best method of all. One of the reasons it has been so difficult to control and destroy the HIV viruses is that it has that chameleon quality to be able to change or mutate itself so that the drug that is being used to destroy its growth becomes powerless . This is why the drug AZT will only work for a couple of years and then lose its efficiency.

Yung-Kang Chow feels that a combination of three drugs at once will be able to outsmart the virus. Since it is known that the virus will mutate, to change so that the present drug will be ineffective, Yung-Kang Chow feels that as the virus mutates and mutates, and mutates, to avoid the ill effects the drugs

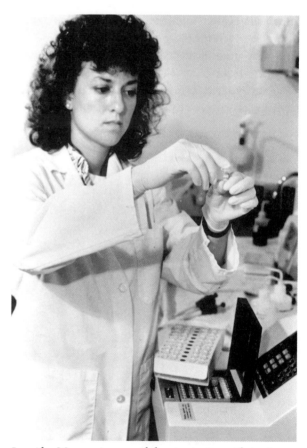

Jennifer Moore, in one of the many research projects on AIDS, performs a polymerase chain reaction test at the Centers for Disease Control and Prevention.

Results for a Western blot test conducted for AIDS research are recorded for analysis.

Larry Wells performs a standard enzyme-linked immunosorbent assay during AIDS research at the Centers for Disease Control in Atlanta.

do to it, the virus should mutate itself right out of the harmful effects it presently has on people.

Yang-Kang Chow plans to use three out of four drugs: two that are approved and presently being sold as anti-HIV drugs—AZT and ddI, and either pyridinone or nevirapine, two experimental ones. Early in 1993, the National Institutes of Health picked 10 yet undisclosed medical sites in the United States to be treating 200 patients with advanced HIV infections.

Part of the wonder of this is that it is against tradition to consider this type of medical treatment. The medical theory has always been to use different types of drugs "aimed at different steps in the life cycle of the microbe. One drug might be chosen because it works against one target in a microbe, a second drug against another target and so on. Such combinations are used in treating tuberculosis," according to a story in the February 18, 1993 *New York Times.*

Since it is known that the HIV virus will mutate to save itself, "[Yang-Kang] Chow's strategy, called convergent combination therapy, is designed to force it to produce several drug-resistance mutations simultaneously in a crucial viral enzyme, reverse transcription. Mr. Chow's strategy was to choose a combination directed at a single target," reported the *New York Times.*

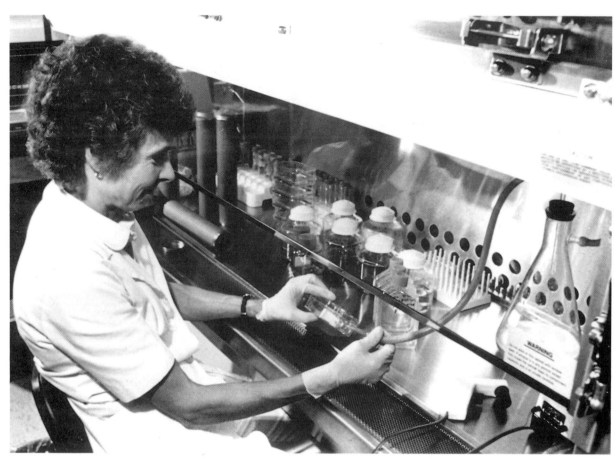

Judith Galphin processes cell cultures in a biosafety cabinet at the Centers for Disease Control and Prevention.

Trying several different drugs, but deciding on AZT, ddI, and pyridinine, he prevented HIV replication. "When the drugs were stopped 21 days after infection, the scientists reported, no viral replication was observed for the next 30 days and no evidence of HIV could be detected with the most sophisticated methods. Even after the drugs were removed at day 56, no viral replication was observed for the next 45 days of the test," according to the same *New York Times* story.

The Knowledgeable Public

People now say thet they are more informed now than they were in 1985. In a June 1993 *New York Times*/CBS NEWS poll, 45% of the people polled said they knew a lot about AIDS, up from 10% in 1985. Those that knew someone who had died from AIDS—26%, up from 15%; and someone who has AIDS—16%, up from 1%; 79% now know that

someone cannot get AIDS by using a drinking glass after an infected person has used it. That is up from 34% in 1985. Sixty-nine percent now know that sexual intercourse is one way of getting AIDS, and 98% said that someone could get AIDS from a blood transfusion.

Some Have It Worse

While the AIDS epidemic is defintely taking its toll on the United States, other areas of the world are hit harder.

Some situations are too sad for words. The country of Uganda in Africa is such a place. It is quickly becoming a country where a boy becomes "the man of the house," sometimes before he becomes a teenager. Such was the case of Julius Keeya Kintu. His father became ill with AIDS five years ago. He taught his son all that he knew about farming their couple of acres. Together they fixed up their house, a "brick and thatch hut," and then his father died.

In late 1992, his mother became too ill to care for Julius and his six siblings. She traveled to her mother's home to die. Julius, at 13, is now the man of the house. "My father taught me how to plant and my mother, she taught me discipline," said Julius. His story was contained in a special report in the *New York Times.*

Ten years after AIDS was first discovered in Uganda, "AIDS- related deaths have left between 1.5 and 2 million children without fathers; most have also lost their mothers. A 1991 census in the hard hit districts of Rakai and Masaka listed 25% of the children as orphans. The government knows that it dare not take them off the land. The land and farming is their only hope.

It is difficult to tell exactly how many Ugandans have AIDS. Only 30% of the people regularly see a doctor, but it is estimated by the Ugandan government that the infection rate there is 9%. By contrast, the infection rate in the United States is four-tenths of 1%.

The social structure of the country has changed. Hospitals are overcrowded. There is no medicine for AIDS in Uganda. Newspapers list page after page of death notices. At one college, 22 of 2,000 were not alive when graduation day came. Funerals that were once days long and involved all of the villagers, now last only for a couple of hours. "The years traditionally allowed for a widow to mourn had been shortened to less than 24 hours, after which it is considered bad luck to grieve," according to a special report in the *New York Times.*

The seven Kintu orphans still live on the land. They are luckier than most. They have a home, the land, and a social worker stays in contact with them to see that they are fed and that "all is well." They do attend school—a two hour walk one way—then come back to tend their fields in the evening. All they want to do is survive.

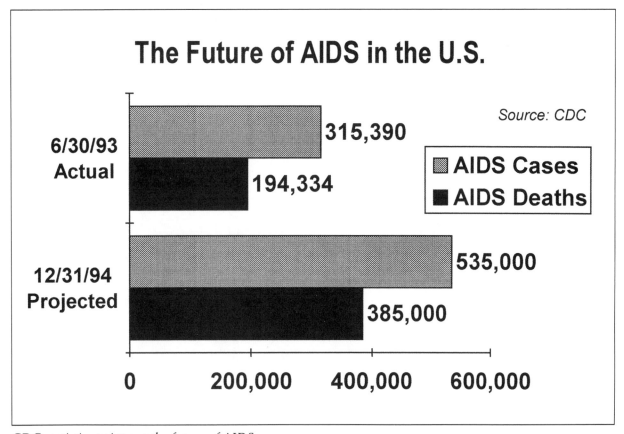

CDC statistics point out the future of AIDS.

A bomb blasted a crater in the basement of New York's World Trade Center. The damage was so extensive that workers had to make some repairs before it was safe for forensics investigators to perform their work.

6

UNRAVELING CRIME MYSTERIES INVOLVES MULTIPLE SCIENCE DISCIPLINES

Forensic science burst into the limelight in 1993, with the massive news coverage of two major events: the bombing of New York City's World Trade Center and the siege—then fiery destruction—of the Branch Davidian cult compound near Waco, Texas. But forensics also was getting close attention in the quieter, more deliberate chambers of courts across the United States, particularly the U.S. Supreme Court, which overturned a 70-year-old standard used to govern the admissibility of scientific evidence in trials.

The events of the year mirrored the broad scope of forensic science, which ranges from tasks that have to be conducted on a moment's notice and often under adverse conditions to procedures that have to be carried out in well-controlled laboratories, then explained in lengthy court testimony. Investigators had to depend on their best field work when they went to work to unravel the mystery of the Trade Center bombing in New York. And even though Texas medical examiners were prepared for the worst, their tasks in identifying the remains of cult members who perished in the cult fire still were daunting. And in other cities and towns at various times of the year, scientific experts—after lab tests and considerable study and experience—testified in court on evidence presented in civil and criminal cases.

The Element of Surprise

When an explosion rocked the World Trade Center at mid-day February 26, federal and New York City officers went on their highest state of alert, Code Red. Task forces, including explosives experts, psychiatrists, hostage negotiators, and chemists, immediately swung into action to preserve as much evidence and prevent as much potential human damage as possible. They were on the front line of a process destined to take months or years to settle.

The World Trade Center occupies seven buildings and 16 acres in the lower Manhattan section of New York City, but its most recognizable features are the twin 110-story office towers—the second-tallest in the world, next to the Sears tower in Chicago. The explosion occurred in the basement, but it sent smoke billowing up through both towers. More than 50,000 workers, in some 900 businesses, and thousands of tourists and visitors can be in the towers at any given time. When the explosion knocked out the towers' electricity, those thousands of people had to walk down dark, smoky stairwells, some as many as 107 stories, to safety. About 30 people were picked up off the roof of the towers by helicopters. In all, the rescue of people from the complex took about 12 hours.

The blast killed six people and injured more than 1,000 others, and the office towers were closed for

New York and New Jersey Port Authority police officers Jim Wheeler (Left) and Steve Vitale survey some of the bomb damage in the World Trade Center.

weeks afterward. Authorities were calling the blast, triggered by a 1,500-pound bomb made with chemicals readily available to the public, the most destructive terrorist act ever on U.S. soil. *(See Chapter 7 for more on terrorism.)*

Typically, investigators face a months-long, painstaking search before finding definitive evidence from such disasters. After a midair explosion of a jumbo jet over Lockerbie, Scotland killed 270 people aboard Pan Am Flight 103 in December 1988, investigators had to reassemble a major portion of the entire airplane. They started their search for clues by crawling on hands and knees over the crash site, collecting bits and pieces of the airplane and passengers' belongings.

While the airplane crash in Scotland spread debris over an 845-square-mile area, the Trade Center debris was confined to a shaky five-story basement crater. The Friday explosion was so intense that it created a 100-by-200-foot crater of metal and concrete debris. Investigators could not safely search through evidence until some structural fortification was complete. Some initial crime-scene searching was necessary, however, but it could not begin until the following Sunday.

According to a March 15, 1993 *Time* article entitled "A Case of Dumb Luck," that first search was fruitful for Joseph Hanlin, a bomb expert and agent for the federal Bureau of Alcohol, Tobacco and Firearms (AFT).

Hanlin, who was among a team of 10 ATF and New York City investigators on the initial inspection, picked up a piece of burned and twisted metal that, to an untrained eye, might look like any other piece of burned and twisted metal. But to him and the nine other investigators on that search, it was evidence, and in a matter of days it proved to be a crucial piece in the massive puzzle.

Authorities said the metal contained enough numbers that, when processed through a car manufacturer's computer system, showed it had come from a yellow Ford Econoline van sold to Ryder Truck Rental Co. and which had been rented recently to a customer through a rental agency in Jersey City, N.J. By Thursday, six days after the bombing, authorities arrested a man who had attempted to get back his $400 deposit on the rented van by claiming the vehicle had been stolen. Investigators suspected that the van had been used to transport the bomb to the Trade Center basement.

As in most investigations, one clue often leads to another. When the bombing suspect was arrested, authorities said they found traces of bomb residue on the rental agreement the suspect had in his pocket. Then, a search of the man's apartment led agents to a self-storage warehouse, where authorities said more bomb evidence was found.

A business card in the man's possession led investigators to another man, a chemical engineer, who was arrested the next week. Searches of these two suspects' homes, and of other persons linked to them, yielded materials and manuals used in bomb-making, authorities said.

Workers clear debris in the World Trade Center.

On Alert, But for What

Although the Trade Center bombing took authorities by surprise, medical examiners had plenty of warning about the potential for deaths near Waco, Texas, where Branch Davidian cult leader David Koresh and his followers had been held captive behind their compound walls for 51 days. The cult members and the law enforcement officers surrounding them all were heavily armed.

Violence erupted February 28 when more than 100 law enforcement officers tried to serve Koresh with a warrant. The officers wanted to search the isolated, rural compound, about 10 miles east of Waco, Texas, for illegal weapons. But Koresh was somehow tipped off that the officers were coming. A gun battle left several people on both sides dead, and others wounded.

But it was still a surprise when the end of the siege resulted from an intense fire that destroyed the 77-acre compound in less than 25 minutes April 19, killing more than 70 people inside. The focus then shifted from the gun-carrying officers to the scientists

Not much was left of the Branch Davidian compound near Waco, Texas, after a massive fire destroyed the cult's residence and killed almost everyone inside.

who would attempt to identify the remains of cult members. Some were burned beyond recognition in a fire so hot that heads and teeth exploded.

Authorities had long speculated that David Koresh and his followers would not surrender peacefully. Attempts to negotiate with the cult leader had failed consistently, and he often was not communicating at all with officials outside the compound. Still the suddenness and intensity of the fire, which independent arson investiagors have said was set by the cult members themselves, surprised some officers, even though law enforcement armored vehicles had started ramming the compound buildings to force an end to the standoff.

An arson investigation team that concluded the cult members started the fire based its evidence on photographs and statements from witnesses at the scene. Officers said they saw a man inside the compound make a sweeping motion as if throwing or spraying something, then act as if he were lighting a match. Infrared photographs taken from a helicopter flying above the compound showed several sources of the blaze.

Daunting Task

The workload facing medical examiners was overwhelming. As Tarrant County (Texas) Chief Medical Examiner Dr. Nizam Peerwani summed it up, according to an April 23 *New York Times* report: "When a corpse is exposed to such intensive heat, the head will often explode. Many of the bodies we have collected so far have no facial parts left, no skull left, all totally incinerated. Many bodies have sustained such tremendous heat damage that we will have to look very, very hard to find evidence of the cause of death. Identification will be another problem, and it is certainly possible that we won't find remains of some of the bodies at all."

To accomplish the mission, Peerwani was depending on a staff that included 41 scientists and technicians, including pathologists, dentists, and an anthropologist.

When forensic scientists started examining the burned bodies in an effort to identify them, they discovered that at least some of them, including Koresh, had gunshot wounds to the head. It took several days to identify Koresh's body, because his skull had been shattered into pieces from the gunshot. But identification was eventually possible through X-rays and dental records. Months later, an FBI agent said the agency had evidence that another cult member shot Koresh as he started to flee when FBI tanks first rammed the compound walls.

Medical and dental records are often the means used to identify burned bodies. But some of the children who died in the Waco fire had never left the compound, and any records of their lives burned in the fire. Adult cult members' records also proved difficult to assemble, because some people were from outside the United States. Texas authorities had to contact international police agencies to assist in obtaining the records. Dental records, for example, can reveal whether a body matches a person's identity when the victim exhibits the same type of dental work, such as a crown or a gap, contained in the person's records.

Many of the bodies had been torn apart as walls and other structural elements of the compound collapsed during the fire, and some victims' skulls were shattered from gunshot wounds. So Texas authorities called in forensic anthropologists to help reassemble the skulls and skeletons. Among the consulting specialists were scientists from the National Museum of Natural History at the Smithsonian Institution in Washington, D.C. The Smithsonian museum houses a reference "catalog" of bones from more than 30,000 individuals, dating back to ancient Egyptians.

The forensic scientists went through a carefully orchestrated series of steps in their work, starting by surveying the death scene and eventually superimposing photographs over reassembled skulls. At the death scene, the investigators took photographs and videotapes, marking the location and relative position on the floor or ground where bodies were found. (See accompanying story, Page 81, for an explanation on investigating explosions and arson cases.)

After the bodies were removed, medical examiners conducted autopsies, and pathologists tried to determine causes of death. In those who died of smoke inhalation, they found a red color in the lungs and excess carbon monoxide in the blood. In the cases of

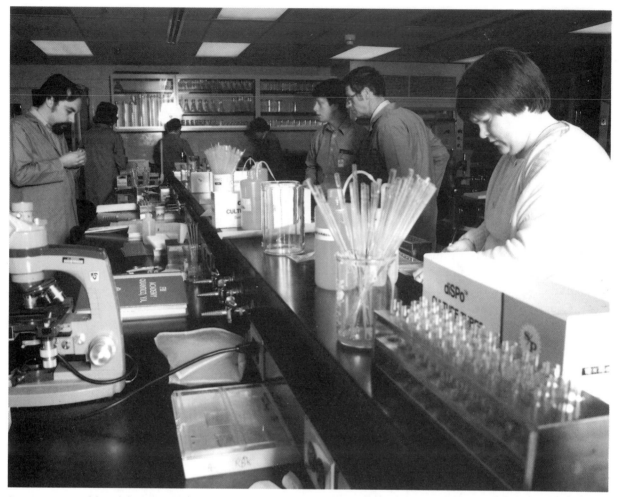

Some state and local forensic science investigators receiving training in serology at the FBI's forensic science research and training center.

burn victims who also had gunshot wounds, the absence of smoke in the lungs indicated the bullet caused the death.

As to deciding whether the bullet came from an arsenal set off by a fire or from a gun intentionally fired, investigators viewed skull markings through a microscope. A gun-fired bullet leaves spiral grooves but a stray bullet does not.

Sometimes bodies were burned so badly that it was not obvious whether a victim was male or female. In this case, investigators studied parts of the skeleton, such as the clavicle and pelvic bones, which reveal gender traits. If the victim was a child, the length of the skeletal bones and the characteristics of the jawbone can help to pinpoint the age within about six months.

To help keep track of all the information they assemble, forensic scientists use the same tool as most other scientists do nowadays: the computer. Special programs help the scientists compare postmortem information with a person's medical and dental records.

But when no records are available on individuals, such as the children whose entire lives had been spent in the Branch Davidian compound, forensic scientists often have to turn to the most modern of techniques, DNA sampling (extracting samples of the hereditary chemical, deoxyribonucleic acid), to determine identities. In such cases, DNA samples are drawn from victims' remains and compared to DNA from relatives.

Whatever the scientists determined from the evidence retrieved from the cult compound may not be fully explained for months or years. Some cult mem-

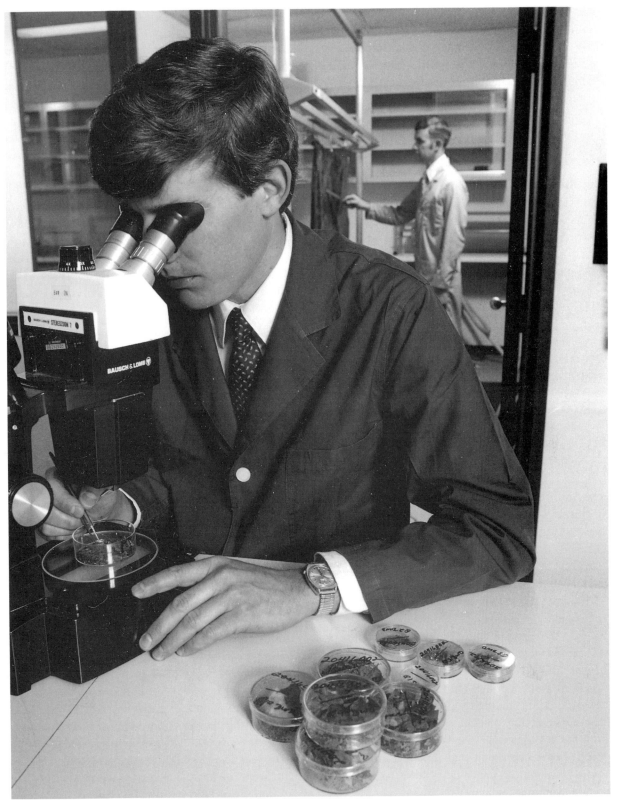

Microscopic examination of evidence is only one of many tasks in forensic science.

bers escaped from the fire, and others already were in custody of law enforcement officers, with criminal charges filed against them. And law enforcement officers are generally prohibited from discussing much evidence when court trials are pending. In September, officials of the National Association of Medical Examiners barred members of the press and the public from Branch Davidian-related sessions of its national conference in Fort Worth, Texas.

Sleuthing for Cause

Forensic science is not always depicted in such a dramatic light as that created by the Trade Center bombing and the Texas cult fire. Less visible and special cases, on both recent and historic events, are often pursued.

James E. Starrs, for example, was searching in 1993 for an answer to a puzzling question over the death of explorer Meriwether Lewis in 1809. Officially, Lewis committed suicide. But Starrs thinks he was murdered. To prove his theory, he has had to master a range of scientific disciplines: geophysics, geology, anthropology, engineering, and archaeology.

Lewis died at a frontier outpost on the Natchez Trace called Grinder's Stand, about 70 miles from Nashville, Tenn. He died of gunshot wounds to the head and chest, which many historians have claimed were self-inflicted. One cause for skepticism about suicide, says Starrs, a professor of law and forensic sciences at George Washington University in Washington, D.C., is the location of the gunshot wounds. It would be extremely rare, he says, for a suicide victim to shoot himself in such a manner.

That skepticism, and other doubts about the circumstances of Lewis' death, has had Starrs studying the guns and ammunition used during that time, in addition to the geology of the burial site and the route Lewis traveled. He also was studying whether Lewis was right-handed or left-handed, a factor in the use of weapons and angles of bullets or slugs. Starrs also was pursuing the possibility of exhuming Lewis' body for examination.

The Lewis case is only one of many historic cases Starrs has studied. Other cases have included the cannibalism questions over the deaths of five prospectors, apparently at the hands of a man named

Alfred Packer, in the San Juan Mountains of Colorado in 1874. Although Packer was convicted and sentenced to hanging for the crimes, questions about the incident led to his being saved from the hanging and even paroled for good behavior. Starrs led an expedition to exhume the bodies of the prospectors. Through scientific analysis, he concluded that they had suffered "defleshing," and their bones indicated they died defending themselves from traumatic blows.

One of the ways Starrs shares his scientific discoveries with others is through the newsletter *Scientific Sleuthing Review*, of which he and Charles R. Midkiff of the Bureau of Alcohol, Tobacco and Firearms are co-editors. The newsletter has published stories on subjects ranging from the historic cases to the latest rulings on scientific evidence in court trials.

A Day in Court

In its first-ever opinion issued on the use of scientific evidence in the courtroom, the U.S. Supreme Court overturned in June 1993 a 70-year-old standard most federal courts used to decide whether juries should hear such evidence. The decision was rendered in an appeal of a California civil case in which parents alleged that birth defects in two children were caused by a drug widely prescribed a number of years ago (but taken off the market in 1983) to relieve morning sickness in pregnant women.

Using the traditional standard, federal courts have applied a "general acceptance" test to determine whether scientific information can be admitted as evidence in a trial. That has predominantly meant that evidence—in addition to being validated through normal scientific methods and procedures—must have been subjected to peer review and generally accepted by other scientists of the same field before it can be admissible. A similar process is used to evaluate articles prior to publication in professional scientific and medical journals.

But in its June ruling, the Supreme Court placed much of the burden of determining the usefulness of potential scientific evidence on federal judges, rather than peer scientists. Judges are now essentially the gatekeepers when it comes to deciding whether "any and all scientific testimony or evidence admitted is not only relevant, but reliable." The ruling, widely hailed as a positive move by several national scientific organizations, is expected to dramatically affect the way science is used to determine the outcome of criminal and civil court cases.

"We are confident that federal judges possess the capacity to undertake this review," Supreme Court Justice Harry A. Blackmun wrote in the court's majority opinion. In making their decisions, judges will consider whether potential evidence has been empirically tested, or subject to testing, using basic scientific methods and procedures. For instance, they will determine whether proposed evidence has been successfully subjected to reproducible experimentation. "Proposed testimony must be supported by appropriate validation—i.e., 'good grounds,' based on what is known," Blackmun wrote.

In the case on which the justices based their ruling, attorneys for the children with birth defects had compiled, through test-tube and animal-testing experiments, evidence that suggested a drug known as Bendectin could cause birth defects. But attorneys for the drug manufacturer argued that the evidence had not been peer-reviewed in the scientific community, had not been published in scientific journals, and was contradicted by published epidemiological (population-based, actual case) studies.

California courts and a federal appeals court, going by the traditional general acceptance standard, ruled against the parents and children. But the Supreme Court sent the case back to the lower courts for trial. The ruling will make it easier not only for the children's attorneys to use their evidence in court, but also for other attorneys to make use of newly developed scientific knowledge, ranging from the potential effects of toxic chemicals on people and the environment to the very personal DNA "fingerprinting," or comparing samples of DNA from crime scenes to DNA from individuals.

How judges will fare in deciding whether information is based on good science or bad science remains to be seen. However, scientific organizations were preparing specific guidelines in 1993 for the judges to use. The Supreme Court ruling technically only applied to federal courts, but state courts were expected to use the ruling as a guideline, especially since many state-court decisions end up in federal court as cases on appeal.

THE EXPERTS EXPLAIN

For this chapter, the editors asked the Bureau of Alcohol, Tobacco and Firearms to explain some of its procedures in investigating crimes such as those that garnered so much attention in 1993. The following account was written by Charles R. Midkiff, an official in the ATF Forensic Science Laboratory in Rockville, Md.

Because disruption at the scene of a fire or explosion is far greater than at other crime scenes, explosions or suspicious fires pose special challenges to investigators. Destruction of materials at the scene make effective laboratory examination of the physical evidence crucial in determining the cause of a fire or explosion, or linking a suspect with the incident.

With only very low levels of the original material likely to remain after an explosion or fire, analytical techniques must be capable of routinely detecting mere traces of a flammable liquid accelerant (substance that causes a fire to advance rapidly) or undetonated explosive. Even though a small amount of the original accelerant may remain unburned, temperatures at the scene evaporate part of the original liquid, changing its composition and complicating identification. In addition, plastics or polymers at the fire scene are degraded, or pyrolyzed, by high temperatures to produce chemical compounds, many of which are the same as those in common petroleum products such as gasoline.

For the detection and identification of traces of a residual flammable liquid accelerant in arson evidence, the analytical method now standard in forensic laboratories is gas chromatography (GC). GC is a technique for vapor phase separation of the components of a complex mixture such as gasoline, which may contain more than 400 individual chemical compounds. Components of a mixture separate during passage through a long

(continued on page 82)

(continued from page 81)

tube or column and enter a detector, producing an electronic signal or peak indicating the component's arrival at the detector and its concentration. Recording of these produces a chromatogram used to identify the type of material present, such as gasoline, kerosene, or diesel fuel.

At a fire scene, samples of debris are collected by the investigator and packaged in airtight containers, such as clean paint cans, for laboratory examination. In the laboratory, traces of residual flammable liquid in the sample are extracted from the debris and concentrated by adsorption onto charcoal. The concentrated liquid is removed from the charcoal and analyzed by GC.

In most instances, investigators use a long, small-diameter (or capillary) column for better separation of the mixture. This is known as capillary column GC, and identification of the liquid by chromatogram pattern is relatively straightforward. In samples highly contaminated with pyrolysis products from wood or plastic, however, the chromatogram is complex and difficult to interpret.

An important area of current research is the development of techniques that will confirm the presence, or absence, of accelerants in a highly contaminated fire-debris sample. The most promising approach to date combines the separation power of GC with mass spectrometry (MS), a technique that identifies fragments of a molecule to determine its molecular weight and structure.

With this combined approach (GC/MS), the chromatogram is examined using a computer data system for the presence and/or combinations of particular chemical compounds typical of a type of accelerant. Although work in this area is still under way, it promises more effective detection of flammable liquids used in arson fires while, at the same time, ensures that an accelerant is not "detected" in the fire debris when, in fact, none exists.

Techniques for detection of traces of explosives in debris form the scene of a bombing have advanced considerably in recent years. Most common explosives contain a significant percentage of nitrogen in their composition, and advantage can be taken of this for their detection. One approach combines gas, or liquid, chromatography with an extremely sensitive nitrogen-specific, infrared chemiluminescent detector known as the Thermal Energy Analyzer®. This system permits detection of traces of a wide range of commercial and military explosives. It is sufficiently sensitive to detect nitroglycerin from double-base smokeless gunpowder used in a pipe bomb on the walls of fragments of pipe recovered at the scene.

The combination of GC/MS also has found application when definitive identification of an explosive is required and only traces of material are available. In some instances, examination of the scene debris fails to detect intact explosive materials, and identification must be made from observation of characteristic residues.

One rapidly developing analytical technique for the examination of explosive residues is ion chromatography (IC). This instrument identifies extremely low levels of ions typical of residues from inorganic explosives, such as black powder widely used in pipe bombs. Research also is under way on application of capillary electrophoresis to identify explosives used in criminal bombings. In addition to extremely high sensitivity, each of these techniques provides results in only a few minutes.

Well-established analytical techniques, such as infrared and X-ray powder diffraction, are benefiting from advances in computer technology. Computer data systems permit rapid searches of files of library spectra and rapid identification of components or elemental profiles. Improved detectors for energy-dispersive X-ray analysis (EDX), which, when combined with scanning electron microscopy (SEM), permit identification of light elements such as nitrogen and oxygen common in explosives quickly and with only tiny samples.

With the continuing threat of criminal and terrorist use of explosives, research will continue to develop analytical techniques offering sensitivity for detection of trace elements, selectivity to ensure accurate identification, and analysis speed for prompt results.

The federal Bureau of Alcohol, Tobacco and Firearms is often called upon to investigate bombings such as this car explosion.

This image—the World Trade Center dominating the lower Manhattan skyline—was shattered in 1993 by a terrorist attack.

7

VIOLENCE OFTEN ERUPTS FROM RELIGIOUS EXTREMISM

Americans, prior to 1993, would watch the evening news or read the morning newspaper and sigh a sigh of relief that a terrorist attack somewhere else in the world took place there, and not in the United States. Somehow, Americans generally felt that such things wouldn't happen on American soil.

What happened on February 26, 1993 changed forever that feeling that terrorism was not real in the United States. On that day, mothers and fathers left for work in the morning. Elementary-school children, who had anxiously awaited the arrival of the day of their class field trip, had dressed in their Sunday best for their trek to, among other places, the World Trade Center. The bombing at the Trade Center that day shook more than just the two 110-story office towers readily identified with the lower Manhattan skyline. It shattered the collective psyche of Americans. It brought terrorism home to U.S. soil, and in a big way.

Almost two months later, Americans saw another form of violence that can erupt from religious extremism, when the 77-acre compound of the Branch Davidian cult went up in flames near Waco, Texas. This time the violence affected more people within the cult than it did innocent bystanders, but the horror still reverberated around the world.

The Psychological Grip of Terrorism
Days after the Trade Center blast, which killed six people and injured more than 1,000 others, authorities arrested suspects who appeared to be linked to international terrorists. Prior to this incident, these terrorists had confined their violent actions to Europe or the Middle East, but this act shook the streets of New York, and Americans were wondering what targets would be next.

It didn't take long to find out. Just weeks after the bombing, authorities arrested a group of individuals allegedly plotting to bomb the Holland and Lincoln tunnels that lie under the Hudson River between Manhattan and New Jersey, as well as the United Nations building, and federal offices.

Gazetta Culbreth, a tunnel toll taker, described the feelings of many in a June 26, 1993 *New York Times* article. "I never saw a day like it in my 26 years on the job. You just knew that everybody coming through had the exact same thing on their mind. Every last one of them. Some asked me if things were safe, sort of joking. But even those who kept quiet, you knew they were thinking about the bombs. I know it's what I was thinking when I came through Manhattan to start my shift."

Post Traumatic Stress Disorder
The bombing has given researchers at Cornell University a window into the psychological effects of post traumatic stress disorder (PTSD), once referred to as "shell shock" or "battle fatigue" in World Wars I and II, The Korean War, and, more recently, the Vietnam War. But PTSD can occur with any type of severe mental or physical trauma. Symptoms are: difficulty sleeping or concentrating, nightmares,

85

flashbacks, fear, guilt, anxiety, panic attacks, or depression.

"Very little information has been available up to now on PTSD as it relates to terrorism. Very few studies have conducted comprehensive assessments of survivors of terrorist attacks," said Dr. JoAnn Difede, a Cornell psychologist leading the team that is evaluating and treating some survivors of the Twin Towers attack. Normally, acts of terrorism claim only a handful of people. With the Towers bombing, more than 55,000 people were in the buildings, and 1,000 were trapped for a considerable length of time. The worst part was not knowing if trying to escape or just sitting still and waiting to be rescued was the right thing to do. This uncertainty gave the psychologists a pool of people on which to study the effects of terrorism.

Researchers at Cornell are hoping to identify the psychiatric and somatic illnesses that accompany PTSD following a terrorist act. And while medication can control the disorder, the Cornell researchers hope to learn ways to cure the persons that suffer from PTSD. Difede added, "PTSD sometimes can control a person's life unless the trauma is somehow resolved."

When determining the effect the disaster had on the mental wellness of those individuals involved, three sets of variables had to be identified:

* First, the specific characteristics of the disaster that put these people in jeopardy, i.e., how quickly the action took place, how long it lasted, and whether it was a natural act or a man-made one.
* Second, the individual differences of the victims, such as personal characteristics, how they were affected, and where they spent their recovery time.
* Third, the psychological response, over time, to the particular disaster.

Initally, it was thought that World Trade Center tenants would break leases and vow never to return after the bombing. However, less than 10 could not cope with returning to the towers. Instead, people have banded together. Management of the towers began visiting tenants at least once a week, sometimes more. Welcome-back letters and coffee mugs were sent to all employees, and "I survived"-type memorabilia were being sold on the streets below.

The Towers are now more tenant-friendly. New security measures were installed. Stress counseling is available to all 55,000 employees. Free parking through another garage has been arranged for the employees. It hasn't all been easy. Many feel that they have been violated, since one's workplace is also an extension of themselves.

But most importantly, the overall feeling among the 55,000 was that they would survive. "If we can overcome this, nothing can stand in our way. The experience has bonded this organization together. We are better for it," Lawrence S. Huntington, chairman of Fiduciary Trust International, one of the first tenants back in the Towers, was quoted as saying in the March 30, 1993 *New York Times*.

Terrorism Goes West

In January 1993, Germany's intelligence organization had warned the FBI that "radical Islamic fundamentalists had relocated to the West and now constituted a major new terrorist threat to the United States and Europe," according to a June 20, 1993 report in the *Hartford (CT) Courant*. The FBI, while thankful to Germany for passing on the information, was confident that they had the situation well in hand and was not too concerned that the radicals were of any real threat to the United States. Israel also had warned the FBI that terrorists were headed our way.

The terrorists "were united by a zealous Islamic fundamentalist ideology—a bitter hatred of the West and its perceived surrogates such as Western-allied Arab regimes and Israel," the June 26 *Times* article said. The fundamentalists feel that separating church and state is "blasphemous," and the lifestyle in the West is considered hostile. The terrorists all attended a church that "preached that the United States is a 'den of evil and fornication' and regularly called upon Muslims to annihilate their enemies."

Abd Al-Rahman, considered the spiritual leader of the Egyptian fundamentalist movement, said, "Muslims must kill the enemies of Allah, in every way and everywhere in order to liberate themselves from the grandchildren of the pigs and apes who are educated at the table of Zionists, the communists, and the imperialists," according to the *Times*. With

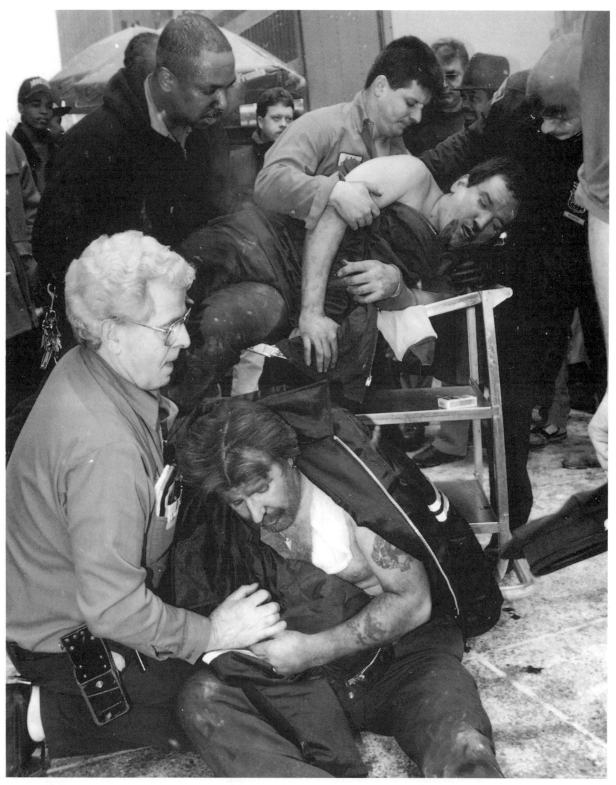

Some of the injured people, being treated first at the scene of the World Trade Center bombing, were among many who may have felt that the United States was immune from terrorist attacks.

such feeling of contempt and hatred toward the people of the United States, the authorities wonder if the bombing of the World Trade Center was a one-time occurrence or if it is just the beginning of a game of psychological warfare.

There seemed to be no understandable reasoning to many Amercans as to why the bombing occurred. Before clues as to the parties responsible emerged, the usual suspects were considered, such as major drug traffickers, Saddam Hussein, and others.

One drug trafficker, when hearing that he was a suspect, was quoted in the March 7, 1993 *New York Times* as saying, "They can take me off the list, because if I had done it, I would be saying why and I would be saying what I want." What makes the psychological effects of terrorism all the more frightening is that there seems to be no logic to it—no way to anticipate which place might be next on the hit list.

Portrait of a Terrorist

Bombers don't wake up one day and decide to become terrorists. It takes years of learning to hate someone or something, consuming the person's every thought. Such was the case of Mahmud the Red, according to various news accounts that appeared after the bombing of the World Trade Center.

Mahmud Abouhalima, known as Mahmud the Red because of his red hair and beard, was born in the small Egyptian village of Kafr al Dawar, a poor town 15 miles from Alexandria. His family, economically better off than most, sent their son to Alexandria University to study to become a teacher, but he returned home before finishing. His friends said that he was consumed with hatred for his native Egypt because it offered little hope for any kind of a better life for those of his generation. He had begun hanging out with members of the outlawed al-Jama'a Islamiyya, or Islamic Group that had the blind Sheik Omar Abdel Rahman as their spiritual leader. This group's mission was to make Egypt an Islamic state. The authorities were watching the group's activities and even arresting some of its members.

In 1981, Egyptian President Anwar Sadat had had some 2,000 Islamic intellectuals arrested, and Mahmud Abouhalima decided it was time to leave Egypt. He went to Germany as a tourist. Within a week, Sadat was killed. Abouhalima asked for political asylum. His request was denied, and he was scheduled to leave Germany in two weeks.

Then he conveniently wed the very accessible girl-next-door in his apartment building, which gave him a legitimate way to stay. He was good to her, provided well, prayed five times a day and avoided alcohol. He social life was spent with the Egyptian immigrant community, especially the orthodox Muslims that he met at the mosques while praying. He would invite his newfound friends to the house and speak only in Arabic, which Soika, his wife, did not understand. She felt that he was with some kind of "underground." "He never said anything about it directly. But I could well imagine it," she said in an article in the October 4, 1993 *Time* magazine.

When she refused to convert to Islam or bear children, the marriage dissolved. After the divorce he married a German, Marianne Weber. She converted to Islam, lived with him in tiny quarters, and left with him in 1985 for a vacation in the United States. Their six month travel visa expired at the same time that the amnesty program for illegal aliens who had worked as migrant farm workers went into effect. Abouhalima said that he was a farm worker. Taken at his word, he was allowed to stay.

For the next five years, he drove taxi cabs in New York City. He was considered a taxi-driving nightmare, running red lights, failing to answer traffic violation summonses, and driving without a license. He was remembered by one passenger as always having lots of Arabic books in the cab and always reading them in traffic, ignoring what was going on around him. He would play Arabic sermons on cassettes in the cab, too. "He had contempt for materialistic America, even though he was here," recalled the passenger in the *Time* article.

After obtaining his "green card" in 1988, Abouhalima went to Afghanistan to fight in the "jihad," or holy war, supporting the mujahedin, the Muslim rebels who had been fighting for 10 years to rid their country of the Soviet-backed government.

Abouhalima returned to the United States in July 1990—it is thought that Sheik Omar arrived around the same time—wearing fatigues and combat boots. He joined up with others who had fought in Afghanistan, and went into the Connecticut countryside to practice target shooting. Ahmed Sattar, director of a mosque in Brooklyn who knew Abouhalima, told *Time,* "I haven't met one person who was sorry he went. Most left America as ordinary men and came back so devout and so proud. The war reminded them of the glorious old days, many hundreds of years ago, when Muslims were fighting the infidel."

Abouhalima began attending the mosque where the Sheik preached. The Sheik was able to quickly take control of those who, like Abouhalima, were educated but unable to obtain anything but menial work in the United States. They felt demeaned, and a little guilty for abandoning their native Egypt. Soon, Abouhalima was working for the Sheik as his driver and body guard.

For the Sheik to gain legal entrance to the United States he had to have a sponsor. Mustafa Shalabi, who had been Abouhalima's boss at the Afghan recruitment center, became the sponsor, but he and the Sheik soon began to struggle over the leadership of the Muslim group. In March 1991, Shalabi was found dead, shot and stabbed. Abouhalima was considered the prime murder suspect, but was never

Cars line up to go through the Lincoln Tunnel, under the Hudson River, from New York to New Jersey. This tunnel, the nearby Holland Tunnel, and other sites were planned targets for terrorist attacks, according to authorities who arrested a number of individuals after the World Trade Center bombing.

charged. Meanwhile, one of his friends, El Sayyid Nosair, was charged, tried, and acquitted of the murder of Israeli-American militant Rabbi Meir Kahane. Abouhalima was also a suspect in that case.

At four o'clock in the morning of February 26, a yellow Ryder van pulled into a gas station, followed by a blue Honda. The attendant thought that he was about to be robbed, but the drivers only wanted gas. The driver of the Honda, a tall red-haired, freckled man, paid. The attendant, curious at that hour of the morning, tried to peek in the van, but the driver hopped out and stood by the van's window to block his view.

Eight hours later, the World Trade Center was bombed.

The gas station attendant has been placed under federal protection. He remembers Abouhalima and Mohammad Salameh in the Ryder van and blue Honda.

Today, Abouhalima sits in jail awaiting trial. He escaped to Egypt only to be tortured by his native government into confessing to the World Trade Center bombing and was then returned to the United States.

The Fear Spreads

The same day the Trade Center was bombed, police were told that the Empire State Building in midtown Manhattan would be next. Thousands of people were evacuated from the building immediately, giving them an early, albeit unsettled weekend, but no bomb exploded. Security at the building, however, was tightened for weeks afterward. Normally, people can enter the Empire State Building through any of several entrances on the front and sides, but entry was confined for a while to one front doorway, and everyone went through a metal detector much like those at airports.

For days after the bombing, commuters also were reminded of the potential dangers. People who walked through New York's Grand Central Terminal on their way to and from commuter trains did so alongside police officers with bomb-sniffing dogs. Such an image does not have a calming effect just before boarding a train that has to crawl through a 50-block underground corridor before emerging above ground.

Authorities also advised airports, nuclear power plants, and other places to tighten security, and to be on alert for any terrorist activity.

Terrorism of a Different Kind

Sometimes, terrorism does not have a religious face, or any face at all, until perpetrators of a crime are caught. Another form of terrorism that has plagued the United States on and off for the past 15 years was on again in 1993, when two letter bombs were sent to two scientists two days apart.

One incident involved Dr. Charles J. Epstein, a geneticist working at the University of California in San Francisco. Two days later, at Yale University in New Haven, Conn., David Gelernter, a computer scientist, also received a letter bomb. Both men were critically injured.

So far, 14 such bombs have exploded over a number of years, with Epstein and Gelertner the 13th and 14th victims. Only one person thus far has died of bomb-related injuries.

All 14 cases involved people in the computer or high-technology areas. It felt that the bomber's motive is revenge, but for what remains unknown. And why did the bomber waited six years from bombing number 12 in 1987 to numbers 13 and 14 in 1993?

The *New York Times* reported receiving a letter from someone who claims to be the bomber. The letter said, "We are an anarchist group calling ourselves FC. Notice that the postmark on this envelope precedes a newsworthy event that will happen about the time you receive this letter, if nothing goes wrong. This will prove that we knew about the event in advance, so our claim of responsibility is truthful. Ask the FBI about FC. They have heard about us. We will give information about our goals at some future time. Right now we only want to establish our identity and provide an identifying number that will ensure the authenticity of any future communications from us. Keep this number secret so that no one else can pretend to speak in our name."

A nine-digit number accompanied the letter. An FBI agent who is now retired said that FC were initials that were on an earlier bomb, but that information had never been made public. He said that only the bomber and the FBI were aware of it.

Psychological Profile

The picture painted by law enforcement personnel of the bomber is of a quiet white man who makes lists. He most likely has very low self-esteem. He is probably a neat dresser, who grew up in Chicago, graduated high school and maybe attended college, but has had a series of menial jobs. He has difficulty getting along with women, feeling that he is physically unattractive. He is probably either in his late 30s or early 40s. Also, the period of time between the event that upsets him and the bombing to avenge the perceived wrongdoing can be a long, making the "why" of the bombing almost impossible to answer.

The bomber's profile continues: he probably watches the bomb go off and keeps souvenirs of the explosions—newspaper articles, and videos—to relive the event over and over again. Each bomb has included a "signature" of the bomber which is not destroyed when the bomb detonates. The signature on a previous bomb was the FC which the retired FBI agent mentioned.

All of this is the bomber's secret, hidden life. He, as with nearly all such criminals, is considered the perfect neighbor, keeping to himself, but always considered the nicest guy on the block, according to a profile highlighted in the June 26, 1993 *New York Times*.

As terrorists go, this bomber may be one of the worst, because law enforcement personnel are no closer to catching him in 1993 than they were in 1978. Whatever has irritated this man so much that it has consumed his every thought and deed for the last 15 years makes him a dangerous person. The terror is in not knowing when or if he will ever strike again.

That was not the case with the Branch Davidian cult in Waco, Texas. Authorities knew the cult was amassing an arsenal, and they went to the cult's compound in February to find out just how many illegal weapons were there. The visit turned into a 51-day standoff that resulted in the total obliteration of the cult compound and the loss of more than 70 lives.

The Cult Mind Set

Cults—groups led by religious zealots—have been around since the beginning of time. In 1534, a group of radical German Protestants, feeling that the end of the world was at hand, took control of the Westphalian town of Munster and proclaimed it to be the New Jerusalem. Jan Bockelson, ("John of Leyden") with a charismatic and religiously obsessed personality, assumed leadership and announced that he was the Messiah.

Bockelson's reign and the cult's existence ended disastrously in 1535 with torture and ultimately death for him and his followers. He and two of his aides were "lofted in cages to the top of Munster's church tower [and] soon fell victim to the ravages of the weather and scavenging birds. . . . [T]he cages remain to this day, a notable Westphalian tourist attraction," said Paul Boyer, a professor of history at the University of Wisconsin, in the May 17, 1993 *The New Republic*. (Westphalia refers to the region in Germany bordering the Netherlands, east of the Rhine River, including the Ruhr Valley).

But what makes a religious organization and its leader good and a cultist organization bad?

Perhaps the biggest and most important differences are that with a religious group, a person is allowed to keep his own thoughts and ideas and—should the desire arise—leave. Those two options typically are not given to cult members, such as 1993's most famous cult organization: the Branch Davidians, of Waco, Texas, under the leadership of David Koresh, who changed his name from Vernon Howell.

Cults prey on the weaknesses of people. Those most affected are people with little or no self-esteem, who are looking for some sort of meaning in their lives. People join cults looking for a sense of purpose—they are trying to become "part of something extraordinarily significant that seem[s] to carry them beyond their feelings of isolation and toward an expanded sense of reality and the meaning of life," according to an article in the March-April 1992 edition of *Psychology Today*.

Cults usually have some cause, which universally is accepted as good. In 1978, in Jonestown, Guyana, 913 people died in a mass suicide. They were Jim Jones and 912 of his followers, of which 276 were children. The group had its beginnings years earlier in San Francisco, where they were called the People's Temple. Jones and his followers wanted to end racism, and decided to build their own little world in the jungles of South America. They chose a place near Georgetown, Guyana, and named their paradise in honor of their leader, Jim Jones.

Their idea—to end racism so that all men and women could live in peace and harmony—sounded great. The method by which Jim Jones was able to completely control the people was not. He would begin by having people sign loyalty oaths to him, then blank power-of-attorney sheets, and then "confessions" of abuse toward their children, treason toward the United States, and various other crimes.

"It was all about forcing members to experience themselves as vulgar and despicable people who could never return to a normal life outside of the group. It was about destroying any personal relationships that might come ahead of the relationship each individual member had with him. It was about terrorizing children and turning them against their parents. It was about seeing Jim Jones as an omnipotent figure who could snuff out members' lives on a whim as easily as he had already snuffed out their self-respect. In short, it was about mind control," the *Psychology Today* article states.

And while some people did not completely swallow Jim Jones' way of life, the consequences of leaving, for most, were too much of a chance to take. There was a policy in force of tracking down and killing any cult members who chose to defect, or leave the group, and should a person succeed in escaping, any family members left behind would be blamed and terrorized in the escapee's place.

But when prospective members first heard of Jim Jones and attended their first meetings, they weren't asked if they would commit suicide for the "cause." They were told of this wondrous person—this prophet—who "could heal the sick and predict the future," the article states.

And like the traveling medicine man of the Old West with his snake-oil potions and miracle cures, the Reverend Jones fooled his followers. He had them drugged so that it would appear that he was raising them from the dead when they came to. And he would go through the trash looking for clues about different people's lives so

he could use the information in "psychic readings." He kept his followers busy with noteworthy projects, thereby depriving them of more and more sleep. He fed them less and less, for the work of the cause came first. Eventually, lack of sleep and food means a "breakdown [in] the ability to make rational judgments and weakens the psychological resistance of anyone," the *Psychology Today* article says. Eventually, membership in the group becomes more important than life itself. They actually believed that he was God, not like a priest, minister, or rabbi who represents God, but as the real supreme being Himself.

Leo Ryan, a U.S. congressman, and several members of the press traveled to Guyana at the request of cult followers' families in the United States to try to convince them to return home. The congressman and his group were found shot to death at the airfield.

Not Again

Back in the United States, some people said that this would never happen again. People would never put their trust in just one person and one cause again. In the spring of 1993, 15 years after the massacre in Guyana, David Koresh and the Branch Davidians proved them wrong.

The Branch Daivdians were an offshoot of the Seventh-Day Adventist Church, and many of their followers were one-time members of the Adventists. The Adventists came from the Millerite movement of the 1840s and were always interested in eschatology, or the second coming of Christ, and the end of the world. Adventist ministers held "prophecy seminars" in motels and would conduct the seminars as a teacher would with study guides, tests, and diplomas.

Koresh, born Vernon Howell, was influenced by mid-19th century theory that used pieces of several books of the bible to "prove" his ideas. The theory is based on the idea that "wickedness will increase as the end approaches. . . . [That] a seven year period of cataclysmic struggle between the forces of evil and the forces of righteousness . . . will persecute God's true believers as he enforces his global military and economic dictatorship," according to *The New Republic.*

Koresh and the Branch Davidians also were considered part of a group called premillennialists. They believe that Christ will return to Earth every 1,000 years, and with the year 2000 quickly approaching, more and more groups like Koresh's are preparing for Christ's arrival.

Experts on millennial groups say that the federal law enforcement officers may have played right into David Koresh's hands, according to R. Scott Appleby, co-director of the Fundamentalism Project, which is sponsored by the American Academy of Arts and Sciences to study fundamentalist movements worldwide. They said that the confrontation within the compound repersented the final struggle between good and evil, which made the Branch Davidians resist all the more.

Groups like the Branch Davidians feel that they have a unique role in history, that they are the center of the universe, and people in positions of authority have little to no effect on them. They play by different rules when it comes to who has authority. Federal law enforcement personnel did not. Law enforcement is viewed "as essentially hostile to their freedoms, said Ron Enroth, a professor of sociology at Westmont College in Santa Barbara, Calif., who was quoted in the Washington Post.

Upon seeing the officers at the compound, the Branch Davidians probably thought, "Here come the forces of darkness against the good guys. Clearly [the agents] didn't recognize that they were playing out this role in just doing their ordinary jobs," said Ted Daniels, editor of the Millennium News, which tracks end-of-time prophecies. Unfortunately, it was recognized too late that the Branch Davidians were willing to sacrifice themselves and their children for their principles, said Appleby. And although Americans have always appreciated and even revered those who would lay down their lives for their country, martyrdom in the name of a cult is neither understood nor praised.

Evidence also strongly suggested that Vernon Howell, or David Koresh, was mimicking a turn-of-the-century cult leader named Cyrus R. Teed who lived near Fort Myers, Fla., according to J. Phillip Arnold, director of Reunion Institute, a center for biblical research in Houston, Texas. According to Arnold, there are quite a few similarities between Koresh and Teed.

Teed was a former Union Army medical corpsman from the Civil War who changed his name to Cyrus Teed Koresh when he started his religious commune called the Koreshian Unity. "I've never heard of anybody else calling themselves Koresh before and I've been reading this stuff for 20 years," said Arnold in a Washington Post report. Koresh is the Hebrew word for Cyrus, the Persian king who, according to the Old Testament book of Isaiah, was the defender of the Israelites and the one God sent to defeat the Babylonians.

Both men were obsessed with the Book of Revelation, which foretells the apocalypse ending of the world. Both also said that God was both male and female. Teed said that he was the incarnation of the Messiah, and, in a vision, he was told to gather 144,000 people that were to prepare for the final judgment. Both men interchanged science and religion with David Koresh using astrology and Teed using egocentric philosophy, which "viewed the Earth as a hollow, concave sphere in which mankind looked out onto three layers of atmosphere," Arnold said.

Robert S. Fogarty wrote the introduction to Teed's 1898 book, The Cellular Cosmology—The Earth a Concave Sphere. He said that "Teed may have been a lunatic, fraud, and swindler; however, to his followers he was Koresh, the prophet whose philosophy was not only divine but a mandate to cultivate the earth and save it for future generations."

Teed was born in upstate New York in 1839. He said that he had his first vision in 1869. He first founded a commune in Chicago and then moved it to Estero, Fla., in 1903. The community boasted 2,000 acres and had its own bakery, laundry, print shop, and school. At its peak, Teed had 300 members living at the commune and 4,000 followers throughout the country.

Teed's trouble started with politics. In the past, the commune had voted in a group for the democratic candidate. In 1906, they formed their own party and ran candidates for county offices on the platform that they would redistribute the wealth and public ownership of utilities. Teed got into an argument with the town marshal, and was so severely beaten that one and one-half years later, in 1908, he died from the injuries.

Arnold felt that David Koresh knew the story of Teed, either by reading Teed's book, or by meeting someone who had been a student of Teed. Lois Roden, the widowed wife of the former leader of the Branch Davidians, who befriended Koresh and took him under her wing, may have been that person.

Whatever the influence, Koresh was not an average criminal. In his own mind, he was not even a criminal—he was the messiah. "If the Bible is true, then I'm Christ," he had been heard to say more than once.

Karl Menninger once said that the signs of psychosis are: "a delusional preoccupation with persecution, usually associated with grandiosity; more or less continuous erratic, disorganized excitement accompanied by irascibility; bizarre delusional ideas coupled with obvious indifference to social expectations; and pervasive convictions of evil or wickedness in self or others," according to an article in the May 2, 1993 *Hartford (CT) Courant*.

Had Koresh been a criminal in the sense that he knew that he was a bad person and was breaking the law on purpose, the raid on his Texas compound might have worked; the blaring music and screaming animal noises might have worked; the persecution might have worked. But Koresh was not a criminal in this sense. He was doing the work of God. He was God, and God could do no wrong.

Agents from the U.S. Bureau of Alcohol, Tobacco and Firearms, the ATF, wanted to talk to David Koresh. Word had it that he was amassing hugh stockpiles of weapons and ammunition in the Branch Davidian compound near Waco, Texas, and that he had acquired the stash illegally. The agents found out the hard way just how many weapons Koresh had collected when they tried to serve a warrant, and the 51-day seige began.

The authorities attempted to deal with Koresh as they had other leaders in hostage-type situations. But psychotics need to be approached on their own terms. He felt that the answers to life were contained in scripture quotes. Perhaps communication with him could have taken the form of biblical quotes counteracting his theories. Psychotics also have "difficulty dealing with ambiguity, threat or impatience," the *Courant* said. Psychotics have trouble appraising reality.

Age and Innocence

All Branch Davidian children were to refer to David Koresh as their father, regardless of who the natural parent really was. Their natural parents, both mother and father, were to be referred to as "dogs." There were 21 children released from the compound shortly after the first confrontation between the cult and the ATF in February. Of those 21, 19 were old enough to respond to questions by the authorities.

They were mesmerized by flushing toilets and warm food. In drawings made of the compound, they drew pictures of fire, explosions, and of castles in heaven. They had been told that there were only two kinds of people: good and evil. All of the good people lived at the compound, and everyone else in the world was evil. They said that they, their parents, and David Koresh would all die by fire. Koresh would then return to Earth and kill the evil people that had killed the Branch Davidians and him. Then they would all be reunited in heaven.

Not all people that become involved with cults are young. At least half of the 6 million people involved are over the age of 25. Some are still trying to find themselves. Still others are trying to fill a void left by the death of a spouse or the empty-nest syndrome (when children leave home after growing up). "They end up joining cults when events lead them to search for a deeper sense of belonging and for something more meaningful in their lives. They do so because they happen to be in the wrong place at the wrong time and are ripe for exploitation. They do so because they find themselves getting caught in the claws of a parasite before they realize what is happening to them," says the *Psychology Today* article.

Koresh's cult, like most, was funded by the savings accounts, wages of those still employed, social security checks, and pension checks of their members. Being able to "pay your way" seems to be an important part of the cult's interest in its converts. The March 15, 1993 *Newsweek* tells of a 25-year-old woman who was living away from her family, with parents that "didn't understand her." A friend took her to a Montana-based New Age group.

Before she was able to free herself from the group, she had "given" them all of her money, including $6,500 for her place in a bomb shelter, since she had been led to believe that a nuclear holocaust was imminent. She started to doubt the validity of the group when, during the building of the bomb shelter she fell, and was told by those in charge that God had made her fall because she still was evil. People who have never come in contact with a cult sometimes have difficulty understanding how anyone could "fall for such nonsense." But, the need to belong to someone or something can make everything seem "right."

True to Form, a Violent Ending

A 51-day standoff between the Branch Davidians and the law enforcement officers ended with the compound burning to the ground April 19, 1993. "I can't tell you the shock and the horror that all of us felt when we saw those flames coming out. We thought, Oh my God, they're killing themselves," said Bob Ricks, FBI spokesman, at a press conference.

In the weeks after the crisis, however, after the situation was analyzed in a noncrisis frame of mind, the ending appeared to fit the rest of the Branch Davidians story. And once again, people are wondering: Can this ever happen again?

Winds off the Atlantic Ocean churned up the waters of the New Jersey shore in December 1992 and piled up boats like sardines.

8

FOR THE WEATHER, A YEAR FOR THE RECORD BOOKS

People say if it weren't for the weather, there would be little to talk about. Well, in 1993, people had plenty to talk about. A one-year period, from August 1992's Hurricane Andrew to the summer 1993's Great Flood, proved to be one of the busiest for meteorologists and most diverse in terms of the types of weather recorded. No part of the country was immune to adverse weather conditions. Temperature highs and lows, droughts and floods, and snow—lots and lots of snow—were all in the weather news of 1993.

A Nor'easter Strikes

On December 11, 1992, a preseason winter storm struck the East Coast with wind gusts up to 90 miles per hour. It crippled the area with flooding, winds, rain, and snow. Hundreds of thousands of homes lost electrical power, thousands of businesses were damaged, the lives of millions were disrupted.

The storm was actually a combination of two storms that came from the West Coast. The first, a low-pressure system, was responsible for a tornado in Monterey, Calif., and flooding in Los Angeles. The second system entered from the Pacific Northwest and was called a jet streak because of its speed. The jet streak actually traveled within the jet stream, a narrow band of air that flows from west to east across the United States. The air moves at speeds between 60 kilometers in the summer to 125 kilometers in the winter. It is located above the troposphere

of the Earth's atmosphere, approximately 20 to 25 kilometers over the temperate zones of the Earth, and varying as much as 7 kilometers above the poles to 28 kilometers above the equator.

The two systems moved across the country, the jet streak moving at 170 miles per hour at 35,000 feet in the North, and the low-pressure system in the South. When the system to the South reached the East Coast storm, it turned north. As the two storms met, "the jet streak sucked air from the top of the low-pressure system, lowering its pressure even further. The system intensified rapidly as it began to move up the East coast," according to a December 12, 1992 report in the New York Times.

At the time, a high-pressure system was over Eastern Canada, creating cold wind. (High-pressure air will try to mix with a low-pressure system whenever possible to equalize the pressure. This movement of the high pressure causes wind.) These cold Canadian winds then mixed with the winds that the low-pressure system had picked up from the warm Atlantic Ocean waters.

This Northeaster, or more commonly, "Nor'easter," resembled a hurricane in many ways. But it wasn't, Lee Grenci, a meteorologist at Pennsylvania State University Weather Communications Group, said in the Times article. "It's a different animal." This storm actually did have an ill-defined eye as it passed over Atlantic City, New Jersey, but an eye is only one characteristic of a hurricane.

On Long Island Sound, the December storm caused beach erosion and damaged homes in places as this in Milford, Conn.

The damage caused by the storm is considered to be the worst since 1950. With its counterclockwise winds off the Atlantic Ocean, it drove the water on to the land, resulting in floods. And, although the tides were only 3–4 feet above normal, the damage was done by the water being pushed onto the land, into the towns, and down the streets.

Churning Up the Jersey Shore

The famous New Jersey boardwalks were strewed about like tossed pickup-sticks, with section from Bradley Beach, Belmar, Point Pleasant, Spring Lake, and Sea Girt found several blocks away. Point Pleasant lost 75 feet of beach and countless feet of sand dunes.

The century-old fishing pier in Ocean Grove, N.J., was swept out to sea during the storm. People in Manasquan, N.J., were evacuated from some of the beach areas by boats and National Guard trucks. And one young man, eager to find dry land, left his beach home by surfboard. Wayne Albright, a meteorologist with the National Weather Service, said, "People who have lived through this storm will have lived through probably the highest tides this century on the southern New Jersey coastline."

Some of the worst damage of all may have occurred to Fire Island, N.Y., which runs parallel to the southern side of Long Island. Homes were lost because of the relentless beating of the surf against the land, and the sand dunes sustained lasting damage.

"This may very well be the beginning of the end of Fire Island," said John Muuss, Director of Public Safety and Emergency Management for the town of Islip. According to an article in the December 15, 1992 *New York Times*, the storm had caused the ocean to breach, or slice, through the 30-mile-long island in many places; any more storms of any size might do irreparable damage.

Islip's town supervisor, Frank Jones, said, "The destruction of the dunes is the thing that is most devastating. We lost houses that can come and go, but there was so much devastation to the dunes that in some places they no longer exist. And that's not a quick fix. You can't scrape the beach and throw some sand up there and put some snow fences. Only God can rebuild the dunes."

Flooding also took place on the Southern shore of Connecticut, from Norwalk in the western part of the state to Stonington and Mystic in the eastern part. Houses along Long Island Sound were pulled into the water by high seas. Because of the shape of the sound, and because the storm pushed more ocean water into it, the waters sloshed around like the water in a bath tub does when a person moves back and forth and back and forth in the tub. Altogether, 12,000 homes were either lost or damaged.

Do rain storms hurt cities? They do if the city is on an island. People went to work in New York City that December morning and suddenly found themselves stranded. They were trapped in flooded cars and in a commuter ferryboat in New York harbor. The tunnels and subways were flooded. Trains in and out of New York City that use underground railways stopped running or were stranded. And, according to the *Times*, there were white caps on the highways.

The Storm of the Century

Three months later, in mid-March, the East Coast was treated to another extraordinary weather system.

The Blizzard of '93, called the Storm of the Century because of its record-breaking precipitation and damage, was the result of the jet stream dipping farther to the south than it usually does. The jet stream usually divides the country's weather, with the colder, arctic weather staying to the north of the line and warmer air to the south. This year, the jet stream dipped much farther to the south, bringing the colder arctic air with it. There it mixed with the warm, moist air of the Gulf of Mexico. Because of the cold arctic air, what normally would have been a low-pressure area of rain, became a windy snow storm—a snowy hurricane.

Tornadoes, spawned by the storm, killed people in central Florida, and snow began falling in sections of Alabama and Georgia unaccustomed to anything but an occasional dusting. Then, the storm walked deliberately up the coast, with a combination of rain, snow, lightening, and wind. More than 100 people lost their lives as a direct result of the storm.

The Red Cross set up shelters for people forced from their homes. T.V. stations devoted the entire days' programming to weather forecasts and storm-related news. Volunteers with four-wheel drive vehicles transported doctors, nurses, and medical staff to and from hospitals, and for some lucky students, schools closed.

Many areas, even in the deep south, received between one and two feet of snow with more in the eastern mountains and some areas of New England. Wind gusts were clocked at over 100 miles per hour from Florida to Massachusetts. Campers and hikers had to either be rescued, or have supplies dropped to them as the storm moved from the South to the North.

In Connecticut, one family removed more than 50 gallons of snow from their attic. Because of the direction of the storm in relation to the house, the snow was pushed under the eaves of the house into the attic. The eaves, at the very bottom of the roof, have tiny holes that allow air to enter and exit to ventilate the attic. The holes are situated so that rain and snow *usually* cannot enter, but a strange wind pattern can change that. However, this family was luckier than some.

The entire town of Sea Bright, N.J.,—1,800 residents—had to be evacuated because of flooding. Sea Bright is situated on a peninsula that has the Atlantic Ocean to the east and a series of bays and rivers to the west that connect to New York Harbor to the north. Birmingham, Ala., received 13 inches of snow, which it fell in a 24 hour period. "At least 18 homes toppled into the sea on New York's Long Island Sound, [and] about 200 homes along North Carolina's Outer Banks were damaged," according to reports in the March 15,1993 *Hartford Courant*.

The storm forced 23 airports to close in the East on Saturday, March 13, causing delays and cancellations of flights across the country. Not only were flights affected in or out of Eastern airports, but flights elsewhere in the country were disrupted because planes were grounded.

Hotter, Drier Days Arrive

As the saying goes, be careful what you wish for, you just might get it. And the people in the East who wished for the long hot days of summer after battling a long, cold winter got their wish—in the form of a heat wave. Figures rose to triple digits and people died as a direct result of the heat that encased the eastern third of the country in early July. Philadelphia and New York City had three days each of triple-digit temperatures. Twenty thousand chickens died in Westminster, Mass., as a result of the heat. Lightning strikes ignited forests in North Carolina and, according to news reports, a dairy farmer said that his cows had stopped giving milk because of the intense heat. "They just stand around in the shade. . . . They've just shut down and quit."

Heat waves are bad enough, but in the Middle Atlantic and Southern states, it did not rain, and crops withered and died. In a "Today" show broadcast in August 1993, one Virginia farmer described watching his fields go from green to yellow to brown and his cattle eating not only all of what he had grown, but also grasses along the highways near his farm. He worried that he would have nothing left to feed them come winter.

Parts of the Southeast, with little or no rainfall during the growing season, experienced one of the worst droughts in years. The State Agriculture Commissioner of South Carolina stated that 95% of the corn crop, 70% of the soybeans, 50% of the wheat, and 25% of the tobacco grown in the state had been lost due to the lack of rain, according to the July 25, 1993 *New York Times*. Neighboring states of North Carolina and Georgia also reported crop failures due to the weather.

History Repeats

While the heat wave of 1993 was miserable, meteorologists say there have been worse years. Jim Wagner, a meteorologist at the National Weather Service's Climate Center at Camp Springs, Md. said that "[c]ool areas are 'just about balancing out' this summer," according to a report in the July 12, 1993 *New York Times*. And while he feels that this heat was not related to global warming, some climatologists say that an overall warming is taking place because of pollutants in the atmosphere.

But, as heat waves go, this was nothing compared to the big one in 1936. According to the *New York Times*, temperatures in New York City then hit 106 degrees. In 1936, there was no air conditioning. People fainted on the job. They slept on the roofs of their New York City buildings. The heat wave was not confined only to New York City, though. Intense heat with temperatures of 120 degrees were recorded in Arkansas, Kansas, and North and South Dakota. Fifteen states recorded temperatures that, as yet, have not been broken. A total of 997 people died across the nation in 10 days, 76 in New York City. Of those, 21 had drowned after jumping in the water as a way to escape the searing heat.

Heat in the city is different than in the country, a city dweller will say. The sidewalks and pavement absorb the heat. Those who could leave New York City in 1936 did so. Mayor Fiorello LaGuardia of New York City ordered all of those who had been jailed for sleeping on the beaches to be released and said that no one else would be arrested for such an offense until after the heat had broken. City pools stayed open until midnight.

In the 1993 heat wave, as in the one in 1936, people just wished that it would rain.

The Great Flood

And rain it did, but mostly in the Midwest. In 1993, the great heat wave in the East and the "Great Flood" in the Midwest resulted from a weather pattern that blanketed the continental United States. What appears to have happened is that nothing was moving in the sky. A high-pressure system known as the Bermuda High, normally located in the Atlantic Ocean off the coast of the southeastern United States, stalled over South Carolina and Georgia. That meant clear skies and almost no possibility of rain in the southeastern United States.

The winds in a high-pressure system travel clockwise, and are called anticyclone winds. The polar jet stream, that usually separates the weather North and South in the United States, flows across the country from West to East. Low-pressure systems move along in a counter clockwise direction. In the winter months this jet stream guides the harsh, winter snow storms across the country, but in the summer, the jet stream is usually much weaker and much farther to the north in Canada, which is why summer temperatures in most of the United States are similar compared to the deep contrast between the winter temperatures in different areas of the country, according to a story in the September 1993 *Storm* magazine.

The summer jet stream moved south into the Central Plains, and the Bermuda High moved west over South Carolina and Georgia. This caused heavy rainfall to engulf the Midwest area for an extraordinary length of time. And while this weather pattern is not uncommon, it is rare for these weather patterns to remain stationary for such a long period of time. The result was not only a flood in the Midwest, but a drought in the Southeast.

The winds traveled down the southeastern coast and into the Gulf of Mexico. When winds travel across water, they pick up some of that moisture. This time, the moisture fell as rain in the Midwest, according to a report in the July 9, 1993 *New York Times*. Meteorologists also said that after the 1992 summer, which was so cool, the Midwest may have retained more moisture than usual in the ground and not had as much as usual evaporate into the atmosphere. Also, a subtropical jet stream moved storms across the Southwest and up the Mississippi valley in the spring of 1993, where the moisture fell as rain on ground still saturated from 1992.

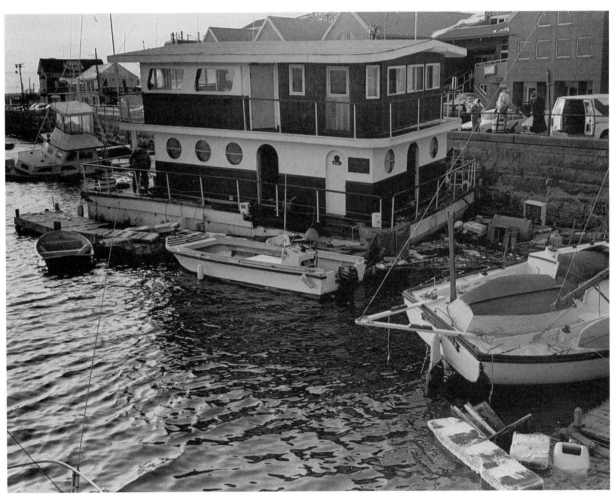

A houseboat named Hurricane Gloria *came to rest amid broken docks and against a sea wall in Newport, R.I., after the Nor'easter in March.*

The eastern high-pressure system also prevented cold fronts from moving in on the Northeast and breaking the heat wave. Climatologists say that there are two naturally occurring reasons for this weather pattern.

The first is El Niño, an area of warm water that develops in the Pacific Ocean every two to seven years. El Niño was responsible for bringing heavier winter rains to the Midwest. So, when the spring rains fell, the ground was already saturated.

The second reason is the eruption of Mt. Pinatubo, a volcano in the Phillippine Islands that erupted in June 1991. The ash and debris that was spit from the volcano filled the skies, became part of the world's jet streams and gave the Earth a cooler-than-normal period of weather.

Generally, from April 1 to June 27, the rainfall in the Midwest should total about 10 inches. But in 1993, the average was 15 inches or more in some areas. Crops of corn and soybeans, usually visible for as far as the eye can see, were not seen this year. Mud replaced the plants.

The flood, involving several major rivers and countless small streams, eventually consumed all or parts of nine states: Minnesota, Wisconsin, Illinois, Missouri, Iowa, North and South Dakota, Nebraska, and Kansas. And by September, the mighty Mississippi River had transported enough water to send some of it on a circuitous route to the Atlantic Ocean. Oceanographers reported finding a freshwater river under the ocean's surface off the Florida coast some 1,500 miles from the mouth of the Mississippi in the Gulf of Mexico. The fresh water apparently was picked up by the Gulf Stream and carried around Florida into the Atlantic.

Fighting the Flood

People in all affected states fought back by sandbagging—building their own levees to protect town and personal property. One man, who owned two acres near Niota, Ill., sandbagged his homestead to keep the waters from flooding him out. At one point, the only way to cross the Mississippi River was by helicopter, since bridges were not usable for stretches of 200 miles and more. People who owned small boats stayed mobile since much of the area had flooded too much for any other form of transportation.

In Prairie du Chien, Wis., population 6,000, the employees of the local radio station, WPRE, spent two weeks boating to and from work. It was the only way to get there since all of the roads were under water. In Glen Haven, another Wisconsin town, a storm dropped four inches of rain in 20 minutes, causing six feet of water to cascade down Main Street, taking everything, including 17 cars, with it. Five wound up in the Mississippi River. The other 12 stopped by crashing into the railroad bridge.

An estimated 26.5 million sandbags were used during the flood to try to keep areas from flooding. Still, the percentage of farmland lost because of the flood ranged from approximately half a million acres to 6 million acres. All-in-all, because of the flood, more than 21 million acres were unproductive in 1993. That worked out to be just less than 17,000 square miles, or the approximate combined size of New Jersey, Rhode Island, and New Hampshire.

As the water rose on the Mississippi River, the barges, boats, and tugs that use the river as a super highway suddenly came to a halt. For as the river rose, the reliability of the river stopped. The banks of the river could no longer be seen. Familiar landmarks disappeared. Five hundred miles of the Mississippi had to be closed. Up to a thousand barges carrying grains, coal, and farm chemicals were trapped, according to a *USA Today* report.

The Final Blow

In the town of Hardin, Mo., the Missouri River attacked the town, leaving the residents with no telephone service, no electricity, and no running water. When the town's 598 residents began trying to put the pieces of the town back together, they discovered a piece missing that was so huge that they might never have it back the way it was.

The river had assaulted their history. It had scooped out a 50-foot hole in what had been their cemetery. The cemetery dates back to 1810 and contained the remains of parents, grandparents, great grandparents, and Civil War ancestors. It had survived countless tornadoes. It had been the town's link with the past.

Caskets were found "down river" each day and returned to the tiny town for identification and reburial. Families that grieved and buried their dead once had to do it again if their family members were relocated. One farmer woke to find 10 vaults in her yard. She lives eight miles east of Hardin.

Ironically, this town is not even located directly on the Missouri River. It is five miles north of the river and about 35 miles east of Kansas City, on the western side of Missouri.

According to the August 2, 1993 *Boston Globe,* only 45 people lost their lives because of the flood due to ample warnings, evacuation plans, no flash floods and protection of human life by levees and dams. By comparison, during the flood of 1889, thousands died, with 2,100 drowning on one day, May 31, 1889.

The Levee Effect

Evacuation plans in the Midwest had been in effect since a series of levees and dams were built after previous floods. Levees are high walls built along the banks of the river to protect an area of land, usually a town, from flood waters. Not all towns chose to build levees. Some felt that their view of the river was too spectacular to block with a levee, others felt that they were too expensive.

The town of Bettendorf, Iowa built a levee system that gives them the best of both worlds. Their levee consists of folding walls of aluminum and concrete that can open up to a height of just over 10 feet and are only 3 feet 7 inches when closed. This system gives the residents a beautiful view most of the time and protection from Mother Nature when necessary. The levees in Bettendorf held, and, while not all levees did, the overwhelming majority of them held back the water. The Army Corps of Engineers said in a report in July 2, 1993 *USA Today* that at least 32 levees had failed on the Mississippi and its tributaries.

Some feel that the levee system works too well. Many years ago, mighty rivers like the Mississippi would flood each year and deposit nutrient soil on the banks, ensuring the farmers a good crop each year. Now, with the levee system, one of two things happens: First, the water can only flood certain areas because of the levees, therefore flooding too much in small areas. Second, the rich soil is no longer being deposited on the farmland.

What a River Wants, . . .

When the river floods too much in certain areas, it deposits the soil in homes and businesses and streets, not where farmers grow crops. What does not wind up going over the banks, flows down the Mississippi and out into the Gulf of Mexico. According to a report in July 26, 1993 *Time* Magazine, protection of existing towns is important, but in the future, "[i]n some cases it may even prove cost effective to relocate entire flood-prone communities."

"In the old days, the Mississippi and its tributaries flooded all the time, moving nutrients from one place to another, creating a diversity of habitats," said Norm Stucky, a biologist with the Missouri Conservation Department as reported in the July 18, 1993 *Hartford Courant.* People are magically drawn to the water. More people live within 100 miles of the coast than in the interior of the country.

But certain parts of the land, the tidal marsh, is a buffer zone between the water and the land. Along the Mississippi and its tributaries there is a flood plain. The purpose of the flood plain is to act as a blotter for the rivers when they overflow. It is to blot up, or store, the flood waters, to slow down the flood by reducing the height and speed of the waters. Keeping the waters within a narrow space makes the waters run more quickly, which makes them more dangerous to anything that gets in their way.

The way water runs through a garden hose is an example of the way the levees and dams control the flooding waters. Normally, water flows out of a hose at a certain speed. If a person were to put their thumb over half of the mouth of the hose, the same amount of water would come out, except it would shoot out farther and faster and would have more force behind it. By not allowing the flood plains to do the work for which they were intended, and by building levees and dams to keep the water off the flood plains, the flooding has actually been worse.

Communities that have a levee or dam between them and the river feel safe and secure. When levees break, water gets trapped behind the remaining levees, making drainage of the waters more difficult and more time-consuming, therefore lengthening the time of the flood. Also, when levees are used to narrow the river's path the river's sediments that would normally be deposited on the flood plain are instead dropped next to the levee wall, which, over time, raises the height of the river. The levee must then also be raised to remain effective.

"In general, a river wants to recreate itself as a river with a flood plain; it's rising in response to these rising levees," said James T.B. Tripp, an expert on floods with the Environmental Defense Fund. "River systems have a way of adjusting themselves in response to human manipulation of the flood plain in ways that can never be entirely foreseen," according to an article in the July 20, 1993 *New York Times*.

Because of this, flood-plain managers are trying a more compromising approach: working with the river, not against it. They are keeping new development away from the flood plain, "preserving or restoring its ecosystems and letting water flow as freely as possible so that natural flood-control mechanisms can work." Different areas of the country are now using the wetlands as natural holding tanks or flood basins.

"They are preserving stretches of flood plain in urban areas which, in between periods of high water, serve as parks, ball fields, and greenways," the *New York Times* article stated. "For too long we've been trying to adjust rivers to human needs, and then we wonder why our rivers are messed up and why we continue to get flooded; it's not a mystery," Larry Larson, director of the Association of State Flood-plain Managers, an organization of professionals engaged in flood plain management and flood control, told the *Times*.

The article gave examples of how some areas have dealt with the issue:

- Tulsa, Okla., decided after the 1984 flood of Mingo Creek to work with nature by creating a more natural flood-control system. The city constructed a series of lakes on Mingo Creek's flood plain. Most of the year they are dry and are used for the town's sporting events. But when there is a flood, they are there to slow down the waters. The lakes are strung together by a series of "trickle trails," used during the dry times as jogging trails and during the flooding as canals from one lake to the next.

- Littleton, Colo., developed a 625-acre park in its flood plain to weaken the effects of the South Platte River flooding instead of rerouting the river.
- North Richmond, Calif., in the San Francisco Bay area, "successfully brought about the creation of a naturally meandering flood channel and restored the stream-side ecosystem in a way that would maintain ecological health while accommodating once-in-a-century floods."

Some ecologists say that the definition of a river is not just the part where the water flows, but also the flood plain and valley in which the river resides. David Johnson, an aquatic ecologist who is assistant director of the School of Natural Resources at Ohio State University was quoted in the *New York Times* as saying that, "[i]t's a question of working with the river or fighting the river. Fighting the river is almost always going to be a losing battle."

David Lanegran, a professor of geography and urban studies at Macalester College in St. Paul, Minnesota, said in the July 18, 1993 *New York Times* that "the river is taking back its old places. You can see the old marshes coming back in the farmers' fields, all the places where the duck ponds used to be. It's almost like a ghost. The water is saying, 'This is where I used to be. This used to be my place.'"

Flood Plains as Ecosystems

Flood plains are productive ecosystems. Like an ocean's tidal pool, which needs the constant rise and fall of the tides to bathe the marsh and the animals that live in the marsh, rivers need their flood plains.

"When they flood in the spring, they become breeding grounds for fish. Most flood plain acreage is wetlands, and about half the country's endangered species require wetland habitat. The riparian zone along rivers is home to distinct assemblages of soils, microbes, plants, and animals that depend on high water tables and occasional flooding," the *New York Times* reported.

The Great Flood of '93, in the history of the river, "is part of the natural cycle of renewal." The river currents lift topsoil from the land, carry it downstream, and deposit it on another piece of land. The

(Left) A firefighter views a van that was thrown onto a sea wall in the Bronx, N.Y., during the December 1992 storm. Another person looks over a stray boat that landed on a car.

(Below) New York City police in protective gear wade along FDR Drive on Manhattan's upper East Side to search stranded vehicles and rescue occupants during the December storm.

An individual makes his way via snow skis across New York City's Fifth Avenue during the March 1993 "Storm of the Century."

heavy rains that usually come before a flood help in the cleansing of river waters for better fish spawning, according to the *New York Times*, and, "the great lesson of the floods may be that humans will have to do a lot more if they are to outwit nature, if that is even possible."

While the "logical" thing might be to give the land back to the river, more is at stake than the wood and stones used to build a house. Part of America's history lies along the banks of the river. The town of Ste. Genevieve, Mo., was built over 250 years ago in 1735 by the French. Many of the homes there were built in the 1700s and 1800s. When the flood hit, the people there used 870,000 sandbags, each containing 35 pounds of sand, to protect their little piece of history.

The boyhood home of Samuel Clemens, who wrote under the pen name of Mark Train, is in Hannibal, Mo. Settled in 1819, the town was used by Clemens as the backdrop for two of his books, *The Adventures of Tom Sawyer* and *The Adventures of Huckleberry Finn*.

Sometimes rivers are rerouted to satisfy the needs of the people living in the town, but even waters have memory. Take Turtle Creek in Kansas City, Kan., for example. The levees on the Missouri River held, but the creek, which had been moved in the 1920s to make way for a road, remembered its old route and subsequently put the road under eight feet of water.

The Year Marches On

As fall approached in 1993, so did the inevitable hurricane season. But it would take quite a hurricane season to overshadow what had already happened during the year.

Cape Hattaras and the outer banks of North Carolina were evacuated in late August because of Hurricane Emily. And, although Emily never made landfall, she still caused enough damage to make the residents of coastal North Carolina speak her name with reverence. Emily approached the islands of North Carolina as the full moon rose from the East. With a 45-mile-wide eye, the sassy Emily tore roofs off houses, flooded homes and businesses, and even claimed a few of the houses as they crumbled into the sea.

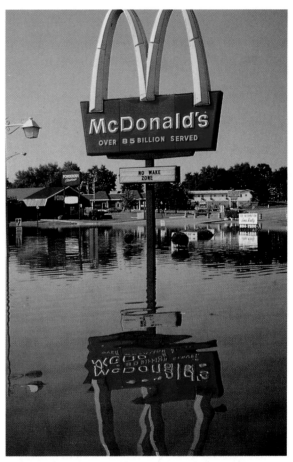

A McDonald's restaurant in Festus, Mo., was under water in July when the Mississippi River flooded.

But in a year where weather has caused heartache and sorrow for so many, Emily showed compassion for the coastal barrier islands of North Carolina, and curved Northeast. The eye never did make landfall. And while the storm churned toward the Northeast, a front moved across New England, coaxing the potential killer out to sea where it died in the cold waters of the North Atlantic.

Unusual Is Usual

Unusual weather in 1993 seemed to be the norm and not the exception in the world:

- In June, it snowed enough in Colorado to close three mountain passes.
- Paris, France experienced the worst rainstorm in more than a decade. The storm caused the Seine

(Top) Members of the Mexico Missouri Army National Guard fortify a levee in Festus, Mo., to try and hold back the Mississippi River flood waters.
(Bottom) This levee in St. Louis, Mo., nearly collapsed along the Des Peres River and placed some residents within 10 feet of the flood water. But rocks and plastic were used to fortify the levee.

Flood waters consumed many homes in the Midwest.

to be poisoned with sewage and 300 tons of dead fish.

• In May, a rain squall dropped 4.5 inches of rain on Hong Kong in one hour.

Then again, weather always has had a major effect on humans.

From the Beginnings

Throughout history, weather has played a major role in shaping not only the landscape, but also in determining which civilizations would endure. Archaeologists now believe they know the reason for the collapse of the ancient Akkadian civilization in 2200 B.C. The Akkadian civilization was located between the Tigrus and Euphrates rivers in the area now known as Syria. They were beaten by a severe 300-year drought, according to an article in the journal *Science*.

Historians say that period of dry weather coincides with the breakdown of the other ancient civilizations in Egypt, Greece, Palestine, and the Indus Valley. Geologists and archeologists say a change in the climate occurred after a volcanic eruption that covered the area with a layer of ash.

Mesopotamia, meaning the land between the rivers, was where the first cities were located. Two countries now cover Mesopotamia: Syria and Iraq. The very first city-states were located in the southern part of what is now Iraq. Middle-school social stud-

Saint Genevieve, Mo., was a town afloat after the Mississippi River overran its banks.

Flood waters stretched halfway up telephone poles.

Fortifying levees involved round-the-clock efforts by National Guardsmen and civilian volunteers. In July in Festus, Mo., people workd to save small business shops.

(Above) Relief efforts for flood victims involved troops and aircraft from many places. Here, Guardsmen at Montgomery, Ala., load a plane bound for the Midwest.

(Right) Sandbagging efforts continued into late summer. Here, troops load sandbags onto a helicopter.

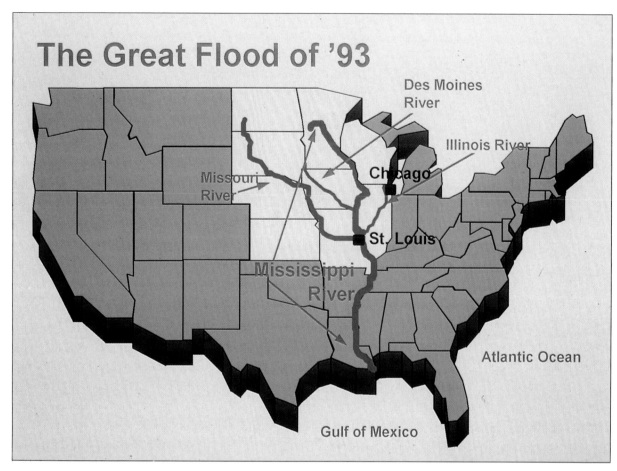

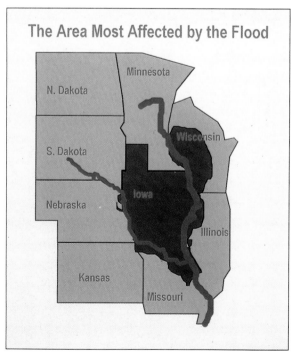

(Above) A map of the United States highlights the Midwest flood zone and some of the rivers involved.

(Right) The dark area shows how extensive an area was affected by the flood.

ies books refer to this area as Sumer. The Sumerians invented a form of writing called cuneiform, which has left behind a well-documented history of the area.

Archaeologists had known since the 1940s about a 300-year gap in the history of Mesopotamia. Marie-Agnes Courty, a French geologist, used a microscope to examine particles on the roof of a house in Mesopotamia. There she found a thin layer of volcanic ash, covered with sand. In areas around the house, sand as much as three feet thick was found.

She saw fewer earthworm holes, and wind-blown pellets and dust, all signs of arid soil.

"That tells you the climate went from good to rotten in a very short time—in the tens of years," said Harvey Weiss, a Yale University archaeologist, who led the American-French expedition. Whether the volcano caused the drought, or if it just happened to erupt at the same time the drought was beginning is uncertain. Which volcano erupted also is unknown.

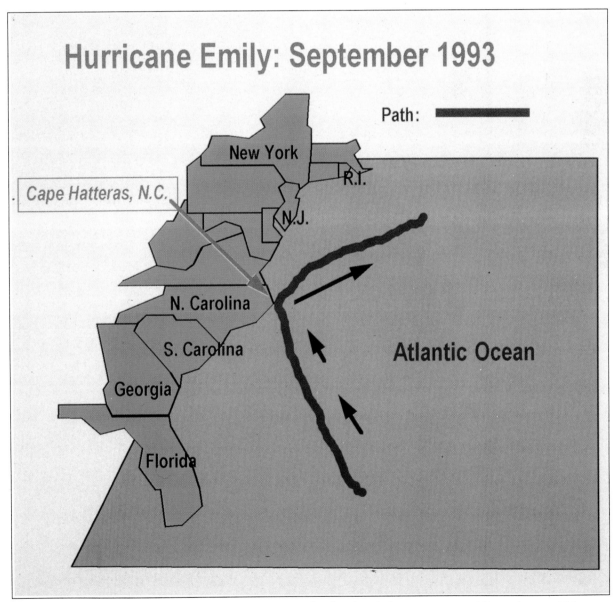

Hurricane Emily skirted the Southeast coast in September but headed out to sea, avoiding what could have been another weather-related disaster.

The Douglas fir tree is among the commercially most valuable commodities in the lumber business, but it also provides habitat for wildlife such as the spotted owl.

9

BIRDS VS. TREES:
A NATIONAL DEBATE

President Bill Clinton knew that his newly proposed policy on timber cutting in the Pacific Northwest would go a long way toward achieving a balance between economic and environmental needs. He knew it because neither preservationists nor loggers were happy.

"We know that our solutions may not make everybody happy. Indeed, they may not make anybody happy," Clinton said in announcing the policy in July 1993. But in achieving a balance, everybody gives up something, he reasoned.

The debate over logging in the Pacific Northwest has been an expensive and bitter one since federal courts started holding up sales of timber from federal lands in the late 1980s. Environmental organizations had a potent cause, the northern spotted owl, to use

A northern spotted owl sits in a tree.

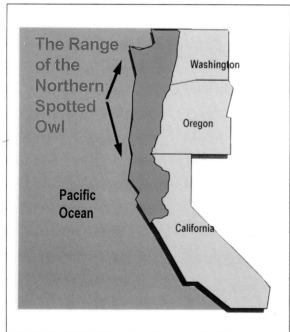

The northern spotted owl's habitat in the United States stretches across three states in the Pacific Northwest.

A forester checks on plantings made after a forest section was logged.

as a reason for successfully suing government agencies they claimed were selling too many trees too fast. The spotted owl, they said, was disappearing along with its habitat, which consisted mainly of the oldest stands of trees in the forest.

But those oldest, tallest, and biggest trees also brought the highest prices in the lumber market. Other, younger trees also were needed from to help satisfy a burgeoning demand for wood products, the timber industry claimed; saving spotted owls meant endangering another species: the human logger.

The owls-vs.-trees debate in the courtrooms came to symbolize a much broader discussion of the meaning and purpose of the Endangered Species Act, a federal law that provides protection for species likely to become extinct unless specific plans are developed to preserve them and their habitats. The law, enacted in 1973, and vigorously debated in courtrooms throughout its 20-year history, was up for renewal in Congress in 1993.

The debate has pitted the environment and economy squarely against each other. While the spotted owl's direct sphere of influence is limited to the Pacific Northwest and northern California region, the outcome of any decisions in the debate are of national importance, due primarily to a growing trend by Americans to take a hard look at how the country's natural resources are managed.

Steeped in Tradition

Timber companies have been buying trees from federal lands for decades, particularly in the West, where the federal government is a major landowner of national forests, national parks, and recreation areas. The two federal agencies that own and manage tim-

(Left) The red-cockaded woodpecker has been on the Endangered Species List for a number of years. But an agreement between the U.S. government and Georgia-Pacific Corp. will help to preserve its habitat in the Southeast.
(Below) The range of the red-cockaded woodpecker stretches across several states in the Southeast.

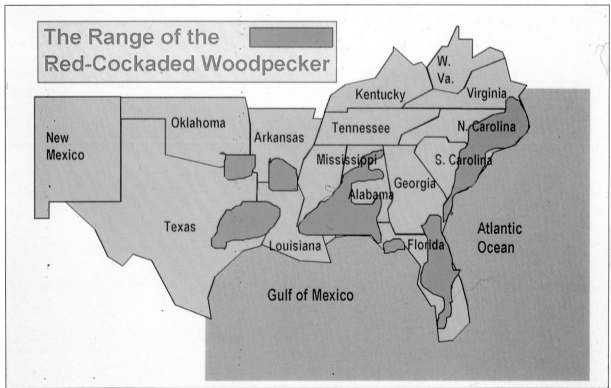

The Range of the Red-Cockaded Woodpecker

(Right) The demand for wood products, such as this softwood lumber from Mississippi, soared during past construction booms.

(Below) Loggers work in a Southern pine forest.

ber for sale are the U.S. Forest Service (USFS), an agency of the U.S. Department of Agriculture, and the Bureau of Land Management (BLM), an agency of the U.S. Department of Interior.

Timber is sold by the federal government from national forests administered by USFS and from lands administered by BLM, but not from national parks, which are managed by another Interior Department agency, the National Park Service. In addition to the federal government, some state governments also sell timber off state-owned lands.

The government agencies' forestry management professionals survey the federal lands, map out areas to be logged, and then offer specific tracts of timber for sale. Timber companies buy the rights to cut trees on these tracts by submitting bids at timber auctions held by the government. Loggers then cut only those trees in the mapped tracts sold at the auction.

The purpose of selling the trees was twofold. First, it was considered sound forestry management to harvest trees on a cyclical basis, much like other agricultural crops are grown on farms but, of course, with decades instead of years in between the harvesting periods. Second, the sales brought in revenue for the government from lands that otherwise just cost money to maintain.

Using the spotted owl as a weapon, environmental groups have shaken both foundations of the government's reasons for selling timber. First, they have claimed that it is best to let forests exist on their own and let Mother Nature take its course. Second, they say administrative and other costs involved in the preparation of some timber auctions amount to more than what the auctions bring in, putting some sales in the net-loss category rather than in the profit margins.

Old-Growth and Second-Growth Forests

At the center of the debate in the Pacific Northwest are old-growth trees—trees that could be 200 or more years old and several feet in diameter. Most of the forests from which timber is sold in the western United States contain no old-growth trees, because they have been logged already.

Older trees yield large pieces of lumber with tight grain and rich color, and the beauty and strength of the wood make it extremely valuable in a commercial market. Virtually no old-growth forests exist on privately owned lands in the West, which makes any available old-growth trees on government lands that much more valuable. But devout conservationists maintain that because of the shortage of old-growth trees, all remaining old-growth habitats should be preserved.

Most of the forests consist of what is known as second-growth trees. These are trees that, depending on the species, may be harvested when they are about 70 years old. They are called second-growth because they have grown in land that was previously cleared by either logging or by natural causes, such as the forest fires, which are common in the West.

After years of studying, the Interior Department's U.S. Fish and Wildlife Service (USFWS) listed the northern spotted owl as a "threatened" species in June 1990. "The listing decision was made strictly on the basis of the species' biological status. The [Endangered Species] Act does not permit economic factors to be considered as part of a listing decision," the agency said in its announcement of the listing.

The Endangered Species Act has two categories, or listings: threatened and endangered. An endangered species is in danger of extinction throughout all or a significant portion of its range. A threatened species is likely to become endangered within the foreseeable future. Each listing carries different parameters of protection that the government require, with endangered status obviously carrying the strictest requirements.

In general, however, the law prohibits anyone from harassing, harming, hunting, wounding, killing, trapping or collecting endangered or threatened species, and it prohibits endangering them during interstate and foreign commerce. In the case of spotted owls, that means their nesting areas cannot be logged.

The northern spotted owl, or *Strix occidentalis caurina*, lives mainly in old-growth forests, but also to some extent in second-growth forests, with its range limited to an area that stretches from British Columbia down the western side of the Cascade Mountains to northern California. As of 1992, the government estimated that about 3,500 pairs of owls lived in the states of Washington, Oregon, and California.

The northern spotted owl is a medium-sized predatory bird, with a round face and dark brown eyes, and chestnut-brown feathers overall, with barred brown-and-white tail feathers. It does not have ear tufts like the great horned owl. Spotted owls don't build nests. They roost in cavities of heart-rotted tree trunks. They feed mostly on rodents, such as flying squirrels, woodrats, and gophers, but they also eat birds, insects, and reptiles.

"The Fish and Wildlife Service found that the northern spotted owl is threatened throughout its range by the loss and adverse modification of suitable habitat and the resultant decline in population," the agency's June 1992 statement said. The primary habitat of the owl was described in the context of old-growth forests: For flying, the owls need large open areas beneath the canopy that forms when the tops of older trees blend together rather than shoot skyward as individual units. The owls also need the fallen trees and other woody debris on the ground, because those elements provide habitat for smaller animals on which the owl feeds.

Since that designation, however, timber companies have been taking an inventory of owls, and many were claiming as late as September 1993 that spotted owls were not only living, but living well, in second-growth forests.

Nevertheless, a listing under the Endangered Species Act requires the government to develop a recovery plan for the species, so an interagency team of scientists has been formed to evaluate alternatives for the spotted owl and the forests of the Pacific Northwest.

Northwest Timber Sales Plummeted

The northern spotted owl is but one species, but its importance has been raised to a significant level because the government considers it an "indicator" species. That means that the status of the owl is an indicator of the state of the entire ecosystem in which it lives. Using this premise, environmental groups claimed successfully in the late 1980s that losses in the owl's population were threatening the forests of the Pacific Northwest. The groups took their case to court, and federal judges initially sided with them.

Prior to the court injunctions that halted or delayed timber sales, the federal government was selling 4 billion to 5 billion board feet of wood a year from the forests involved in the dispute. A board foot of lumber is the equivalent of a piece of wood that measures 1 foot long, 1 foot wide, and is 1 inch thick. In lumber language, a 1"x12" plank that is 10 feet long would contain 10 board feet of wood. A 2"x12" plank would contain 10 board feet in a 5-foot-long section. It takes about 10,000 board feet of lumber to build an average single-family house. Much of the harvest from these forests is of the Douglas fir species, a highly regarded softwood in the home-building business.

Since the courts have limited sales in the owl's range, however, government timber sales have plummeted. The estimate for 1993 was projected at 2 billion board feet, about half the previous level.

The reduction in federal timber sales, combined with the effects of automation within the timber industry, plus the fluctuations in the overall economy over the past few years, has meant a loss by some estimates of as many as 20,000 jobs for the Pacific Northwest timber industry.

The decrease in timber sales translated to a loss of thousands of timber jobs, and a dramatic rise in prices for a dwindling supply of lumber. Timber companies often blamed the environmentalists' lawsuits for causing the job losses and price hikes. However, environmentalists claimed that an increase in automation in the timber industry, combined with the industry's exporting of whole logs overseas, contributed heavily to the situation.

Under the plan proposed by President Clinton, logging would continue at a low level, so that protection of the forests and the animal species within them can be assured. The 1995 harvest is projected to be about 1.2 billion board feet. But to help alleviate the economic hardships, the president proposes to spend $1.2 billion training people for alternative jobs and providing for economic and community development.

"This issue has been one which has bedeviled the people of the Pacific Northwest for some years now," Clinton said in announcing his decision. "The time has come to break the logjam, to end the endless delay and bickering, and to restore some genuine security and rootedness to the lives of the people who

Wildlife biologists for Georgia-Pacific Corp. prepare to attach a U.S. Fish and Wildlife Service identification band to a young northern spotted owl. The identification is part of a joint study between industry and government to determine the true population of the owl in northern California.

have for too long been torn from pillar to post in this important area of the United States."

Clinton said he had based his decision on a balancing test: whether the plan was "scientifically sound, ecologically credible, and legally defensible," and whether it "provides an innovative approach to forest management, to protect the environment and to produce a predictable level of timber sales."

Forest products industry representatives blasted the president's plan as economically devasting, while some environmental groups claimed the plan didn't go far enough to protect the forests and animal species. And even though the president has chosen a plan, the issue was far from settled. Legislators from the Pacific Northwest vowed to offer still more alternatives, and the federal courts involved still have to approve any—including the president's—solutions. Also, new lawsuits were filed by the forest products industry after Clinton's announcement.

Not Just the West

The uproar over the president's plan for the Pacific Northwest forests, in many ways, overshadowed an earlier successful effort by the Clinton administration and timber and environmental interests. In April, U.S. Secretary of the Interior Bruce Babbitt announced a "first-of-its-kind agreement which balances sound timber management and strong conservation measures to protect endangered species."

The agreement, between the government and Georgia-Pacific Corp., a major player in the wood-products industry, provided for protection of the habitat of the red-cockaded woodpecker while still allowing "reasonable" harvests of Southern pine logs.

The red-cockaded woodpecker, which was listed as an endangered species in 1970, resides in forests of 12 states in the Southeast, from Texas to Virginia. The bird nests and roosts exclusively in older, living pines. As these trees were felled over a number of years as the region developed economically, the woodpecker's population declined. The current population is estimated to be 10,000–14,000 birds in about 4,000 family groups.

The red-cockaded woodpecker is typically 7 inches long, has a white patch on its cheeks, a red cockade, and clawed toes that point in two directions. The woodpeckers nest in clans, including three to seven adults, from April to June, and produce three to four eggs. They eat insects.

While the spotted owl debate centers mostly on federally owned lands in the Pacific Northwest, the woodpecker agreement involves 4 million acres of land in the Southeast owned or leased by Georgia-Pacific.

"This agreement provides a breakthrough in establishing cooperative public and private efforts to save an endangered species," Babbitt said. "In the past, our government has rarely provided guidance to corporations about what they need to do to comply with the Endangered Species Act. They've forced corporations to guess, with the only enforcement tool being the threat of a lawsuit. But with some government leadership, we can move forward to protect species and avoid costly and unpredictable lawsuits. That's the course set by this agreement."

The agreement calls for Georgia-Pacific to conduct forest-management practices, including timber harvesting, "with the objective of sustaining indefinitely the active red-cockaded woodpecker colonies present." The company and the government agreed to conduct cooperative research efforts on forest characteristics and the woodpecker's survival. Georgia-Pacific agreed to pay the government $5,000 a year for five years to help fund the research.

Elements of Georgia-Pacific's plan include:

- Locating and marking all active red-cockaded woodpecker colonies on the company's 4.2 million acres of timberland in the Southeast.
- Providing adequate foraging habitat for the birds within a half mile of the colony center.
- Maintaining a 200-foot buffer zone around a colony.
- Providing at least 80x120 acres of forage habitat for each colony.
- Prohibiting new roads in colony areas.

Under the Endangered Species Act, private landowners are not responsible for providing recovery plans and actions for threatened and endangered species. The law only prohibits anyone, including private landowners, from doing anything that would disturb or destroy the affected animals.

A Balanced Approach

Other than taking no action at all, which was not a viable alternative since the spotted owl has been placed on the threatened species list, President Clinton had essentially 10 alternatives from which to choose a direction for the future of Pacific Northwest forests and animals.

The alternatives were developed by a team of scientists of various disciplines and from a number of government agencies. *(A mini-glossary of terms appears on page 127.)*

Of the alternatives, 10 were considered by the president for implementation. Though Alternative Nine was chosen, brief summaries of the others follow. The summaries, and any quotes within them, are based on the content of *Draft Supplemental Environmental Impact Statement,* published in July 1993.

The Federal land that encompasses the territory of the northern spotted owl consists of 24,260,700 acres in Washington, Oregon, and northern California. In that area, the spotted owl is only one of 42 species of animals that are listed or proposed for listing as threatened or endangered. The other species include the marbled murrelet, grizzly bear, and northern bald eagle. The 10 alternatives divide the land into the following categories:

Designated Areas

Congressionally Reserved—These lands have already been designated by the government. These lands include: Wilderness, Wild and Scenic Rivers, National Wildlife Refuges, National Parks, some Research Natural Areas, and others. The acreage of these areas does not change through the 10 alternatives.

Late-Successional Reserves—These areas would change for each alternative. They would be held and managed for the protection of the habitat of species in late-successional, or old-growth forests that are inhabitated by the northern spotted owl. In most of the alternatives, some thinning of the young trees, called silvicultural treatment, would be permitted.

Managed Late-Successional Areas—These are areas that may have to be sacrificed for the good of the whole at some time in the future. That means that silvicultural treatments or fire-hazard-reduction treatments would be allowed in order to avoid destructive forest fires, disease, or insect epidemics.

Adaptive Management Areas—These areas exist only under alternative nine. This is an area of educational commitment to learn more about ecosystem management. Each area is the subject of a different focus, such as how to use late-successional forests to their fullest, and how to improve the land that lies along the rivers, streams and lakes.

Administratively Withdrawn Areas—These are areas of federal land that were not scheduled for timber sale previously and, therefore, are not now included in the allowable sale quantity (ASQ). These areas include recreational facilities, areas that are not suitable for timber removal, visual retention and riparian areas, and areas necessary for the protection of certain species.

Riparian Reserves—This is the space of land that lies along the rivers, lakes, and streams that is considered unstable or potentially unstable should the trees be removed.

Matrix—This is all federal lands not identified in the designated areas above. It is the area where all scheduled timber harvesting will take place. Each of the 10 alternatives specifies the particular number of green trees, snags, and logs left after each particular type of action.

Summaries of Alternatives

Alternative One. This plan most benefited the environmentalists and had the least regard for the loggers. "Essentially all old-growth forests would be protected, significant protection of forests adjacent to streams would be provided to protect fish, and some forest cover would be retained in areas where timber cutting is allowed, to permit spotted owl dispersal."

Matrix standards and guidelines would be as follows: retain at least six large, green trees per acre, two large snags per acre, and two large logs per acre.

Ten percent of the matrix is to be at least 180 years old with plans to bring the remaining 90% to a 180-year rotation. Twelve percent of the area would be available for scheduled timber cutting.

Alternative Two. This plan most benefitted the old-growth forests plus other areas that were considered necessary for the northern spotted owl's population. There would be limited salvage and silvicultural practices in protected areas. Forests adjacent to streams would be highly protected. In timber-cutting areas, the forest canopy would be retained.

Matrix standards and guidelines would be as follows: retain at least six large, green trees per acre, two large snags per acre, and two large logs per acre. Twenty percent of the area would be available for timber cutting.

Alternative Three. This plan would treat late-successional reserves differently, depending on where they were located. The Eastern Cascades of Oregon and the Cascades of Washington and California would be treated differently than the other late-successional reserves.

Matrix standards and guidelines would be as follows. Ten percent of the matrix in either late-successional or the oldest possible trees in stands of five to 10 acres would be retained. Four large, green trees per acre, 12 large logs in decay, with two to 10 logs in the eastern areas would be retained, as would appropriate levels of snag to support 40% of potential population levels. Nineteen percent of the area would be available for timber cutting.

Alternative Four. This plan would "protect the most ecologically significant late-successional forests and additional areas identified to protect spotted owls. It would maximize protection of forests adjacent to streams in order to protect fish, and would provide for the retention of some forest cover in areas where timber cutting is allowed."

Matrix standards and guidelines would be as follows. Retain green trees, snags and coarse woody debris at levels specified in current forest-management plans. Additional snags would be required in the Eastern Oregon and Washington Cascades, and California Klamath Physiographic Provinces. Nineteen percent of the area would be available for timber cutting.

Alternative Five. This plan, recommended by the Scientific Analysis Team, would implement the migration strategy. It would add riparian buffers, added protection for the marbled murrelet and endemic species protection to the plans.

Matrix standards and guidelines are the same as for Alternative Four. Twenty-three percent of the area would be available for timber cutting.

Alternative Six. This plan "was designed to protect the most ecologically significant late-successional forest and additional areas determined to be necessary for spotted owl population viability from the Scientific Panel on Late-Successional Forest Ecosystems."

Matrix standards and guidelines are the same as for Alternative Two. Twenty-three percent of the area would be available for timber cutting.

Alternative Seven. This plan best paralleled the recent report developed after the listing of the spotted owl, the *Final Draft of the Northern Spotted Owl Recovery Plan.*

Matrix standards and guidelines are for the retention of green trees, snags, and woody debris as specified in the recovery plan. Thirty-four percent of the area would be available for timber cutting.

Alternative Eight. This plan would provide protection for the most ecologically significant late-successional forests and additional areas for the spotted owls. There would be miminal protection for riparian buffer zones by rivers and streams.

Matrix standards and guidelines would be for the retention of green trees, snags, and woody debris as outlined in Alternative Nine, the preferred plan. Twenty-seven percent of the area would be available for timber cutting.

Alternative Nine. This is the plan chosen by President Clinton as the best of both worlds. It is a combination of four different plans that were developed for the management of the old-growth forests.

"Old-growth forests and other habitat would be protected where they overlap with Key Watersheds. Adaptive Management Areas would be designated to achieve social and economic objectives while learning more about ecosystem management." Under this plan, the land allocations, designated areas, and matrix uses are as follows:

Congressionally Reserved: 6,983,100 acres (29%)
Late-Successional Reserves: 7,052,600 acres (29%)

Standards and Guidelines: Thinning or other silvicultural treatments require review before being approved to assure that these treatments are necessary and beneficial to the late-successional reserves. Activities in the Western and Eastern Cascades are considered separately and are reviewed below. Disposal of dead trees is based on guidelines set forth in the *Final Draft of the Northern Spotted Owl Recovery Plan,* and is to be limited to areas of loss in excess of 10 acres.

West of the Cascades—No logging will be performed in stands that are older than 80 years. Thinning may occur on stands up to 80 years of age, after which, silvicultural treatments are to be performed only if beneficial to the stands.

East of the Cascades and the Eastern Portion of the Klamath Province—Additional management activities are allowed in this area due to the overall dryness of this section. Guidelines are adapted from the *Final Draft of the Northern Spotted Owl Recovery Plan.*

Adaptive Management Areas: 1,487,700 acres (6%)

Standards and Guidelines: Ten different areas have been identified and designated for the development and testing of ecological, economic, and other social objectives. These adaptive management areas are to be prototypes of how forest communities might be run.

Riparian Reserves: 2,231,300 (9%)

Standards and Guidelines: Fish-bearing streams, lakes, and reservoirs—There is to be a space equal to two times the height of the trees, or 300 feet, whichever is higher, on either side of the water.

Permanently flowing waters without fish are to have a space equal to one tree, or 150 feet, whichever is greater.

Intermittent streams or wetlands that are less than one acre in all other watersheds are to have a buffer of one-half of one tree or 50 feet.

Administratively Withdrawn: 1,652,900 acres (7%)
Matrix: 4,853,300 acres (20%)

Standards and Guidelines: For National Forests in the Oregon Coast Range Physiographic Province, the Olympic National Forest, and the Mt. Baker-Snoqualmie National Forest (areas with high stream density), management of the matrix is based on current plans. In the remainder of the National Forests in Oregon and Washington, 15% of the area designated for cutting is to be retained, with it being split into small sections of one-half to four acres in size.

Alternative Ten. This plan would protect late-successional forests and other areas of spotted owl population. This plan is similar to Alternative Six.

Matrix standards and guidelines would be retention of at least six large, green trees per acre that are larger than the average in diameter, two snags per acre, and two large logs per acre. Twenty-three percent of the area would be available for timber cutting.

A Trend Toward Ecosystem Management

The events in the Pacific Northwest illustrate how the government is emphasizing total ecosystem management of forests, rather than just considering what may have been considered as best for the trees. Thinning a forest, or clear-cutting a section of it every 70 years, may have been considered the best approach in the recent past toward preserving the health of the trees.

But the forest contains more than just trees. It contains spotted owls, and red-cockaded woodpeckers, and other species. And management of the forest involves more than just management of trees. Management now involves looking at the entire ecosystem.

MINI GLOSSARY

Adaptive Management: A process by which scientifically driven management experiments are implemented, with test results used to improve forest-management plans.

Administratively Withdrawn Areas: Areas of the forest that federal agencies have decided to withhold from timber sales.

Late-Successional Forest: A forest in mature or old-growth stage.

Reserves: Areas that have been withdrawn, either by federal agencies or by Congress, from timber sales.

Silviculture: The science and practice of controlling the establishment, composition, and growth of vegetation in forests.

Snag: A standing dead, or partially dead, tree that is at least 10 inches in diameter at breast height and at least 6 feet tall.

(Above and opposite page) Two views of the Everglades in Florida. Known as the "River of Grass," this is one of the country's largest freshwater systems being polluted with animal and farming waste.

10

RIVERS, LAKES, AND THEIR WILDLIFE

In 1972, Americans decided they weren't going to take it anymore: rivers and lakes were dying; the life had been sucked out of them from overuse—from both business and pleasure. They spurred the passage of a law to clean up the nation's waters.

The Clean Water Act, now 20 years old, is still a long way from returning U.S. rivers and lakes to the days before the Industrial Revolution, when the devastating pollution of waterways began. The book *A River Runs Through It*, which was made into a movie, was written about the Blackfoot River in Montana. The movie was filmed 16 years after the book was written. In those 16 years the quality of the Blackfoot River had deteriotated to the point that it could no longer be used as the setting for the movie, and another location had to be found.

While many urban dwellers in the United States today think of Montana as a pure and unspoiled rural mecca, the Montana natives weren't surprised with what the movie crew found. "The Blackfoot has been over-mined, over-cut, over-fished, over-recreated, and overlooked," Becky Garland, president of the Big Blackfoot Chapter of Trout Unlimited was quoted as saying in the October 1993 edition of *E, The Environmental Magazine*.

The Environmental Protection Agency, the EPA, listed the Blackfoot in its 1990 National Water Quality Inventory as having elevated toxins. There are 2,279 miles of rivers in Montana that fall into that category, and 28,000 miles in all of the United States. These toxins were responsible for the killing of some 26 million fish in 1990 alone. "The public perception is that the rivers are cleaned up, that they're better than ever, because the goo is gone. But if water quality is improving, then why are all the fish dying,"

said Kevin Coyle, president of American Rivers, in the *E* article.

Coyle lists "the four horsemen of river destruction" as dams, diversion of water, alteration of channels and land development, according to the January 26, 1993 *New York Times*.

Dam Effects

Dams do exactly what they are supposed to do. They stop the water. But that is not good for either the river

The Miami River in Florida is a heavily traveled waterway, creating a high demand for its resources.

or the life it supports. River-flowing nutrients become trapped by the dams and cannot flow downstream. Dams also change the water temperature—too hot or too cold and the insects on which the fish feed will stay away. Many Western rivers are long and have multiple dams. This repeated breaking of the rivers' natural patterns can be devastating to the life of the river.

Rivers are a good source of residential water, especially in the Western United States. Unfortunately, diverting the water for human consumption has proven detrimental to the rivers. According to the *Times*, that use "has simply dried up many rivers and streams for much of the year, with the result that their ecosystems are, in Mr. Coyle's words, 'ghosts of what they use to be.'"

Rivers have been rechanneled in an effort to drain land more efficiently, build roads where the rivers used to be, and protect towns from the seasonal flooding of the rivers. This type of tampering with

Mother Nature "reduce[s] the variety of habitats critical to biological diversity," the *Times* article said.

The development of waterfront property, with its removal of view-blocking vegetation, has eliminated the area necessary between the water and the land. Draining the land between the water and the buildings makes the water flow more rapidly. Not only does this erode the land, but it leaves less water in the river for the drier seasons.

Pollution Sources

There are two types of pollution sources. They are called point and nonpoint sources. Point sources are forms of pollution in which chemicals, waste, and other pollutants are dumped directly into the water. They are the ones that governments—local and federal—attacked in the 1970s. Nonpoint pollution sources are not as easily visable but can be just as—if not more—lethal. Nonpoint sources of pollution include farmland and streets, where water runoff can contain chemicals and pollutants deadly to water and the creatures it supports.

The Clean Water Act of 1972 stated that its intent was "to restore and maintain the chemical, physical, and biological integrity of the nation's waters." First tackled were the most visable problems: the rivers in cities. And the efforts to clean up these rivers, to keep industry from using them as sewers, and for cities to control what is dumped in them has been successful. Wastewater treatment has greatly improved because the federal government has spent $56 billion on new plants since the act was implemented, according to *E* magazine. People now use the rivers as recreational facilities.

Competing uses of the nation's waterways often causes environmental stress, and diligent watchfulness is necessary to avoid further harm. In New York Harbor, a baykeeper in a small boat is dwarfed by one of the many freighter ships that travel the waterway.

The act stated that all rivers were to be clean enough for swimming and fishing by 1983. In 1990, the EPA's Water Quality Inventory found that 37% of the rivers did not meet the swimming and fishing guidelines. Only 36% of the nation's 1.8 million miles of rivers were checked, so the 37% may or may not be completely accurate. And industry is still releasing toxic waste in some locations.

Rivers Reflect the Land

"Rivers are the catch basins for all our land-use practices—farmers spraying their fields, homeowners spraying their lawns, logging, grazing, everything. And our land-use practices are causing aquatic species to go extinct at a rapid rate. The invertebrates are shouting out most loudly, telling us some rivers are dying," said Coyle.

According to *E*, quoting a recent study by the Nature Conservatory, 65%–70% of the "bottom of the food chain" aquatic creatures are considered rare to extinct. Examples of the bottom-of-the-food chain species are crayfish and freshwater mussels. Mussels are filter-feeders. They draw the water into them, extract the nutrients, and expel the water, then repeat the process. Since they are not very tolerant of pollution, and succumb to it easily, they are one of the first and—also one of the most reliable—warning signals of trouble.

With the Clean Water Act up for renewal in 1993, a bill to do so was introduced in the Senate by Max Baucus (D-MT), head of the Committee on Environment and Public Works, and John Chaffee (R-RI), the committee's top minority leader. Voting was scheduled for the fall of 1993.

The EPA would like to see river testing shifted from point to nonpoint sites. The federal government, however, allocates more funds for cleanup if specific sites are monitored.

It's not difficult to find the source of pollution when dead fish cover the river near an industrial treatment plant. Nonpoint sites are more difficult to find. The farmer that sprayed his land last month, only to have rain wash the herbicide into the river is a much more elusive polluter than a chemical plant.

More than 20 years after the enactment of the Clean Water Act, the main culprit is no longer big business polluting rivers and streams. "According to the Conservation Foundation, nearly five tons of soil erode off of one acre of farmland each year in the U.S., carrying sediment (the number one pollutant), fertilizers, herbicides, and insecticides into rivers and streams," reports *E*.

Agriculture—as a big business instead of a family business—has had a major effect on rivers. Crops are now sprayed with many different chemicals and herbicides instead of being tilled as the family farmers once did. The 1990 Farm Bill encourages farmers to use fewer chemicals and control the chemical runoff, but financially, farmers are paid more by the U.S. Department of Agriculture (USDA) to grow as much as possible. They are paid on the five-year average of their fields. This discourages farmers from crop or field rotation, and from reducing the use of pesticides.

Urban runoff is also a problem. Residential areas use a substantial amount of lawn pesticides only to have much of it wash down the streets and into storm drains that carry the pollutants into the rivers.

One of the biggest concerns is the quality of the water in rivers and lakes today, compared to the quality of the water when the colonists first arrived in America.

"Our national fixation on cleaning up the nation's most polluted water resources to minimally acceptable standards has blinded us to the imminent decline of existing pristine water bodies. If the current course remains unchanged, the consequence of continued neglect of outstanding water resources in the United States will be equally mediocre water quality everywhere," says a 1992 report of the National Wildlife Federation.

Recreational Effects
But pollution from the land to the water is not the only source of water pollution. Anyone who uses the

Boats pass through a channel in the Charles River in Massachusetts.

water for boating may very well be partly responsible for pollution. Each year, boaters using gasoline-powered engines inadvertently spill small amounts of fuel when filling their tanks. Everyone has seen the shiny rainbow-colored waters around boatyards.

The Oil Pollution Control Act allows the Coast Guard to fine any boater up to $10,000 for negligent spills, and up to a six-month jail term could await anyone that "produces a sheen on the water." But people normally don't spill gasoline on purpose, and the Coast Guard is rarely there when such small spills occur.

Andre Mele, author of *Polluting for Pleasure*, figures that the 12 million gasoline-using boats in the United States are responsible for 400 million gallons of unburned gasoline being spilled into waterways each year, either from tank-filling, or from two-stroke outboard engines, when they are running.

He calculates that as five times the amount spilled by the *Exxon Valdez*, an oil tanker that ran aground and dumped oil into waters off Alaska. According to Ken Zerafa of the EPA, two-stroke outboard engine release volatile organic compounds, called VOCs, into both the air and the water. "In a typical two-stroke engine," Zerafa explains in *E*, "extra fuel that enters the cylinder on the intake stroke is used to expel the exhaust gases."

Boaters also pollute by dumping garbage and raw sewage into the water. While the Coast Guard can and does routinely check boats for "a reasonable amount of garbage," the 1972 federal Water Pollution Control Act "requires all boats to be equipped with Coast Guard approved holding tanks or treatment systems. This law also prohibits discharge of even treated waste in many areas," reports *E*. Despite the law and the Coast Guard patrols, violators still break the law and are rarely caught.

Los Angeles County officials, deciding that they had had enough of the filth, started placing dye tablets in the heads (toilets) of visiting boats. This way, when a boater illegally pumps his toilet at sea, he can be more easily spotted and fined. According to *E*, more than 225 fines have been levied so far.

Many of the boaters have complained in the past that there are very few places where they can pump out their holding tanks. But The Clean Vessel Act of 1992 should soon take care of that problem, Taxes on marine fuels should raise $40 million in the next five years. This money is to be used to build and maintain more pump-out facilities for boaters.

Changes in Paints

Another problem even more deadly than the previous two is the type of bottom paint used by boaters. Bottom paints contain tributyltin (TBT), a tin compound. Trouble with TBT was first discovered in the 1970s in France, when Pacific oysters being harvested were found to have deformitites. Then in Britain, the female dog whelk snails were found with not only female sex organs, but also with penises.

The problem was directly linked to TBT in the mud and bottom sediment near marinas and boat yards. Mike Rexrode, of the EPA, quoted by *E*, said that "[t]hese deformities are caused by very tiny amounts of TBT—just .02 parts per billion in the case of the Pacific oyster, and .7 parts per trillion in the case of the dog whelk snail." In 1981, France banned the use of TBT paints for all boats under 25 meters, or 82 feet in length.

Deformities have been found in the oysters in Coos Bay, Ore., and TBT poisoning has turned up in Chinook salmon, mud crabs, and green algae, after which Congress passed the Organotin Antifouling Act in 1988 to prohibit TBT paint for all boats except those made of aluminum. The new bottom paint is made now with copper. Copper corrodes aluminum, hence the exception to the rule.

The change in bottom paints has led to better-than-expected results. The deformity rate dropped 80% in one year and after three years the rate of deformity was only 10%. Unfortunately, the success rate from the change in bottom paint has not been as good as in France. TBT is still showing up in Puget Sound, Wash., Galveston, Texas, Narraganset Bay, R.I., and in Lake Erie. In Puget Sound, it is more than 1 part per billion, and it is being found in the middle of these lakes and bays. There doesn't seem to be any logical explanation for this, and very little funding to find out why, reports *E*.

Messing with Mother Nature

While many people played in freshwater ponds and lakes during the summer, researchers from the New England Aquarium seined those ponds in the Northeast looking for the elusive brindle shiner. The brindle shiner, they say, "could be vital to aquatic life in the New England coastal plain," according to a story in the July 26, 1993 *Boston Globe.*

The aquarium's spokesmen feel that possibly 40% of Massachusetts' native freshwater fish are headed for extinction, due in part to more and more of the coastal wetlands being encroached upon by waterfront development. Also, larger, alien sportsfish have invaded the habitat of the native fish and use the smaller, native fish for food. Since the 1960s, their numbers have decreased to the point that marine researchers are worried if the breeds will survive.

For a species to be placed on the endangered list, research needs to be submitted that shows the decline in the particular species' numbers. The problem with the brindle shiner is that no one ever kept records as to population, and the Northeast, with its tremendous coastal population already interfering with coastal plain species, has not helped.

"The East has been treated as a write-off," said Leslie Kaufman, chief scientist for the Edgerton Research Lab at the Aquarium and the leader of the brindle shiner project.

Paul Nickerson, chief of the U.S. Fish and Wildlife Service's endangered species division in the Northeastern United States, said that the only fish from the Northeastern waters to be listed on the endangered species list is the short-nosed sturgeon. Although three others have been submitted, the Fisheries and Wildlife Service still does not have the records necessary to add them to the list.

Karsten Hartel, associate curator of the Museum of Comparative Zoology at Harvard University, has been working closely with Nickerson. Hartel is near publication on a book listing all freshwater fish species in Massachusetts, and first suggested the search for the brindle shiner. The book, *Inland Fishes of Massachusetts,* is the first complete book on this subject since 1865. The findings are disturbing:

Of the 85 species listed in the book, 60%, or 51 species, have been brought to the state from other regions of the country. One species, the piranha, has even been found in Massachusetts, but it is felt that it is not reproducing in the New England climate. The rainbow trout, originally from the Northwest, and the large-mouth bass, a native of the central and southeastern United States, are favorites of anglers, but detrimental to the native varieties that are smaller and serve as food.

The Northeast also has unique problems. There are fewer freshwater fish in New England partly because the area was under Ice Age glaciers until 10,000 years ago, and species haven't had the development time necessary for expansion. Also, after the Ice Age, many of the water paths were no longer usable as mountains and the salt water of the oceans blocked them.

Although freshwater fish appear to be in jeopardy, it is important to mention that this is not a problem particular to Massachusetts, or even New England. "There is a mass extinction going on in the world," the *Globe* quoted Kaufman as saying. "In this part of the country, the loss of fauna is similar to everywhere else, except there are fewer species and they are less attended to."

The Colorado River, south of Lake Mojave is an example of the same problem in the West. It has become the first major river in the United States that no longer has any native species, because exotic species were added and because the natural flow of the river was changed.

The Columbia River now has one variety of salmon on the endangered species list because dams have interfered with the migratory patterns of the fish. If the salmon cannot return upriver to spawn, the breed will die.

Most Endangered List

A 1993 list of the United States' top 10 endangered rivers was published by American Rivers, a conservation group. It ranks the rivers on "their importance as natural resoures and to human health, the degree of threat they are experiencing, and the imminence of threats the rivers are facing," according to a report released by American Rivers.

Congress passed the Wild and Scenic Rivers Act 25 years ago and rivers in every section of the country are still under attack from sewage, farming and industrial pollution, dams, and mining, according to a report in the April 21, 1993 *San Francisco Chronicle.*

Every year, American Rivers publishes a list similar to the famous lists of "the 10 most wanted

The recreational demand is high for waterways in the United States, especially at places such as the Okefenokee Swamp in Georgia.

criminals" or "the 10 best (or worst) dressed people in America." Listed here are the 10 most endangered rivers and the 15 most threatened rivers in America, according to American Rivers:

Rio Grande/Rio Conchos system—(Colorado/New Mexico/Texas). This system presently poses the greatest danger to human health because of "headwaters-to-mouth degradation and untreated sewage discharges and pollution from industrial plants along the Mexican border."

Environmental cleanup depends on the North American Free Trade Agreement, (NAFTA), but conditions are some of the worst seen in years. Near Brownsville, Texas, where the mouth of the river is located, 50 babies have been born in an 18-month period with anencephalia, a deformity where the brain does not develop. Usually a baby dies within days, although some live to adulthood with a severe form of mental retardation.

Columbia/Snake system—(Idaho/Washington/Oregon). Listed as first on the 1992 endangered rivers list, it has dropped to number two in 1993 because of the condition of the Rio Grande.

This river system was listed in 1992 because of the "alarming declines in native salmon populations brought on by the adverse effects of power dams and the loss of habitat and flows on the river," says American Rivers. Juvenile fish are transported by barge instead of free-moving waters because of the way water is released through the dams. American Rivers said that miminal work had been done in 1992 to improve the situation.

The Everglades—(Florida). Called the "River of Grass," it is one of the United States' largest freshwater systems that is being polluted with animal and farming waste, causing declines in the population of wading birds in the Everglades.

Anacostia—(Washington, D.C./Maryland). The Anacostia is heavily polluted because of leaking sewage, channelization, poison runoff, sedimentation, and dumping. This pollution is occurring within 1.5 miles of the U.S. Capitol and is considered the most endangered urban river.

American Rivers said that to a large degree, the Anacostia's problems are due to the Army Corps of Engineers trying to straighten the river and to control

The short-nosed sturgeon is the only Northern freshwater fish on the endangered species list.

it for better flood control. That has resulted in a faster river that has eroded the banks and stream beds of nutrients and vegetation, according to reports in the April 21, 1993 *Washington Times*.

American Rivers was then quoted in the April 25, 1993 *Washington Post* as saying that the Anacostia has been subjected to environmental harassment since the 1700s, when it was an export site for the tobacco industry. Once a 40-foot-deep river, it is now a muddy creek because of the silt buildup. Although the Anacostia Watershed Society calls the river "lifeless concrete ditches rushing the river's toxic waters to the Chesapeake Bay," American Rivers feels that it can be saved.

Virgin River—(Utah/Arizona/Nevada). The Virgin River is presently undammed, but 12 dams have been proposed to be built even though two species of fish that are presently on the endangered list inhabit the river. This river also flows through Zion National Park.

Rogue and Illinois system—(Oregon). The cutting of old-growth timber here threatens not only the spotted owls, but also the salmon.

Penobscot—(Maine). Even though the Atlantic Salmon are being restored to this river, a hydropower dam has been proposed.

Clavey—(California). Two hydropower dams have been proposed for this river that runs through the Sierra Nevada Mountains.

Alsek and Tatshenshini system—(Alaska and British Columbia). This river system was listed because it was threatened with an acid-producing copper mine in Windy Craggy nearby. However, the listing probably will be discontinued in light of recent developments.

According to an article published in the June 26, 1993 *Vancouver Sun*, the proposal to build a copper mine in Windy Craggy has been defeated. Instead, it will become a provincial park.

The June 24, 1993 *Washington Post* quoted Premier Michael Harcourt of British Columbia as saying that the 2.5-million-acre watershed, about two times the size of the Grand Canyon, will become part of the existing park system in Alaska. Canada's Yukon Territory and, with 21 million acres, would become part of the world's largest protected wilderness to cross national boundries.

"While we recognize there will be economic costs from this decision, the benefits to the global environment from this world wilderness reserve are unmatched," Harcourt said.

Vice President Al Gore, who had considered the copper mine "an environmental nightmare waiting to happen," said that Harcourt had acted "boldly and with foresight to protect and preserve the natural heritage of one of the world's most important rivers."

The June 23, 1993 *Wall Street Journal* said that if this copper deposit had been mined it would have produced 1% of the world's copper for the next 25 years.

Platte—(Nebraska). This river supports a very large portion of the migratory birds. The Kingsley hydropower dam located on the river and presently up for relicensing, is a major factor in the life of the river.

Most Threatened List

American Rivers also lists 15 threatened rivers. They are listed below in alphabetical order.

The Animas River—(Colorado). There is a federal project for marginal farmland that will divert much of the water from the river.

Beamoc System: Beaverkill (lower) and Willowemoc Rivers—(New York). The local towns worked to protect the rivers, which were listed as endangered in 1992. The Beaverkill's upper section is one of the world's best-known trout streams. The lower Beaverkill and its tributary, the Willowemoc River, have been hurt by the local land use.

Blackfoot River—(Montana). The original setting for the book *A River Runs Through It*, it is threatened by timber harvests, cattle grazing, mining, overfishing, and stream diversions. Local and National groups have worked hard to clean up the river. Their efforts resulted in the river being removed from the 1992 endangered list.

Eleven Point River—(Missouri). One of the original eight Wild and Scenic Rivers, exploratory drilling for lead has begun near the river. The possible threat to water and the environment from lead could be extensive.

Great Whale River—(Quebec). An important area for shorebirds and waterfowl, this area is threatened by the James Bay Hydroelectric Project, which would flood not only the wildlife lands, but also the homelands of the Cree and Inuit Indians. New York state has canceled its contract for power with the proposed plant, but the developer was still planning to build.

Little Bighorn River—Wyoming. A hydropower project is threatening wildlife, Indian rights and the environmental health of the northeastern Wyoming system.

Los Angeles River—California. This river is 58 miles long, but only 12 miles are still in a natural state. The rest of the river has been diverted, buried underneath the city, or used in Hollywood movies. Now the U.S. Army Corps of Engineers wants to enclose the remaining 12 miles behind concrete walls to control flooding. American Rivers feels that more natural options are available.

Moose Creek—(Alaska). In Alaska, any water body that is navigable is considered owned by the state. The state can then issue mining permits on these waterways. In 1992, this happened to Moose Creek, located in the Denali National Park. After public controversy, state lands in Denali were closed to mining, but mining permits issued earlier still exist. Also, the state wishes to obtain ownership of all submerged lands—over 200 rivers and lakes—thus allowing development to take place.

Skokomish River—(Washington). Because of the Cushman Project, which includes two hydroelectric dams and reservoirs, native salmon are near extinction, less water now goes to the Olympic Penninsula River, the river estuary is in danger of dying, and the Skokomish Indian Tribe's cultural, economic and treaty rights are in jeopardy. Efforts are being made to improve the operation of the project.

St. Mary's River—(Virginia). A southern Appalachian Mountain stream, it is in danger of acid rain pollution from the Ohio and Tennessee Valleys. Virginia has now issued 17 new fossil-fuel-burning power plants that could cause more harm to this and surrounding ecosystems.

Susquehanna River—(Pennsylvania). Nitrogen and phosphorus nutrients that are nonpoint pollution from agriculture, sediments from erosion, and toxins all pose a threat to this river, which drains into the Chesapeake Bay.

Tennessee River—(Kentucky). Aquatic life in this river in Southwest Kentucky is contaminated due to toxic and hazardous pollution in the river and the soils near the river due to hazardous waste discharges and leaking landfills.

Thorne River—(Alaska). Part of Alaska's Tongass National Forest, it is being threatened by pressures to clearcut the old-growth trees within its watershed.

White River—(Arkansas). The fish in this river are suffering from oxygen deprivation, and low dissolved oxygen content from both a large amount of animal waste that washes into the river and the dam operations.

Yuba, South—(California). Flood control dams have been proposed for this river. Local groups are trying to obtain National Wild and Scenic River Designation for the river to protect it from the dam.

"Our rivers have become the repository for our environmental abuses. We need to take care of our circulatory system or the body will die," Kevin Coyle, president of American Rivers was quoted as saying in the April 21, 1993 *Washington Times.*

Coyle was further quoted in the *Oregonian* on April 21, 1993 as saying that "our rivers are becoming sterile and polluted. By making the public and political leaders aware of just how poisoned, dredged, dammed, and overdeveloped our rivers are, the prospects for protecting and restoring rivers everywhere improve immeasurably."

But What About the Fish

Rivers and streams are of great importance to both the water cycle and the movement of nutrients and minerals from the land to the oceans. They provide people with drinking water, nourish the plants and animals on which people rely for food, serve as avenues of transportation, and provide one form of energy. Throughout history, civilizations built homes, villages, and cities on waterways. But the

Manatees, among Florida's threatened water creatures, often get too close to some of the many boats in the states' coastal river waters.

waters, rivers, and streams especially, are in danger of being destroyed. Although six major factors presently threaten the waters, their recovery is probable through hard work.

Rivers and streams contain a plethora of teleost (bony) fish. At present, there are some 22,000 known species, with approximately 100 new species being discovered each year. One reason for the high number of fish compared to birds (that only have two new species, on average, discovered each year) is that fish are more isolated in their environments.

If trout in river "A" never mingle with trout in river "B," there is more of a chance of river "A" trout developing differently than those in river "B." There also are many more species of freshwater fish in the Eastern half of the United States than in the Western half, and more species in the Mississippi River than in all of Europe. One reason is simply that more rivers and streams in the East are isolated from each other. Western rivers, though fewer in number, tend to be longer than their Eastern counterparts.

Many different fish could be on the endangered and/or threatened list but because of incomplete data, few are listed. There are six factors that influence the well-being in lotic (moving water) environments. They are:

- Habitat loss and degradation
- Spread of exotic species
- Overharvesting
- Secondary extinctions
- Chemical and organic pollution
- Climate change

In the past 100 years, three genera, 27 species, and 13 subspecies of North American fish have become extinct. The reasons were detailed in an article in the January 1993 *BioScience* magazine. In 82% of the cases, more than one reason contributed to the loss of the species. The reasons for the loss of species are as follows: Habitat loss, 73%; species introduction, 68%; chemical pollution, 38%; hybridization, 38%; and overharvesting, 15%.

Habitat loss and degradation has occurred basically through change of the rivers and streams through dams, deforestation, agriculture, and human involvement with the waterways.

As for species invasion, the Food and Agriculture Organization (FAO) of the United Nations lists many species of exotic fish that have been introduced to America's rivers and streams. The carp, thought to have originated in China, is known to have existed in Europe in the 11th or 12th century and in England by the year 1500. They were introduced to Africa around 1700 and the New World around 1850.

Carp have not only integrated themselves into the habitat of the native fish, but they have also increased water turbidity because of their bottom-feeding habits. While not all species invasions are bad (Carp can help control aquatic weeds, and mosquito fish and guppies are used for mosquito control worldwide), they have forced many native fish into extinction.

While there have been no examples of extinctions due to overharvesting in North America, overharvesting, coupled with other influences, has hurt certain fish populations. In the tropics, fish exploited for both food and as exotic pets (tropical fish) are more seriously threatened.

Secondary extinction occurs when the loss of one species upsets the "balance of nature" to the point that the other species becomes either rare or common. An example of this happened at Flathead Lake in Montana.

The Kokanee salmon was introduced for the benefit of fishermen, grizzly bears, and bald eagles. Shrimp were then introduced as food for the salmon. But the shrimp ate the zooplankton that had originally been the salmon's food. Then, to escape the salmon, the shrimp dove to deep water where the salmon could not eat them. Soon, the salmon died due to starvation, which meant that the bears and eagles also had no food. There was a decline in the number of bears, and the eagles that had used the lake as a migratory pit stop went elsewhere. The lake, no longer a favorite fisherman's hangout, affected the local economy.

Luckily, rivers and streams are living pieces of nature. Literally tons and tons of water move through them, which gives them an excellent chance to repair and cleanse themselves when disturbances occur. How long that repair takes depends on what disruption occurs. In a review of over 150 case studies of the recovery of freshwater systems, *Bio-Science* reported, assaults to the water known as pulse events—chemical spills, etc.—were easier recoveries for rivers than what are known as press disturbances—habitat alterations, the changing of the river's channel, dam building, etc. The recovery time for the press disturbances usually ran into decades.

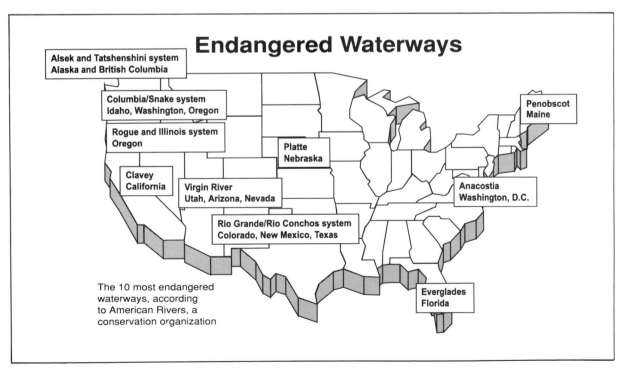

Endangered Waterways

Alsek and Tatshenshini system
Alaska and British Columbia

Columbia/Snake system
Idaho, Washington, Oregon

Rogue and Illinois system
Oregon

Clavey
California

Virgin River
Utah, Arizona, Nevada

Platte
Nebraska

Penobscot
Maine

Anacostia
Washington, D.C.

Rio Grande/Rio Conchos system
Colorado, New Mexico, Texas

Everglades
Florida

The 10 most endangered waterways, according to American Rivers, a conservation organization

A reduction in power plant emissions has helped reduce the concentration of sulfates in the atmosphere since 1970, helping to reduce the amount of acid rain over most of the United States.

11

ENVIRONMENTALLY SPEAKING

Researchers at the U.S. Geological Survey had good news in 1993 about at least one aspect of the environment. The researchers recorded a decline in the concentration of sulfates, key elements of acid rain, at 26 of 33 monitoring sites around the country between 1980 and 1991. Sulfates, sulfur byproducts, produced mainly by fossil-fuel-burning power plants, and the measurements indicated that reductions in sulfur dioxide emissions from power plants was paying off.

The news was not so good about nitrates, another key element of acid rain. Nitrate concentrations declined by significant amounts at only three of the 33 sites, and showed a "downward trend" at 24 other sites. Nitrates are byproducts of nitrogen oxides, which are produced by emissions from automobile exhausts and power plants.

While government officials and scientists called the Geological Survey's 1993 report encouraging overall, the figures indicate the complexity of maintaining or improving the nation's air quality. Scientists grappling with the issues of acid rain, the ozone layer, and the theory of global warming, however, are not dealing with a problem that appeared just before the Clean Air Act was passed in 1970. Some of today's problems are centuries old. Acid rain and ozone are discussed in this chapter, and global warming in the next chapter.

Acid Rain

More than 300 years ago, in 1661, scientists observed that industrial emissions in England had a bad effect on the well-being of plants and people. Pollutants, traveling by air, crossed the English Channel between England and France. Observers of this air pollution suggested that building better chimneys on factories,

located on the outskirts of town, might dilute the pollutants before they wafted off to distant places.

Not until 200 years later, in the mid-1800s, would Robert Angus Smith, a chemist and Britain's first alkali inspector, discover "acid rain." Smith's published report on acid rain explained the problem in Manchester, England, where the closer a person came to the city, the more acidic the air became. The sulfuric acid that he found in the air caused metals to corrode and clothing to fade. He also noted that acid rain damaged plants and materials.

Smith coined the phrase "acid rain" 20 years later in his book *The Beginnings of Chemical Climatology*, which described the principles of acid rain. Detailing experiments in England, Scotland, and Germany, he linked the wind, coal combustion, nearness to the water masses, and how much and how often it snowed. He offered suggestions for ways to collect and analyze precipitation.

A Century Is Lost

Unfortunately, Smith was ahead of his time and his findings were either ignored or simply overlooked by the scientific world for nearly 100 years. Then, in the late 1950s, Smith's work inspired Eville Gorham, a Canadian ecologist. After receiving his doctorate in botany, Gorham moved from England to Sweden to study the effects rainwater had on healthy ecosystems. He then moved to the Lake District in northern England to continue his work. One of the first things that Gorham noticed was that the quality of the rainwater depended on the direction of the wind that had channeled the water there. To the south was the industrial section of the Midlands, to the east, the Irish Sea. Rain from the south contained sulfuric acid, from the east it contained salt.

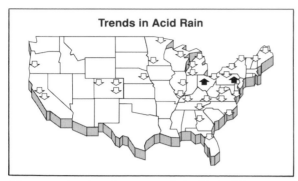

Trends in Acid Rain

Most monitoring sites around the United States recorded a decrease in acid rain between 1980 and 1991. But two sites—Delaware, Ohio and Leading Ridge, Pa.—showed an increase.

This led Gorham to study the effects of acid rain on the ecology. At first, he had difficulty deciding where to start. He wasn't sure how different organisms would respond to different levels of acidity. To begin, he looked at the levels of sulfuric acid in one area—such as a city—and compared them to the number of deaths from respiratory problems in the same place. He discovered that higher levels of acidic pollutants in a city corresponded with a greater number of bronchitis cases; more sulfate particles in the air coincided with more cases of pneumonia; and more tar correlated with more lung cancer.

In the early 1960s, after Gorham moved to Canada, he showed that acid in the rain that was close to industrial areas directly correlated with industrial emissions. He also noted that acidic aquatic ecosystems directly related to acidic precipitation.

Though he presented a more complete picture of acid rain's effects, Gorham had not been the only scientist working on the theory of acid rain after Smith.

- In 1911, two English scientists noted that the degree of acidity increased or decreased the closer or farther one was from Leeds, England, an industrial town. They also noted that plants did not grow as well, nor did seeds germinate as quickly in an acidic environment.
- In 1919, an Austrian soil scientist discovered that something that fell from the atmosphere was responsible for the acidic nature of the forest soil.
- In 1921 and 1927 a Norwegian limnologist noticed a correlation between trout production and the

acidity of rivers and lakes. A limnologist is a scientist who studies the physical and biological characteristics of bodies of fresh water.

- In 1939 a Swedish scientist correlated acidity and the toxic effects of aluminum to fish.

Hans Enger, a soil scientist, in 1948, established a method to collect chemicals in precipitation throughout Europe. Using Enger's data, meteorologists in Sweden, England, and the United States began looking for atmospheric acidity.

Scientists did not realize until the late 1960s that the acidic problem was far more widespread than their own particular area of expertise. They were all collecting separate data on the growing, common problem of air pollution.

Egner's work was expanded and eventually came to be known as the European Air Chemistry Network. Nearly 20 years worth of Egner's data was used in the early 1960s by Svante Oden. Oden also used the work of two other Swedish scientists, Carl Gustav Rossby and Erik Eriksson. They worked with the movement of air masses, and they, too, had used Egner's data to test their ideas. Oden concluded that invisible strands of pollution could be moved long distances via the air masses and could cause chemical changes in rural areas far away from the cities and industry where they orginated.

In 1967 Oden published his findings on the theory of acid rain. Some of his conclusions were:

- Acid rain occurred in particular regions, at both the source of the pollution and, through movement with the air masses, where it eventually landed.
- Water—both fresh and sea—were becoming more acidic.
- Air pollutants that contained sulfur and nitrogen traveled between 100 and 2,000 kilometers before landing.
- Most acidic damage in Scandinavia was due to sulfur that was airborne from Great Britain and Germany.
- The ecological consequences of this form of pollution would be a change in lake chemistry, a decrease in fish, a leach of toxic metals from land to water, decrease forest health, more plant diseases, and accelerated damage to materials.

Oden wrote of a "chemical war" among nations in Stockholm's newspaper *Dagens Nyheter*. In 1968, his article appeared in *Ecology Committee Bulletin* and was met with great interest by the scientific community.

Problem of Acid Rain Officially Recognized

In 1972, the Swedish government sponsored research on acid rain and presented its findings to the United Nations Conference on Human Environment. This was the first time the phenomenon was listed as an international air pollution problem during a worldwide conference.

Although most of this was new to the rest of the world, Canadian scientists had long suspected the problem. They had observed that sulfur dioxide emissions above metal smelters were related to acid rain. In 1960 and 1963, Eville Gorham and his colleagues had reported ecological problems around the smelting facility near Sudbury, Ontario.

Oden's main contribution to the world of science is that his findings gave validity to the work of other scientists who were skeptical of what they had found. Gorham, for instance, thought that acid rain was only a local problem until Oden's work showed that the pollutants could be transported over thousands of kilometers.

In 1972, Gene E. Likens of Dartmouth University and F. Herbert Bormann of Yale University began a study on a small watershed in New Hampshire. They studied the chemistry of the water and found it highly acidic, even far from the pollution source. In 1974, they reported that rain in the eastern part of the United States was more acidic than the normal—from 100 to 1000 times more acidic. The cause of this was probably the sulfur and nitrogen oxides from industry and electric power plants.

This was the turning point for acid rain. Newspapers had picked up the story. No longer was this something that scientists discussed in theory. This was now a global problem.

And now, places that have survived 2,000 years of droughts, wars, floods, and famine are no longer able to withstand acid rain. Phidias' sculptures in the Parthenon in Athens, Greece have been removed and replaced with fiberglass replicas. Acid rain would have destroyed them if they had remained out in the open much longer. The Taj Mahal in India, the Coliseum in Rome, and The Rheims cathedral in France have all been damaged by acid rain. According to a story in the March 1993 UNESCO *Courier*, emissions of sulfur dioxide and nitrogen oxides from foundries and power plants, motor vehicles, and heating sources have traveled great distances, causing even greater damage to some of the world's treasures.

Even though the Clean Air Act was amended to be a more forceful tool in the battle for cleaner air, the atmosphere today contains 23 billion kilograms (kg) of pollutants such as lead, sulfur dioxide, carbon monoxide, and nitrogen oxide, among others. Broken down, this means that for every human alive on Earth today, there are 112 kg of particles per year to be inhaled. Government economic incentives should reduce that number by two-thirds by the year 2005.

Any wet substance carries acid rain. That includes not only rain, but also snow, fog, and drizzle. The snow that falls in areas with little melting until the spring affects the wildlife that reproduces each year in the streams. The snow melts into the streams and rivers, and the acid causes sterility and embryo malformation of the wildlife offspring. Forests are also affected. Acid rain has been blamed for the destruction of birches and maples in eastern Canada. And although Canada and the United States have pledged to reduce the sulfur dioxide emissions, the demand for energy in industrialized North America make that pledge difficult to uphold.

Another detriment from acid rain is its effect on the ozone layer.

Where Has All the Ozone Gone?

"Ozone is a molecule of oxygen (O_3) that absorbs certain wavelengths of biologically damaging ultraviolet light. It is the only gas in the atmosphere that does so and, therefore, is an essential part of Earth's ecological balance. The evolution of the land life is believed to be tied closely to the formation of the protective ozone layer," reported the July-August 1993 *Environment* magazine.

Scientists started examining the upper atmosphere in the late 1800s when, out of curiosity, they went looking for differences in the air temperature at different levels of altitude. In 1902, Teisserenc de Bort reported that as altitude rises, temperature decreases up to about 10 kilometers, but then it increases for another 40 kilometers, which would be about 50 kilometers up from Earth's surface. From 10 to 50 kilometers came to be known as the stratosphere. This is where most of the ozone is located.

Sydney Chapman, a scientist at Oxford University, was the first person credited with explaining the makeup of ozone. Ozone is made when an oxygen molecule (O_2) is split by cosmic rays. Each of these oxygen atoms is then combined with an (O_2) molecule to form ozone (O_3). Sometimes, these single oxygen atoms bump into the ozone, breaking it apart and forming two oxygen molecules. ($O_3+O=O_2+O_2$). According to Chapman, this process of atoms and molecules bumping into each other goes on constantly so that ozone molecules are being created and destroyed at the same rate. Therefore, the amount of ozone stays the same.

But Chapman's theory was found to be flawed. The oxygen atoms were destroying the ozone molecules, but only at one-fifth the rate he suspected. Scientists thought that, perhaps, something was reacting with the ozone to destroy it, but ozone reacts with nothing. They thought that maybe it had something to do with the trace atmospheric gases, but the amount was so minute that the scientists didn't think that the gases could affect the ozone.

Then, they thought that these trace elements might be involved in a catalytic chain reaction with the ozone. "A catalytic chain is a series of two or more chemical reactions in which one chemical, [known as] the catalyst destroys another chemical without itself being destroyed. The chain can be repeated indefinitely until all of the chemical is destroyed or until the catalyst is removed by some competing process," reported the magazine *Environment*.

In 1950, David R. Bates, a mathematician from the University of Belfast, Northern Ireland, and Marcel Nicolet, an atmospheric scientist at the Institut d'Aeronomie Spatiale de Belgique in Brussels, Belgium, were the first to recognize that oxides of hydrogen(HO_x) could be effective catalysts in the destruction of ozone. Then in the mid-1960s, John Hampson, a scientist working at the Canadian Armaments Research and Development Establishment in Quebec, and B. G. Hunt, a scientist with the Australian Weapons Research Establishment, were

both working on the effects, if any, of ballistic missiles on the atmosphere during their re-entry. Hampton showed that hydrogen could destroy ozone in a catalytic reaction. Hunt looked at Hampton's results and figured out the rate of ozone destruction.

In 1970, Paul J. Crutzen, an atmospheric chemist, first suggested that oxides of nitrogen (NO) were also a catalyst. He also said that oxides of chlorine, sodium, and bromine also could damage ozone, but there was no need to worry about them, since they did not occur naturally in the stratosphere.

Scientists had turned their attention to the SSTs (supersonic transports) and their environmental impact. The SSTs' fuel was made of nitrogen oxides, sulfate particles and some water vapor. Environmentalists questioned whether the water vapor would cause either the loss of ozone, contribute to more of a cloud cover, or both. But the 1970 scientific conference called to decide if the SSTs were environmentally acceptable—"Study of Critical Environmental Problems" (SCEP)—dismissed the possible water vapor and nitrogen problems.

In 1971, Harold Johnston, a chemist at the University of California, Berkeley, discounted the SCEP's findings, saying that SSTs did pose a threat to the stratosphere.

One year later, the National Aeronautics and Space Administration (NASA), concerned with the space shuttle's solid rocket boosters, wanted to know what effect chlorine would have on the stratosphere. While it had been known that chlorine was released into the stratosphere from volcanic eruptions, the amount was small. The amount from the rocket boosters would be more than what a volcanic eruption released. In July, a NASA study revealed that the rocket boosters would release hydrogen chloride (HCl) in a stream behind the shuttle as it re-entered Earth's atmosphere through the stratosphere. Despite this finding, it was concluded that this would not have a negative effect on the stratosphere.

Ralph J. Cicerone and Richard S. Stolarski, both from the University of Michigan, received the contract from NASA to check their findings. Both men felt that the HCl might break down into hydrogen and chlorine with the then-free chlorine causing a catalytic chain reaction that would destroy the ozone. In the spring of 1973, they reported their findings to NASA.

At Harvard University, two other scientists, Michael E. McElroy and Steven C. Wofsy, had heard the results of NASA's original impact study and began considering the ramifications of chlorine in the stratosphere. McElroy previously had worked with NASA, studying chlorine chemistry on Venus and knew that chlorine could destroy all of the ozone in an atmosphere. Within a year, McElroy and Wofsy had designed a model that would show the destruction of ozone by chlorine.

Both groups of men were present in September 1973 at the International Association of Geomagnetism and Aeronomy (IAGA) meeting in Kyoto, Japan. McElroy dealt with the NO_x in atmospheric photochemistry. Stolarski then spoke about chlorine chemistry. He summarized the team's work, relating it not to the space shuttle, but to volcanic eruptions. McElroy and Wofsy then updated their paper to include the work they had done on chlorine as it related to the ozone. Stolarski and Cicerone also mentioned in their paper that chlorine was better at destroying ozone than was the nitrogen.

Focus Shifts to CFCs

The space shuttle and the SST forced the scientists to consider the effects manmade pollutants would have on the stratosphere, but shortly after the IAGA meeting, in 1974, two chemists, Mario J. Molina and F. Sherwood Rowland, both from the University of California at Irvine, identified chlorofluorocarbons (CFCs) as a source of stratospheric chlorine. CFCs are synthetic and are used in refrigerants, insecticides, and as propellants in aerosol cans. The United States banned the use of CFCs in 1978 and started the drive for international cooperation in this matter.

The election of President Ronald Reagan, however, put a stop to the United States' drive to reduce or ban the use of CFCs. Politics got in the way of the environment, when Anne Burford, head of the Environmental Protection Agency, discounted the story of ozone loss due to CFCs. According to the May 10, 1993 issue of *Time* Magazine, Du Pont Corp., a company that had invested millions of dollars in research toward finding a suitable substitute for CFCs, stopped its research after Reagan's election and challenged Rowland's findings.

The whole yes/no use of CFCs hinged on the debate of CFCs' lifespan. Du Pont scientists argued that CFCs had a short lifespan. In 1980, Du Pont organized the Alliance for Responsible CFC policy, which had members from both the users and producers of CFCs. This, according to Senator John Chaffee of Rhode Island, was an extremely strong lobbying group in favor of keeping CFCs in use. "I remember a parade of CFC users coming through telling me what I was going to do to their refrigeration business if they were denied these marvelous CFCs," Chaffee said, according to *Time*.

A 1983 National Academy of Sciences update suggested that the danger from CFCs might not be so bad if the production level did not increase from its present level. Du Pont assured the White House that the CFC market would remain constant but would not be increasing. Yet from 1982 until the Montreal Protocol in 1987, CFC production rose from 750,000 metric tons to over 1,100,000 metric tons, an increase of almost 350,000 metric tons. That was about a 7% increase a year.

In 1984, when Ralph Cicerone spoke at Columbia University and suggested that the CFC market was growing, he was questioned by Du Pont's manager, Donald Strobach, who said that Cicerone's figures were incorrect. However, Cicerone's figures were supported as true by the EPA and the Rand Corporation.

In 1986 the EPA confronted Du Pont with independent studies that showed the CFC growth. Du Pont, in September of 1986, reversed its stand and agreed that controls on CFC production were needed, and resumed its quest for a CFC substitute. It also agreed to stop producing CFCs by the year 2000.

In the period of delays and squabbling that lasted from 1978 to 1988, almost 19 billion pounds of CFCs were produced in the world.

Rowland's interest in fluorocarbons began when he heard of James E. Lovelock's work with fluorocarbons in the lower atmosphere. In the early 1970s Lovelock had taken measurements for several consecutive years in both the Northern and Southern Hemispheres. He found fluorocarbons in all places he measured. In Lovelock's research, he suggested that these fluorocarbons could be used to follow the movement of air. The scientist saw no link between them and the environment.

Lovelock had kept records of CFCs and noted that nearly all were still in the atmosphere, meaning that they were not being destroyed, absorbed by another element, or chemically changed.

Rowland was interested in what Lovelock had discovered, and began studying the fluorocarbons. Molina joined Rowland in the fall of 1973. Soon they uncovered that CFCs could work as the catalyst to break down and destroy the ozone.

In June 1974, Rowland and Molina revealed their findings. They said the use of CFCs was adding chlorine to the environment and that these CFCs had a life span of between 40 and 150 years. Futher, the two men felt that there was nothing that could destroy the chlorine other than eventual sunlight in the stratosphere.

But when the sunlight broke down the CFCs, it would produce chlorine atoms, which would destroy the ozone. Rowland and Molina concluded that even if CFCs were stopped immediately from entering the stratosphere, with the amount already there, coupled with the CFCs' lifespan, it would still take a great deal of time to remove the chemicals from the stratosphere. Their work suggested that enough had already been released into the atmosphere to begin depletion of the ozone.

Nature Also Is a Culprit

While people contribute most to the problem of ozone depletion through chlorine-producing products like CFCs, the weather also plays a role. "The chlorine is there because of humans but nature occasionally causes the Antarctic winter to be colder than others. The phenomenon of converting manmade chlorine to forms which destroy the ozone is worse in some years," said David J. Hoffman, senior scientist at the National Oceanic and Atmospheric Administration monitoring laboratory in Boulder, Colo. He said that the upper level ozone destruction was due, in part, to the cold.

He added that with the chlorine/cold combination "you can expect to be setting new records every once in a while." Ozone depletion at the lower altitudes is due to the sulfur residue left by the 1991 eruption of Mount Pinatubo in the Philippines, he added.

Michael Oppenheimer, a senior scientist with the Environmental Defense Fund, said, "Nothing can be done about volcanoes, but we can and must swiftly eliminate ozone depleting chemicals." Scientists still point to chlorine products as the most damaging to the ozone.

News of these findings were released to the general public in September 1974 when the American Chemi-cal Society prompted the *New York Times* to print a story on the subject. The article blamed the aerosol can for the problem. The television network CBS picked up the story and ran it nationwide, causing widespread concern—that exists to this day—about the problem of possible ozone depletion.

The hole in the ozone is measured each year. The figures of October 1993 brought both good and bad news. The good news is that the hole over Antarctica was not as large as it was last year—which was recorded as the largest ever. The 1993 hole measured 9 million square miles compared to 1992's measurement of 9.4 million miles. In comparison, the land surface of Antarctica measures 5.4 million square miles.

The bad news is that readings taken by NASA show an area 3.4 miles thick where the ozone has been completely destroyed. The 3.4-mile stretch is between the altitudes of 8.4 and 11.8 miles. Ozone is measured by its thickness, or density. It is not measured in feet or liters, but in something called Dobson units, which calculate the thickness of the ozone as if it were lying on the Earth's surface. About 300 Dobson units equal one-tenth of an inch. Russian and American satellites have taken readings near the South Pole of less than 100 Dobson units, with the lowest number of 88 units recorded on October 6, 1993.

Today, some scientists think that ultraviolet light that enters through the hole in the ozone is already doing irreparable damage. According to the June 1993 *Omni* magazine, ultraviolet light is harming sea life in the Antarctic waters and increasing skin cancer. Signs of ozone loss have appeared over Australia, too. And while people are concerned with CO_2, CFCs are 18,000 times more efficient at promoting global warming. According to the magazine *Omni*, it will take nearly 100 years to wipe out the effects of CFCs after their use has ended.

Other Causes Investigated

But, according to two teams of astronomers, CFCs may not have been the first substantially damaging substance to disrupt Earth's ozone. The researchers have uncovered evidence that a star (supernova) that was as bright as the full moon exploded 340,000 years ago, emitting radiation that could have damaged the ozone and sunburned Stone Age people.

According to a February 25, 1993 *New York Times* report, one of the teams was Italian, led by Dr. Giovanni

F. Biganami. Working with him were scientists from the Instituto di Fisica Cosmica del CNR of Milan and the Universita di Cassino, Italy. The other team was American, led by Dr. Gehrels and Dr. Wan Chen of NASA's Goddard Space Flight Center in Greenbelt, Md.

The supernova that exploded is said to be a faint star named Geminga, one of the brightest sources of gamma ray radiation on the sky. This star was about eight times as massive as the Earth's sun before it used up its fuel, collapsed, and exploded. Its explosion occurred at a distance of less than 195 light years from Earth, which is close enough for it to have destroyed about 20% of the ozone in the stratosophere, but far enough away to not have caused any mass extinctions on Earth. Human beings would have felt the pain of sunburn and, according to Dr. Gehrels, the solar ultraviolet radiation might have caused human skin cancer and cataracts, and damaged marine life.

The Italian team studied images of the remnant star and determined that it was moving at a speed of 60 miles per second across the sky. With that information they were able to chart its point of origin.

The American team linked the supernova explosion to a huge gas bubble made up of hot, thin gas near the edge of the solar system. The bubble, shaped like a peanut, is referred to as the "local bubble," and is believed to be between 320 and 490 light years long. The gas inside the bubble is believed by astronomers to be only 1/100th as dense as normal stellar gases.

Dr. Gehrel's group bases the birth of the remnant star on the pulsar's rotation rate. Pulsars begin by spinning very rapidly, then slowing down at a standard rate. Calculating its present rotation rate to be about four turns per second, the star would be about 340,000 years old.

DNA and Ozone Depletion

The effects of ozone depletion today do not eminate from such dramatic sources as a supernova explosion, and the consequences are not as visible as a quick sunburn.

Dr. James Regan is to head a three-year study on the effects of exposure to the ultraviolet-B radiation. According to the May 25, 1993 New York Times, Regan will use human DNA to measure the effects of the cancer-causing ultraviolet-B radiation (UV-B), which is the type that most often causes skin cancer. The mon-

itoring, according to Regan, is an inexpensive way to watch for increases in this type of radiation, which has become more of a concern as evidence mounts showing the depletion of ozone in the stratosophere.

"We take human cells, and we extract the DNA. This is naked DNA in a water solution. We put this in a quartz tube so that it absorbs all the wavelengths, and we seal that up and put it wherever we want to and leave it out for whatever period of time we wish to measure," Regan said.

A dosimeter, which can be made for about one dollar, is a radiation-measuring device about a half inch in diameter and about four inches long. Traditional light meters can measure light in a 180 degree arc. The dosimeter can measure it in a full 360 degree arc.

Dr. Larry Cupitt, director of the methods research and development division at the EPA's Atmospheric Research and Exposure Assessment Labratory said that the researchers will "use the DNA dosimeters in conjunction with spectroradiometers to help characterize changes in the amount of UV-B across wide areas of the country," the Times reported. The researchers also will be measuring what connection the surface pollution has in the measurement of the UV-B. "We know that there are legitimate questions about effects on the immune system in addition to the skin cancer and cataracts effects that are normally cited. Until we can get the data on what the UV-B flux is at the surface, we will not have a good handle on whether or not environmental changes are occurring," Cupitt said.

In another study that was conducted by Regan and the researchers at the Caribbean Marine Research Center in Exuma Cays, Bahamas, twice the genetic damage as was suspected was recorded by the ocean-borne dosimeter based on the normal measurements of UV-B radiation that was made with spectroradiometers.

This exposure to the UV-B causes "cyclobutane rings to form between adjacent chemical building blocks in the DNA strands whenever genetic damage occurred," the Times reported. These rings determine the damage.

"The important point of this dosimeter, with regard to getting the higher doses, is that this represents the worst case. There is no pigment, there are no DNA repair systems, there is no shielding by protein. In other words, you cannot get more UV-B damage to DNA under any other circumstances," said Dr. Regan.

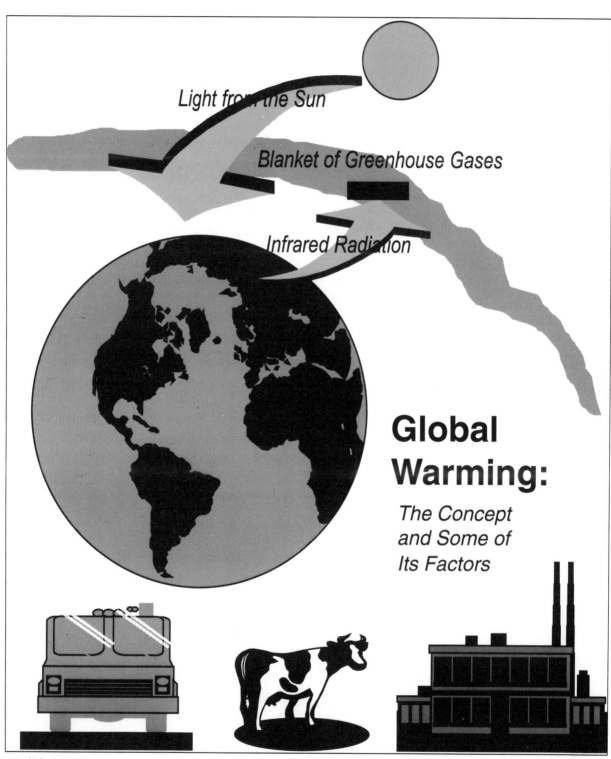

Light from the Sun

Blanket of Greenhouse Gases

Infrared Radiation

Global Warming:

The Concept and Some of Its Factors

In global warming, or the greenhouse effect, light from the sun passes naturally through a blanket of gases to warm Earth. Infrared radiation is then sent back into the atmosphere, but instead of passing through the blanket, it is absorbed due to an increase in the concentration of gases such as carbon dioxide and methane. A number of factors contribute to the greenhouse effect. Among them: emissions from industry and vehicles, and the release of methane gas by cows.

12

THE DEBATE OVER GLOBAL WARMING

In winter, by looking at the cloud cover, a person can tell something about the temperature. If there are a lot of clouds, then the temperature will not drop much overnight; if the sky is clear, the temperature will probably drop significantly before the sun rises again. This is because the clouds act as a blanket around Earth. They trap the air that the the sun warmed during the day and keep Earth warmer at night. Conversely, if there is no cloud cover at the end of the day, Earth's heat escapes, causing the temperature to drop rapidly after nightfall.

"Global warming" works in much the same way. This phenomenon is based on the greenhouse effect, where heat is trapped on Earth's surface by gases like carbon dioxide (CO_2) and methane. These gases act as a blanket around the planet, not allowing heat to escape. This trapped heat can raise Earth's temperature, which can contribute to changed climatic patterns.

But global warming was not, by any means, just a topic of 1993. Scientists have been concerned about global warming since the Industrial Revolution. In 1896, a Swedish chemist named Svante Arrhenius, showed through numerical calculations that the amount of coal that the world was using was enough to have a sizable effect on the Earth's temperatures. He said that doubling the amount of CO_2 in the atmosphere could raise the planet's temperature some 4 to 6 degrees Celsius.

Even earlier, other scientists studied atmospheric gases in relation to Earth's heat. In 1827 Jean-Baptiste-Joseph Fourier noted that possibly the CO_2 in the air helped to keep Earth warm by trapping its heat. Arrhenius also looked into the work of an American scientist named J. Tyndale, who in 1863 observed that even small changes in the makeup of the atmosphere could bring about climatic changes. T.C.

Chamberlain, another American scientist, felt that the periodic glaciation was somehow caused by CO_2.

During the early 20th century, scientists studied the sources of the CO_2 in the atmosphere. Arrhenius felt that industrial processes and burning fossil fuels were most responsible. Other scientists looked to volcanic eruptions as the cause. In 1919, an American scientist, C. Schuchert, said that "life and its abundance are conditioned by the amount of CO_2 present in the atmosphere." Sixteen years later, Alfred J. Lotka, a physical chemist, made the connection between industrial use of fossil fuels and the amount of CO_2 in the atmosphere. Based on industry's 1920 rate of coal use, he felt that the amount of CO_2 in the atmosphere would double in the next 500 years. In 1935, V.A. Kostitzin, a French ecologist, came up with a model of linear and quadratic equation describing the atmospheric circulation of oxygen, carbon, and nitrogen, according to the July-August 1993 issue of *Environment*.

A direct link was made between industrial CO_2 and global temperatures in 1938 by G.S. Callendar, a British steam technologist. Using temperature records from more than 200 weather stations worldwide, he showed that temperatures were rising, and he said they would continue to rise since human activity was bringing about the change. His theory was dismissed by the Royal Meteorological Society for two reasons: The increase was to only be one-half degree difference by the 22nd century, and the warming trend was viewed as a welcome change. Callendar also said that the 10% increase in CO_2 from 1850 to 1940 was directly responsible for the warming trend observed in northern Europe and North America since the 1880s.

Earlier in the 20th century, it had been thought that the oceans could absorb CO_2 without detriment to the oceans or to humans. That was disproved in 1957 by oceanographers Roger Revelle and H.E. Suess. They said that most of the CO_2 would stay in the atmosphere and eventually raise the temperature of the Earth.

In 1958, Charles Keeling, a chemist at the Scripps Institute of Oceanography started measuring the CO_2 in Hawaii. While he noted that the amount of CO_2 increased each year, he measured a large difference between the spring and fall measurements. This was due to the annual growing and then dying of green plants each year. His seasonal plotting of the amount of CO_2 and the sawtooth graph that resulted has come to be a symbol for the greenhouse effect.

Also in the 1950s, G. Plass, a scientist with the Ford Motor Company established fairly accurate estimates of surface temperature changes to CO_2.

In 1963, at a conference held by the Conservation Foundation, Plass's and Keeling's findings on CO_2 were reviewed. The conference ended with affirmation of serious biological, geographical, and economic consequences, and a conclusion that a rise of Earth's temperature of 3.8 degrees due to a doubling of the CO_2 within the atmosphere would cause glaciers to melt and low-lying areas worldwide to flood.

During the 1960s and 1970s, research continued in the area of carbon dioxide and how it would affect Earth's future. In 1979, four scientists warned the U.S. Council on Environmental Quality that a warming trend would have disastrous consequences on human life if significant changes were not made. President Jimmy Carter's science advisor, Frank Press, also suggested that this was an issue of international importance, and the U.S. National Academy of Sciences launched a study into the greenhouse effect.

A Global Focus

It was not until the 1980s that the scientific community started demanding worldwide cooperation. While studies were done on the consumption of fossil fuels, different conclusions were reached. There were, however, two points on which all agreed: 1) with the amount of fossil fuel reserves left, should they be removed at faster rates, there could be environmental damage to Earth, and 2) since these environmental changes would be different all over, the effects on specific countries or areas could not be predicted.

In 1985, V. Ramanathan and Ralph Cicerone discovered that methane, chlorofluorocarbons, and ozone in the lower atmosphere were as dangerous as CO_2 in the area of global warming. Environmental groups initiated studies on this subject and held conferences to discuss the results. Scientists from 29 developed and developing nations participated in SCOPE 29. It was decided that there should be an immediate reduction in the rate of carbon emissions. Earlier groups had not met with the same conclusion. They felt that data gathered in the past was not reliable for use in climate prediction today.

Bert Bolin of the University of Stockholm, and three of his colleagues edited the report from the SCOPE 29 conference. It summarized the greenhouse gas concentrations and how it related to climate changes. Three central issues emerged: how to deal with uncertainties in science, the importance of research carried on at an international level, and setting research priorities.

Bolin helped to create the Advisory Council on Greenhouse Gases (ACGG), which followed up on the recommendations of the 1985 conference. It was disbanded in November 1988 with the formation of the Intergovernmental Panel on Climate Change (IPCC). About 30 nations signed immediately as members.

The summer of 1988 turned out to be one of the hottest on record, which made global warming a hot topic in many news stories. James E. Hansen, director of the National Aeronautics and Space Administration's Institute of Space Studies, testified before the U.S. Senate that, "[t]he earth was warmer in 1988 than at any time in the history of instrumental measurements. [T]he global warming is now large enough that we can ascribe with a high degree of confidence a cause-and-effect relationship to the greenhouse effect. And . . . our computer climate simulations indicate that the greenhouse effect is already large enough to begin to affect the probability of extreme effects such as summer heat waves," reported the July–August 1993 *Environment*.

Those in the scientific community were split. Many felt that Hansen had spoken prematurely on the subject. However, it no longer mattered. The subject now had national attention. A flood of articles on the subject were published. In 1989, 32 bills were introduced and 28 days of hearings were held by nine congressional committees. Global warming was now ripe for public debate, and its potential effects were points of concern.

Some damage may have already begun, with the rising sea temperatures to blame. Coral reefs that protect tropical islands from flooding and are home to sea plants and animals are in danger of being destroyed. According to a June 1993 announcement by Yale University, biologist Leo W. Buss and electrical engineer J. Rimas Vaisnys found that rising sea temperatures disrupt the normal rhythmic digestive contractions of tiny organisms linked to coral polyps, which could cause lethal fluctuations in gas and nutrient concentrations, and permanent damage to coral reefs. For some unknown reason, the polyps react chaotically when the water temperature rises above 93 degrees. The water temperature needs to be below that for the normal to and fro swaying of the polyps during the digestive process.

Another casualty of the global warming war may turn out to be mass extinctions of species—far more than were ever caused by meteor hits, according to Dr. Mark E. Patzkowsky, assistant professor of geosciences at Pennsylvania State University. "In the last 550 million years, there have been five mass extinctions like the one that did in the dinosaurs. Most effort has been placed on understanding these events, but if we look at the geologic record, most of the species that went extinct did so in the times between the mass extinctions," he said. Of all species to become extinct, 4% were during mass extinctions, 96% occurred during the so-called normal times, or between mass extinctions.

Dr. Patzkowsky and Dr. Steven M. Holland, assistant professor of geology at the University of Georgia, who are working together, told those in attendance at the 1993 meeting of the Society for Sedimentary Geology, that there are only four reasons for mass extinctions: asteroid or meteor hits, volcanic explosions, sea level changes, and glaciation.

The researchers, looking at the number of brachiopods then and now, found that about 75% of them went extinct about 455 million years ago. The researchers, looking at the rocks from that time period have been able to determine that the extinctions were due to oceanic changes. "Changes in the rock types indicate changes in the climate and ocean chemistry. Various parts of the rock record indicate changes in temperature, turbidity, nutrients, and possibly oxygen content of the ocean. All these can affect the ocean's organisms and what we need to do is look closely to see which changes are actually associated with the extinction event," said Patzkowsky.

Different types of rocks indicate by their composition what was happening during a particular period. Carbonate rocks made up of a variety of sizes and types indicate warm, shallow, tropical oceans, while those made up of the oceanic organism's skeletons like the brachiopods and clams indicate cooler, temperate climates. More shale in the rocks means an increase in ocean turbidity and more phosphates in the rocks means more nutrients in the oceans. Organic-rich shales and limestones also point to a decrease of oxygen at that time. All of these changes point to a change in sea level. Patzkowsky feels "[t]hat for the times between mass extinctions, sea level is very important."

Geoengineers now are looking for ways to stop global warming. One of the best and easiest ways to begin the process is to repair the damage already done. Trees are about 50% carbon in composition and they absorb carbon during their growing period, which lasts 40 to 50 years on average. Trees that are cut down and burned or allowed to rot are a major source of CO_2 and methane being released into the atmosphere. As an example, ecologists estimate that the Golfo Dulce Forest Reserve in Costa Rica can keep the equivalent of 8.7 million metric tons of carbon from being released in the atmosphere, according to an article in the June 1993 issue of *Omni* magazine.

Researchers are still looking for new forms of energy to replace the petroleum that is now used. "Oil constantly pulls carbon from deep in the ground where it's been locked away for tens of millions of years and spews it into the atmosphere," *Omni* reported.

One option available, according to *Omni,* is a forest in the ocean. Marine algae that will absorb vast quantities of CO_2 can be grown in the seas. The brain child of biologist John Martin of California's Moss Landing Marine Laboratory, the idea came from a mystery that had the biologists puzzled.

In certain areas of the Pacific Ocean, nutrients such as nitrogen and phosphorous are plentiful, but phytoplankton—microscopic plants—are scarce. After discounting the water temperature and amount of light, researchers came to realize that the iron content was low. Fertilizing the water with iron enabled phytoplankton to multiply. Martin's suggestion was simple. Add iron to the ocean and let the phytoplankton multiply and absorb the CO_2.

Martin thinks that this may have already happened at the beginning of the last ice age, about 18,000 years ago. Some scientists think there was three times more phytoplankton and far more dust then than there is today. While this is circumstantial evidence, which does not prove that the plankton were fertilized by the excess dust, Martin and the other scientists find it likely.

Geologist Jorge Sarmiento of Princeton University is not so convinced. He thinks that eventually the plankton would no longer be able to handle the evelated levels of CO_2, and krill, who feed off of plankton would die and form a level of CO_2 on the ocean floor. These deposits would then be digested by bacteria, with that process requiring oxygen. So much oxygen would be needed that a dead zone would be created in the southern oceans. The bacteria would then release nitrous oxide and methane—greenhouse gases far worse than the original CO_2. Martin disagrees: "Some phytoplankton also produce dimethyl sulfide. That stimulates cloud formation, which should add to the cooling effect."

Although skeptical, the American Society of Limnology and Oceanography (ASLO) has endorsed a small test of iron fertilization of the sea to test Martin's theory. If his grant is approved, he hopes to fertilize 50 to 100 kilometers about 400 miles south of the Galapagos Islands. Any plankton growth should then be visible from the satellite launched. If successful, future generations could look to this technique as a way to lower the temperatures on land.

The Arctic Tundra

Now a new source for CO_2 has been found. The Arctic tundra, which covers 20% of Earth's surface, has carbon trapped in its permafrost layers. The tundra, which lies in the northern parts of North America and Eurasia, is treeless with only low shrubs. The ground consists of a subsoil layer, then layers of permafrost. The subsoil layer freezes and thaws each year. The permafrost, made up of layers of dead roots and plants, stays permanently frozen regardless of the season. Now researchers from San Diego State University are seeing

changes in the permafrost. The tundra has not yet been destroyed, but the potential for disaster exists if the greenhouse effect warms the planet.

Carbon, presently trapped in the permafrost, would be released if the temperature of the permafrost were to rise. George Vourlitis, a researcher from San Diego State University thinks that, "these permafrost layers have been accumulating carbon for years and years. As long as the permafrost remains intact, the carbon is pretty much entombed."

Some decomposition and release of carbon takes place in the permafrost, but without oxygen, which acts as a catalyst in the decomposition process, it would take place at a very slow rate. Further, more carbon dioxide always has been absorbed by the plant matter through photosynthesis than was lost through decomposition. The dead plant matter in the permafrost that would normally decompose at the temperate or tropical latitudes cannot do so in its frozen state. But, should the permafrost thaw and the plants decompose, a tremendous amount of carbon dioxide would be released into the air. This would raise the temperature and cause more CO_2 to be released.

Steven Hastings, an ecologist at San Diego State University, said in the November 1993 *Earth* Magazine that this has already started happening. Hastings said, "It's an early warning sign, an alarm bell of global warming. This is strongly suggesting that, yes indeed, global warming is happening and it's going to get worse before it gets better."

In the early 1980s, researchers noted that there had been a shift in the carbon balance in the tundra. Walter Oechel led a team of researchers from San Diego State University. They were to study how the increasing levels of CO_2 were affecting the Arctic ecosystems.

The experiment consisted of erecting greenhouses at Toolik Lake, which is located 125 miles south of the Arctic Ocean on Prudhoe Bay. The CO_2 level was registered every three minutes during the summer months. They found that the CO_2 level varied each day throughout the study, and that the plants were giving off more CO_2 than they were absorbing.

These experiments were carried on over the next five years not only at the same location, but also along a north-south line from Toolik Lake to Prudhoe Bay. The research team again received the same results with the plants emitting more CO_2 than they were absorbing.

Really Global Warming?

The six summers that these experiments were conducted coincided with higher-than-usual summer temperatures in the Arctic. The warmer temperatures allowed part of the permafrost to thaw and release some of its stored carbon. Now the research team is wondering if these were just six warm years in a row or is this phenomenon an indication that global warming is beginning. They do know that over the last 100 years, scientists have measured a warming of the permafrost over the tundra, and a rise in the surface temperatures. But, where climate is concerned, this warming could be normal. And while this may or may not be global warming, Hastings points out that this shows us what could happen if a persistent increase in temperature occurs.

But if this is the beginning of global warming, what effect would the carbon that is trapped in the permafrost have on Earth? Scientists know that the tundra holds about 7% of the world's carbon. But, they also know that if this warming should begin, and the permafrost should thaw and release the carbon, other ecological factors would kick in.

For instance, certain plants grow bigger and faster in CO_2-enriched atmospheres. The University of Michigan conducted a study in an underground laboratory that proves this, *Earth* magazine reports. Scientists were able to double the amount of CO_2 in the atmosphere, mimicking the conditions that they think will be the norm in 50 years. "What we've discovered is that increasing the atmospheric CO_2 content causes plants to store carbon in the soil faster," *Earth* quoted James Teeri, biology professor at the University of Michigan, who headed the project on global change. Professor Teeri could not say if the CO_2 would then have a tendency to leave the soil at a faster rate.

If global warming were to be the norm, new species of trees and a changing landscape would eventually take place, but increased growth of Arctic plants would not be evident in the near future. "Given 50 to 100 to 200 years—the whole ecosystem will change," said Hastings. Then this new plant growth would be able to absorb some of the CO_2 and put the atmospheric carbon back in balance.

Global warming and the stored carbon in the permafrost still have scientists coming up with a variety of possible outcomes. Previously, it was thought that the middle and lower latitude plants would absorb the excess CO_2 that might be emitted by the higher-latitude plants.

But two researchers at the University of Virginia suggest that this might not happen. Tom Smith and Hank Shugart used a computer to simulate what a climate change would do to the Earth's vegetation. Taking into account the loss of species, the rate of their replacement, changing the carbon concentrations in the soil, and migrating plants, the team suggested that the plants and soil would lose more CO_2 than it would retain and that over the next 100 years, 200 gigatons of carbon would be lost from plant ecosystems.

Other Carbon Reserves

Tundra lands are not the only ones that hold carbon. Other carbon-rich soils are found in boreal forests and peatlands. A study recently completed by researchers from the University of Exeter in England showed that carbon in the peatlands make up 3% of Earth's land area and contain approximately 528 tons of carbon—about 3.5 times the amount in the tropical rain forests.

Peatlands have a lot in common with the tundra's permafrost. Both are waterlogged, lack oxygen, and contain a particular group of low shrubs and mosses. The Exeter research team is concerned with the commercialization of the peatlands, which would involve draining the land for farming and mining the land for fuel. The draining of the peatland also would release CO_2.

According to University of Michigan botanist Howard Crum, the release of CO_2 would take place at an even faster rate if global warming would occur as it would dry up most of the peatlands. In his book, *A Focus on Peatlands and Peat Mosses*, Crum wrote, "Carbon dioxide locked up in oxygen starved peat is not likely to be freed by decomposition as long as cool, wet acid conditions prevail. But should the climate become warmer and drier, as it has in the postglacial past, the decay of peat would be greatly accelerated. . . . It is possible that a warming trend over the last century has already set the world's peat to a slow burn by encouraging oxidative decay."

Obviously, the role of Earth's carbon-holding areas—the permafrost and peatland—is complicated, and destined to remain one of the focal points in research and discussion of the concept of global warming.

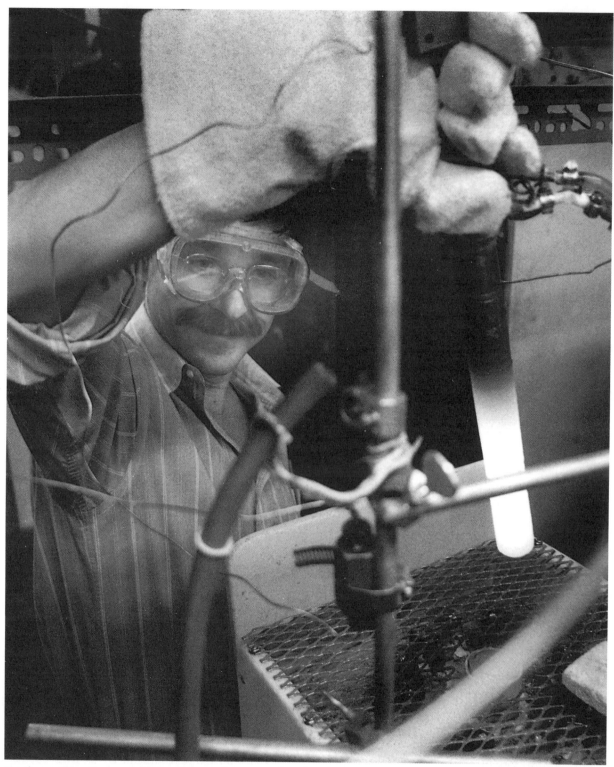

Professor Tim Grove at Massachusetts Institute of Technology retrieves a vessel of lab-made magma from a furnace. Grove and his colleagues have re-created in the lab the molten rock that nature produces in some of the world's most violent volcanoes. Using a special furnace and pressure tank, Grove and his colleagues melted natural lava from an eruption.

13

VOLCANOES AND EARTHQUAKES: RUMBLINGS FROM THE DEEP, TREMORS FROM FAULTS, AND SPEWS FROM MOUNTAINTOPS

The year 1993 began with a deadly bang for scientists. Six were killed January 14 when the Galeras volcano more than two miles high in Colombia's Andes Mountains erupted as the men conducted research. Still, the efforts to understand why the Earth shakes and spews goes on. Whether the source of the shaking and spewing is under water, on flat land, or from the mountaintop, scientists are constantly seeking clues to Earth's rumblings, tremors, and spews. The more they discover the more likely they can avoid such accidents as the one in Colombia.

Rumblings from the Sea Floor

In 1977, Jack Corliss and two companions squeezed into a 25-foot spherical diving vessel called *Alvin* and descended through the darkness of the Galapagos Rift, an underwater volcanic ridge located 200 miles west of Ecuador. There they explored the Pacific Ocean floor at a depth of 1.5 miles, hunting for the greatly suspected, but never seen, "hot springs of the Deep."

Today, scientists not only know what these dynamic hydrothermal vents look like, they actually have seen them. Further, they have not only seen them, they now believe them to be the place where all life on Earth actually began.

"I saw a veil of shimmering water. It reminded me of the way air wavers above hot pavement," said Corliss, in the November 1992 *Discover* magazine. With *Alvin*'s robotic arm extended into the "veil" (a sheet of rising water), a thermometer in its hand, the water temperature was measured at 44 degrees. Water that warm on the ocean's floor was unheard of. Corliss had found the first marine hydrothermal vent.

In these vents, the sea water trickles down through the sea floor through layers of minerals to the hot magma deep within Earth. There it is heated and forced back up the cone of minerals that has been formed through years and years of this action taking place. The water rises in two different styles: either as the "shimmering veil" that was first seen by the Corliss team, or as a turbulent thrust of water known as "black smokers."

"It was totally amazing. I began to wonder what all this might mean, and this sort of naive idea came to me. Could hydrothermal vents be the site of the origin of life?" said Corliss. Scientists are still trying to solve the age-old question of where life began, but it is difficult to trace the beginnings of time back 4.6 billion years. But scientists agree that there two criteria necessary for the beginning of life: "life" had to be able to reproduce itself, and it had to be able to carry and pass on information.

"Self-replication is the cornerstone of any definition of life," goes a line in the *Discover* story. And for life to continue, information needs to be passed from one generation to the next. It is only when this information is somehow accidentally changed that evolution takes place. It is not clear how this process took place. However, "[e]volutionary biologists have traced our family tree to bacteria, one-celled organisms that have been found in rock formations 3.5 billion years old. But even these "primitive" creatures were already quite sophisticated. They had genes of DNA and RNA and were made of protein, lipids, and other ingredients. Something simpler must have preceded them," according to *Discover*.

The trenches deep below the ocean's surface used to be thought of as geologically dead, with only the tiniest population of sea life existing there. It now seems that the opposite is true. "The abysses are the birthplace of the fissures where the ocean plates are moving apart, so that the kind of fissures along the mid-Atlantic, say, mirrors the coastlines of the once united continents between which the Atlantic emerged," reported the November 2, 1993 *New York Times*.

The abysses are filled with all sorts of sea life. The 1977 expedition spotted foot-long giant clams. In 1993 scientists spotted "thickets of tiny tube worms, odd growths of beard-like bacteria, legions of tiny white crab-like creatures and, on rocks facing some mineral towers, delicate networks of colonial organisms whose tentacles reached out toward the monoliths like worshipers at a temple," the *Times* reported. Scientists believe these things to be coral.

Godzilla of the Pacific

The water that percolates down through the layers of Earth to the magma, where it is warmed enough to be forced back up to the ocean's floor, is filled with minerals. In the 1980s, zinc, silver, gold, and copper were some of the valuable minerals that led to the undersea "gold rush."

This discovery led then-President Ronald Reagan in 1983 to claim all water areas 200 miles from the shores of the United States as territory belonging to the United States, in an effort to protect any claim

the country might have to these minerals. However, private companies still feel that it is too costly to attempt any mining ventures at this time. "The work on the ridges is really in its infancy," said Dr. Randolph A. Koski, an economic geologist on the voyage and a member of the U.S. Geological Survey. Thus far, he says, less than 1% of the ridges have been studied at close range.

Hydrothermal vents take different forms. Some are small slits in the ocean floor, while others, such as one dubbed "Godzilla," are tall towers of minerals, covered with odd creatures.

Godzilla stands 15 stories tall and is located in the Juan de Fuca Ridge, in the Pacific Ocean off the West Coast of the United States. Water emitted from Godzilla is a hot 750 degrees, but the icy ocean waters that mix with it provide enough water pressure to keep it from boiling.

"By some estimates, up to 70% of the Earth's internal heat flows through such zones, which every 8 million years filter a volume of water equal to all the world's oceans. Such processes play major roles

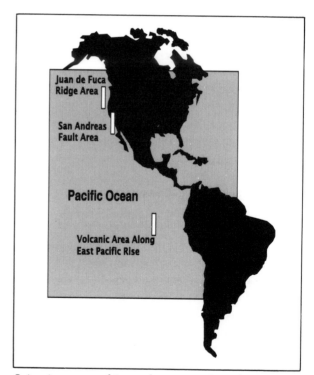

Scientists researching volcanoes and earthquakes have concentrated much of their efforts in these areas over the past year.

in determining the planet's heat and chemical balances," reported the *New York Times*.

The Breakthrough

No one knows how the water flows through these ridges. It is believed that deep hot rock causes sea floor cracks. Water then seeps down into these cracks to where the magma lies. This hot fluid then sucks the minerals out of the Earth's crust, sending them up to the ocean floor. But scientists stress that this is still an educated guess. "The dynamics are basically unknown," said Dr. H. Paul Johnson, a member of the voyage team, and a physicist at the University of Washington.

General knowledge of life on the ocean floor probably would have remained about the same had it not been for a small National Oceanic and Atmospheric Administration laboratory in Newport, Ore., that was electronically linked to a previously secret Navy network set up to listen to ocean noises and enemy submarines.

In just four days, in June 1993, the lab recorded a sea-floor eruption along the Juan de Fuca Ridge. For the next two days, the lab continued to record eruptions, which seemed to be moving south to north. Sea quakes shook the 25-mile-long area. Scientists thought that, perhaps, a new ocean floor was forming.

Alvin Takes a Trip

Alvin is a 25-foot research submersible, which has spent 30 years in service to marine research. (*See Chapter 14 for more information on* Alvin *and the newer submersibles.*) According to the *New York Times*, the inside of *Alvin* consists of a 7' titanium sphere that carries the pilot, a crew of two, and all of the scientific equipment and life support gear needed. *Alvin*'s support ship, *Atlantis 2,* floats high above on the ocean's surface. It is 210 feet long and is the same age as *Alvin. Alvin* has two mechanical arms that it can use to hold things for closer examination. Its exterior racks hold cameras, temperature probes, animal traps, water-sample bottles, sonars, and magnetometers.

Atlantis 2, Alvin, and 52 people left Oregon for Ecuador on October 9, 1993. Alvin dived 11 straight days. The scientists measured the water temperature at each vent, but for the first few days, there was no

sign of new life or mineral chimneys. The next three days produced little more. A lot of bacteria was seen in the water and ocasionally a clump of bacteria would break loose and swirl around, causting scientists to think that bacterial storms were related to recent eruptions of magma. Through the night, mechanical sensors and other equipment were towed from *Atlantis 2.* Using these, scientists pinpointed the southern end of the quake as the origin of the greatest and strongest signal. That area was nicknamed "the Source."

The Source

The second week of dives proved less eventful than the first, and the weather was no longer cooperating. *Alvin* descended more than 1,000 fathoms for the one last search. After a couple hours of searching, Dr. Jack R. Delaney, a University of Washington geologist and leader of the expedition, and his team, as the saying goes, "hit paydirt."

"It's hot. It's got tube worms all over it," said Robert J. Grieve, *Alvin*'s pilot. According to the *Times*, "[a] riot of life flourished on and around the unworldly monolith, which loomed three or four stories high. The tube worms were four or five inches long, their red tips emerging from brown outer cases. The chimney's surface was spread with mats of white bacteria and iridescent, dark red palm worms about an inch long. Smaller still were orange worms covered with tiny bristles. The chimney's surface also crawled with swarms of miniature lobsters known as galatheids."

There also were two kinds of coral with spines, polyps, and tentacles. "We've never seen corals among tube worms before. It's going to be neat to figure out how the corals make a living," said Dr. Cindy Van Dover, a biologist on the voyage from Woods Hole Oceanographic Institute in Massachusetts.

Around the tower lived even more marine life: large anemones with mounds of tentacles, orange-brown spider crabs with bodies the size of dinner plates, and more coral with its tentacles reaching toward the chimney. Scientists saw five chimneys in all on that last day of exploration. Some were tall with swarms of sea life around them; others were small, surrounded with only the very tiniest of sea creatures. Water temperatures ranged from normal to 43 degrees to 543 degrees. Dr. Delany felt that this volcanic field might be new. Since very little is known about chimney growth, future studies are planned.

"Catching the event at the beginning and watching its evolution is an essential part of the understanding process," Dr. Delany said. He then added, "It's exciting as hell! I'm blown away that they pay me to do this stuff."

Earlier in the year, another team of scientists had explored a large concentration of sea-floor volcanoes in the south Pacific Ocean off the coast of South America.

Volcanoes in the Making

Six hundred miles northwest of Easter Island in the Pacific Ocean, there's a whole lot of shaking going on. In an area about the size of New York state, 1,133 sea mounts and cones are making their presence known. Some of these cones are more than a mile off the ocean floor, with their peaks as close as 2,500 feet to the ocean's surface.

According to Dr. Ken MacDonald, a professor of marine geophysics at the University of California, Santa Barbara, several of the cones could begin erupting at any time. "We thought we would find a few dozen new volcanoes. Instead, we found over 1,000 that had never been mapped before," said MacDonald. But that is not surprising since only 5% of the ocean floor has been mapped.

One benefit of the discovery may be the access miners will have to the vast amounts of minerals that will be brought to the ocean's bottom or even beyond. While the mining of the minerals is still in the planning stage, anything in the future is possible. Also, the discovery will reopen the debate about whether volcanic activity like this can add enough heated water to the oceans to change the water temperature, causing serious problems with weather patterns. For instance, the Easter Islands are fairly close to the area where El Niño forms. Scientists are concerned about the possibility that the heated water could intensify the El Niño weather pattern.

"Volcanic action on the ocean floor is part of the whole of understanding El Niño. More power to guys like Ken MacDonald," said Herbert R. Shaw of the United States Geological Survey.

Tracking the Volcanoes

To study the volcanic field, Scripps Oceanographic Institute in La Jolla, Calif., towed two scanning devices, with one attached to the bottom of the boat and one attached to the stern. They then sent down a series of pulses to the ocean floor and recorded the signals sent back to them. MacDonald said that this allowed them to be able to map out the cones and also tell which ones had recently erupted.

Some of the cones were so close that they formed a mountain range that was 300 miles long. "The area of intense volcanic activity covers 55,000 square miles near the East Pacific Ridge, a ridge running from north to south where two of the huge plates that make up Earth's crust, the Pacific and the Nazca plates, are separating," reported the New York Times. These plates are pulling apart at a rate of eight inches per year. That is faster than any other plate separations on Earth.

There is intense volcanic activity as magma oozes from the planet's core and fills in the cracks. These are small but continuous flows and not major volcanic eruptions. The magma warms the water in the immediate area, thus making it a drawing card for uncharacteristic marine life species that now inhabit the area. Fahrenheit temperature here has been measured to be 800 degrees. This area of intense volcanic activity lies 10 to 300 miles west of the East Pacific Ridge between 16 degrees and 19 degrees south latitude and 113.5 degrees and 117 degrees west longitude. While this area is not directly on the East Pacific Ridge, Professor MacDonald said that the same huge underground pool may be feeding both.

"The ocean is pockmarked with thousands of small volcanoes. Ninety percent of all volcanic activity is on the ocean floor," said Dr. Haraldur Sigurdsson, professor of oceanography at the University of Rhode Island. He estimates that about seven-tenths of a cubic mile is pushed up into the ocean floor every year. That is about five to ten times the amount that erupts on land. The only water eruption that has been witnessed occurred on the Juan de Fuca ridge.

Scientists from the U.S. Geological Survey and the University of Hawaii feel that there is a connection and that it should be researched. Some say that if the warm temperature in the area heated up a little more, it could trigger a change in the atmosphere.

Those who disagree say that there is a barrier layer of warm water that is between 650 and 1,650 feet from the surface. Known as the thermocline, it would prevent the warmer water from rising to the surface. "The ocean is so big and even if you are putting a lot of heat in a few spots, it just does not have much effect," said Dr. William Chadwick, a volcanologist at the National Oceanic and Atmospheric Administration in Newport, Ore.

Professor MacDonald said, "I have always been one who thought the idea was hogwash, and I remain extremely skeptical," but he now thinks the idea may have some merit. "It is definitely warming the water. The question is: Could there be periods when maybe a hundred of these volcanoes are simultaneously active, creating so much heat that it climbs up the water columns and gets transmitted into the atmosphere. It's still considered unlikely."

Where the Fault Lies

Far below the California homes, schools, and shopping centers and malls, a monster, some would say, exists. He has no claws or teeth or blazing eyes, but he is still a danger to all who live in southern California. He is "the fault."

A fault is a crack in Earth's crust, and a number of these cracks exist in California. Particular faults in the Los Angeles area are called blind thrusts. "They are blind because they do not break through the surface, and scientists cannot see them directly," according to a story published in the August 24, 1993 New York Times. "They are thrusts because when they break, one side of the fault moves up over the other at a steep angle, focusing energy toward the surface. Mountains, hills, folds, and scarps are formed in the process." If it is a strong thrust, people and objects can be thrown with great force into the air, while a mild thrust would go almost unnoticed, creating only gently rolling hills. Malibu, Beverly Hills, and the Hollywood Hills are all the products of mild thrusts.

Geologists refer to this system as the "Los Angeles earthquake dilemma" and in relation to other geophysical problems, this is considered a big one. All of the experts agree that the faults are under the city, but little is known about when the next thrust will take place, if it will be big or little, or when the last thrust happened.

So, since doing something is better than doing nothing, scientists have spread out over the basin in search of answers. They are measuring ground movements, looking in excavation sites for evidence of buried streets or parking lots, and looking at oil seeps in Malibu and Beverly Hills.

Scientists also are using a method called thumping. Thumping is using flat-bottomed jackhammer-type tools that send sound waves three to six miles down. Listening devices called geophones then pick up the reflected sound waves. This reveals the geologic structure below. Plans are being made to use the thumpers on some streets in Santa Monica and some of the freeways in the area.

Further experiments are planned to set off 60 underground explosions along a 100-mile line through the Los Angeles region. The reflected waves should show images of buried thrust faults. In 1994, an experiment involving an air gun firing will be conducted off the coast. Researchers hope to capture the reflected waves from Earth's crust, hoping that this will give them a good view under the mountains north of Los Angeles.

"These blind faults under L.A. are five miles down," said Dr. Schwartz. "You really can't put your hands on them. Just defining where they are and their extent relies on modeling and a lot of interpretation."

"We are in a funny position of saying to people, 'Look, we have this hazard here, but we don't know the size of it, we don't know how often it moves and we don't know its geometry. It's a scary structure, if it exists. Yes, it would be bad if it moves, but we can't give you a probability. It could happen tomorrow or in a thousand years.' It's not a very satisfying answer, but that's where we are."

The Southern California Earthquake Consortium was set up in 1991. Through this, and with help from the National Science Foundation, dozens of scientists are trying to find these faults and advise local disaster officials. Dr. Thomas Henyey, the program's director, and a geology professor at the University of Southern California, said, "We've been slow to realize that the earthquake hazard in southern California involves more than the San Andreas fault." And while a devastating magnitude 8 earthquake is expected in the near future along the San Andreas, the Los Angeles basin "lies over a convergence zone—a complicated geologic region that could produce a smaller but more damaging magnitude 7 earthquake amid populated areas," according to the *Times*.

Beneath the thrusts faults lies a deeper, horizontal fracture zone. Dr. Thomas Wright, a leading expert on the Los Angeles basin, thinks this is where colder, harder rocks meet warmer, softer rocks, "forming a brittle-ductile transition." This area of basal detachment is nine miles down. The top rocks are sliding over the lower layer.

Blind thrust faults start in that sliding horizontal zone, and form steep ramps that move toward the surface. Each fault is a part of a larger system and is being pushed along by the huge North American and Pacific crustal plates, which meet in California. The place at which they meet is called the San Andreas fault.

Three major thrust-fault systems are presently being mapped, said Dr. Thomas Davis, an oil consultant from Valencia, Calif. These are:

- The Elysian fault. This huge fault begins offshore, where it rises under the Channel Islands. It then cuts over to Santa Monica, pushing up the Santa Monica Mountains. Next it crosses to West Los Angeles, Hollywood, Beverly Hills, and Hollywood Hills. It then goes under the downtown area and forms the hill on which Dodger Stadium sits. Finally, it travels east through Whittier, Monterey Park, and La Hacienda Heights, forming the Puente and Coyote Hills, ending around Chino. The top edge of this fault is about three miles below the surface.
- The fault beneath the Palos Verde peninsula, which extends to San Nicholas Island.
- The fault that lies under the San Gabriel Mountains, forming the Sierra Madre fault system along its foothills. This area has produced quakes of consequential size since 1985 and is considered active.

Tools of the Trade

In researching faults, scientists use many different types of tools to test their theories and make their work easier. Dr. John Suppe devised a method for inferring thrust fault geometry based on surface-fold geometry. Using geometry, "he can look at the shape of the folds and backtracks to determine what kind of deformation it took to create the folds. From that, he can calculate the depth, dip, and size of ramps," reports the *Times*. Dr. Suppe, who grew up on a street that lies over a fold, says, "you'd never know it from looking around the neighborhood."

Other researchers are using different methods to study faults. "Some are applying advanced geodetic surveys to see if the faults are locked or moving," reports the *Times*. The science and math of "geodesy" helps to map exact points on the Earth's surface. The shape and movements of large areas of land can then be calculated, correcting for variations in gravity and magnetism.

This allows the scientists to take advantage of the Department of Defense satellites, of which at least four are flying overhead at any particular time, says Dr. Kenneth Hudnut, a geophysicist at the Geological Survey office in Pasadena. Their location, along with distant quasar, are used to pinpoint exact locations on Earth's surface.

To find out how much compression is occurring across the Los Angeles basin, Dr. Hudnut has county surveyors lay down special receivers as they are mapping roads and property lines. The signals bounce off the satellites and their positions are calculated. This allows Dr. Hudnut a chance to define a regional picture of fault motion and mountain building. Reports the *Times*: "It will take another five years of data collection to measure possible slip rates on the faults," Dr. Hudnut said, but preliminary results indicate that the Los Angeles basin is closing at a rate of about seven millimeters, or about a quarter of an inch a year. "Strain could be accumulating on one or many faults," he said, "or the whole region could be slipping slowly and quietly."

Still other scientists are taking other approaches. Dr. Dolan is examining open trenches looking for clues about past earthquakes. "They map sediment, collect charcoal for dating soils and look for evidence of past movement."

Dr. Dolan thinks that faults in Los Angeles are nearly all paved over. The Hollywood fault has a one-block stretch that is not paved, but is covered with vegetable plots. And in the Santa Monica fault, there are 200 unpaved yards remaining.

Preliminary reports show that the Hollywood and Santa Monica faults do not move for thousands of years between quakes, but the San Andreas fault breaks every few hundred years. When quakes occur because of these blind thrusts, the damage can be great. Unfortunately, scientists cannot give much advice to disaster-preparedness officials about what to expect. But, residents may want to batten down the hatches, observes Dr. Henyey.

Just as scientists want to be able to predict more about earthquakes, they also would like to know more about volcanoes, so a repeat of 1993's tragedy might be avoided.

When Volcanoes Blow Their Tops

Subtle changes take place in the volcano before it erupts. "When a volcano becomes distended with upwelling magma, it moves a tiny distance, often just inches, away from the earth's center of gravity, slightly reducing the strength of the gravitational field at the volcano. Highly sensitive instruments can record such a change," according to the February 9, 1993 New York Times.

"As pressure on rising magma drops, dissolved gases escape like bubbles from champagne. First, lighter gases predominate, then heavier ones. An increased share of the lighter gases may herald fresh magma and an eruption," continues the report.

What happens when a volcano explodes sounds simple enough on paper. But for Dr. Stanley N. Williams, volcanologist at Arizona State University and lone survivor of the Galeras volcano eruption in the Colombian Andes, it is anything but simple. On January 14, 1993, Dr. Williams watched as two other scientists inside the crater and three on the rim opposite him were trapped by an explosion. He was on the Eastern rim and could do nothing to help anyone but himself. Six researchers were killed that day as they were setting up monitoring equipment on Galeras, 13,680 feet high in South America. This was not Galeras' first eruption. Major eruptions with lava flows occurred in 1936 and 1945. Since it became active again in the late 1980s, there have been several minor eruptions, the latest in July 1992.

That year, 90 scientists from 15 countries had gathered in Pasto, Colombia as part of a United Nations effort to reduce the number of deaths resulting from natural disasters. An eruption was predicted to take place sometime in the next decade, and would be a significant threat to the area. Three hundred thousand people live in Pasto, which lies at the bottom of the volcano, only a few miles from the crater. A total of 400,000 live within the danger zone.

The January tragedy is not without its reward, however; the measurements made at Galeras will help greatly in predicting the periods of instability of volcanoes in the future. "Chemical clues in vented gas and subtle shifts in the volcano's overall gravitational field, they say, may eventually give scientists a new kind of alarm system," the Times reports. "They could tell us when we're getting into a dangerous period and more surveillance is needed," said Dr. John Stix, a volcanologist from the University of Montreal and one of the meeting's organizers.

Not All Alike

Volcanoes have distinct personalities, and the actions of one have little to do with how another volcano may or may not react. Galeras stole six lives with no warning. Yet Hawaii's Kileuea warned the public quite adequately before her eruption of January 2, 1993. The aim of the Galeras meeting was to discuss the different methods available to scientists to measure volcanic activity.

According to Dr. Geoff C. Brown, a geologist from the Open University in Britain, minute changes in gravity near the volcanoes could be an indication of a volcano becoming active. The gravity keeps magma in check. But when the volcano is gravitationally off, even by just a few inches, the magma will rise.

Gases also rise out of the volcano as it becomes active. According to the New York Times, "As the magma rises near the surface and undergoes a huge drop in pressure, dissolved gases come out of solution (like carbon dioxide bubbling out of a bottle of soda or seltzer). At first the lightest gases predominate— carbon dioxide, followed by water vapor." The longer the magma sits and ages, the light gases are replaced by heavier ones such as sulfur dioxide and hydrogen chloride. So geochemists feel that if they could monitor the gases, they would know of the arrival of new magma and the possibility of an eruption.

On January 14, 1993, both gravitational and chemical clues were the subject of the day's work. With nearly all of the day's assignments completed, only a few of the scientists remained. "Suddenly, the crater's floor began to lurch and the top of the volcano exploded in a frenzy of hot rocks and lava, killing six of the scientists as well as three nearby tourists," reports the *Times*. "I heard this huge boom, and then rocks the size of televisions started falling around us," recalled Dr. Andrew McFarlane, a geologist at Florida International University, who suffered broken bones and burns but lived to tell about the ordeal.

This eruption was the largest in five years, according to the measurements taken of the volcanic cloud height and the release of seismic energy. Luckily, there was no release of lava, which would have meant disaster for possibly thousands. Another good piece of fortune was that many American scientists were barred from attending the conference by the U.S. State Department, fearing some sort of retaliation against the United States through the scientists by Colombian drug lords. The loss to the science community could have been far worse had all attended.

And, as with most disasters, some good has come out of this: Global attention has now been focused on volcanic forecasting and the problems that come with it. New funds are now being devoted to this type of research. "The important thing is that people follow through with this research and make an impact," Dr. Williams reflects.

Not all follow-through is in the field, however. Some of it takes place in laboratories.

Making Magma in the Lab

At Massachusetts Institute of Technology (MIT) scientists have re-created the molten rock associated with the world's most violent volcanoes—those found in the "Ring of Fire" in the Pacific Ocean. This has enabled them to make the first reliable estimates of how much water is dissolved in magma. They have known for some time that the water was there and that it contributed to the explosiveness of the volcano, but they did not know how to estimate the amount of water.

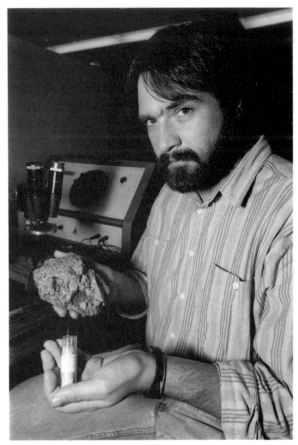

Graduate student Glenn Gaetani holds a lava rock like the kind that has been melted and re-created as magma at the Massachuseetts Institute of Technology.

"That's because the water is completely released as a gas during the explosion. As the liquid magma approaches the surface, the solubility of water in the magma decreases and it boils off. As a result, people could only guess at the amount of water present, although conventional wisdom held that it was low," comments Timothy L. Grove, a professor in the Department of Earth, Atmospheric and Planetary Sciences (EAPS). The MIT scientists found that the Ring of Fire magma contains "four to eight times more [water] than previously thought," according to Professor Grove.

Professor Grove, working with Glenn A. Gaetani of EAPS and Wilfred B. Bryan of Woods Hole were to report their findings at the December 1993 meeting of the American Geophysical Union. In essence, they developed new techniques that allowed them to re-create in the lab the high temperatures and high pressures that exist in magma chambers under the surface of the Earth. Using a special furnace and pressure vessel, they melted natural lava—the end product of an eruption—under a variety of experimental conditions. The procedure "directly reproduces the conditions under which [Ring of Fire] magmas form," said Professor Grove. Overall, Professor Grove said, the work and the estimates it has resulted in "will allow people to develop realistic models of the processes that lead to the generation of these magmas."

Understanding a Volcano

Earth's crust is like the head of a baby. It is made up of several sections that can overlap where the sections meet. The head has sections that can overlap, making the birth of the baby easier for both the baby and its mother. As a baby grows, the sections finally grow together, thereby forming a hard, solid skull. The Earth's crust is similar except the sections, or plates as they are called on the Earth, never grow together. They overlap and are constantly sliding back and forth over each other. This movement of plates is responsible not only for earthquakes, but also for volcanic action.

The volcanoes along the Ring of Fire form when the cold, dense, water-laden oceanic crust of one plate sinks down into the Earth's mantle at the border of another lighter plate. "But when the dense crust gets to a certain depth, the minerals that store the water become unstable, and the water is released and rises up into the overlying mantle," observes Professor Grove.

That water interacts with and induces melting in the mantle, and the resulting water-bearing magma then rises through the mantle and into the overlying crust. The water finally boils off as a gas as the magma ascends through the last 10 kilometers of the shallow crust and the pressure drops.

While such subduction volcanoes—named for the "subducted slab" that takes the water down—account for only 20% of the volcanic activity on Earth,

they are the most violent. "It's this decompression and boiling of water that makes them so dangerous," according to Professor Grove. Hence the interest in defining how much water is dissolved in these volcanoes' magma.

Melting Rocks

The researchers on the project conducted experiments without water in the magma at both high and low temperatures and pressures. In these experiments they found that the composition of minerals preserved in the natural volcanic rock closely resembled the experimental mineral compositions produced by melting the lava with relatively high amounts of water and at a relatively low pressure and temperature. After reviewing the MIT scientists' work, Trevor Falloon of the University of Bristol in the United Kingdom wrote in an accompanying News and Views article in *Nature*, "their conclusion seems inescapable: [these] magmas must have high and significant water contents."

The most difficult task was finding something in which to put the test material. It turns out that the water and hydrogen gases critical to the experiments can escape through most materials at such high temperatures and pressures. In tackling the problem, the geologist turned to MIT researchers in materials science. "That's one of the great things about this place—you can talk to people doing different things, and often get an idea for doing an experiment in a better way," observes Professor Grove. The materials science researchers "turned us on to a new fabrication process for the pressure vessels that we were using that significantly increased their upper pressure and temperature limits."

Because of the new technologies that can now be applied to the study of very old volcanic rock, Professor Grove feels that research in the study of rocks 500 million years old will now contribute to our understanding of the early Earth.

And because of the laboratory and field work scientists are performing coast to coast and under water, a greater understanding will emerge as to the causes and predictability of earthquakes and volcanoes.

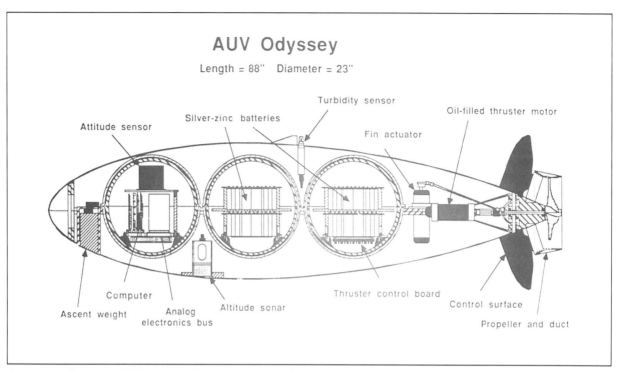

AUV Odyssey

Length = 88" Diameter = 23"

Attitude sensor

Silver-zinc batteries

Turbidity sensor

Fin actuator

Oil-filled thruster motor

Computer

Ascent weight

Analog electronics bus

Altitude sonar

Thruster control board

Control surface

Propeller and duct

Schematic diagram of the AUV Odyssey. The vessel is only 2.15 meters long.

Members of a 1992 expedition to Antarctica prepare to deploy the AUV Odyssey.

14

ROBOTS EXPLORE THE FINAL FRONTIER

"To explore strange new worlds,
To seek out new life and civilizations,
To boldly go where no one has gone before,
These are the voyages . . ."

These words from the popular television show "Star Trek" no longer apply to space exploration. Space, thanks to sky labs and space shuttles, is no longer the final frontier. Today, the last remaining area of exploration lies deep beneath the oceans. Space exploration has proceeded at a faster pace than has study below the waves.

While the space program has sent astronauts up repeatedly in spacecraft for exploration and experimentation, ocean research is being conducted by robots. Robots have been used by the U.S. Navy, oil companies, and even salvage companies to look for sunken treasure on ships located on the continental shelf. But the real treasure—the ocean itself—has stayed beyond reach. Now, with the new breed of sophisticated deep-sea diving machines, the last frontier is closer.

"It's the wave of the future," says Dr. Charles D. Hollister, a senior scientist at the Woods Hole Oceanographic Institute in Massachusetts. The institute is building several different designs of underwater robots.

"The abyss is the last frontier on this planet. We know almost nothing about it. These remote tools have the potential to synoptically [as a whole] explore, study, and characterize its properties, whether biologic, geologic, or chemical. We're on the threshold of a new era," thinks Dr. J. Fox, an oceanographer at the University of Rhode Island.

Uses for the robots are added daily. They will be able to find life forms that have yet to be discovered—plants and animals that live at depths that the human body cannot tolerate. They will also help in studying the ocean's effect on climate and in studying "black smokers," erupting undersea volcanoes. And they can help map the world's coasts and coral reefs.

How Deep Is Deep

Because water pressure increases with depth, a person can only dive to a certain depth of water without some sort of protection. An individual sinking to the bottom of a 12-foot pool can feel the pressure of the water. Twelve feet is only 3.65 meters. Light from the surface can be seen to a depth of 100 meters. A person in a diving suit can go to a depth of 600 meters, and the deepest dive made by a military submarine is 900 meters. Some robots are now able to descend to a depth of 11,000 meters, which is 11 kilometers, or nearly seven miles. That is two kilometers more than the height of Mount Everest. At the depth of 11,000 kilometers, the water pressure is 16,000 pounds per square inch (psi), compared to 32 psi at the surface.

Types of Robots

Robots now being built to explore the ocean depths are of two different types—manned and unmanned.

Alvin is a manned robot and one of the first of its breed. It carries a crew of three. Thus far, he has had a three-decade career and has taken crews to mid-ocean ridges and to the site of the sunken luxury ocean liner, the *Titanic.* Most recently *Alvin* was the vehicle scientists used to travel to the Juan de Fuca Ridge off the west coast of the United States. (*See Chapter 12 for related information regarding the Juan de Fuca Ridge.*)

According to the March 1993 *Science* magazine, many feel that the Navy, which contributes a major share of the finances for the robots, would like to see the scientific world shift to the newer, unmanned *Jason.*

Jason has been in use by the scientists at Woods Hole Oceanographic Institute since the late 1980s. It hangs on a cable, which is attached to *Medea,* a submarine that carries most of *Jason*'s power and some media equipment to watch *Jason* at work. Media equipment is then attached to the main ship overhead, and the cable is used to send information to the mother ship. An educational show broadcast to many schools nationwide has shown *Jason* as he explored the Sea of Cortez.

If money were the deciding factor, *Alvin* would retire and *Jason* would live. The cost of *Jason* at today's prices is $5 million, with Alvin's cost being a pricey $50 million. A small but growing number of scientists hold that remotely operated vehicles— (ROVs) like the unmanned *Jason*—are the way to go, because they are cheaper and safer to operate. *Alvin*'s followers say that nothing can take the place of human hands and eyes guiding it through the dark passages below. But *Alvin*'s competition comes not only from ROVs, but also from the newer autonomous underwater vehicles, or AUVs, that can work underwater for months at a time and can be built for even less than *Jason.*

Retirement may be what the future holds for both *Jason* and *Alvin,* since the AUVs came to be. Testing on this new breed has been in progress at The University of New Hampshire, the Massachusetts Institute of Technology, Woods Hole, and the Monterey Bay Aquarium Research Institute in California for some time, and the results look promising. The new AUVs combine robotics, thrusters, sonar, and sensors with artificial intelligence. They "think" for themselves via a computer onboard. They aren't tied to a mother ship like *Jason,* and they have a great field of motion. And while *Alvin* has a total under-

water time of 12 hours, AUVs can stay submerged for several months or more.

More Players Getting into the Game

Different institutions are designing their ideal underwater robot. *Odyssey* is 7 meters (23 feet) long and can travel 800 kilometers (497 miles) under ideal situations. It was designed by the Massachusetts Institute of Technology.

"Over the next three to five years, this technology will be used routinely to accomplish a lot of the stuff we're talking about now," remarks Richard Blidberg, head of the Marine Systems Engineering Lab at the University of New Hampshire, reported in an article in the July 26, 1993 *Boston Globe.* The "stuff" to which he referred is:

- the monitoring of underwater environments for long periods of time—especially around "black smokers."
- mapping unknown areas of the ocean topography.
- monitoring the ocean currents.
- finding sources of pollution.
- monitoring fish populations so that fish harvests won't lead to endangering their populations.

The AUV prototype named *Odyssey* was tested in the Antarctic waters during the winter of 1992–93. One of its data-collecting duties was to check the thickness of the ice which, over time, should indicate any evidence of possible global warming. It also measured the magnetic field under the ice at the South Pole. This, scientists feel, will help give them the information necessary to arrive at a geological theory of plate tectonics, according to a report in the April 1992 *Technology Review.* It is capable of staying down and covering 170 miles of territory— something that *Jason,* with a tether connecting it to its equipment, or *Alvin,* with only 12 hours of submersible time, could not do.

More progress has been made by Woods Hole with *ABE, Autonomous Benthic Explorer,* which is much larger than *Odyssey. ABE* will be stationed underwater for a period of one year, stationed at a mooring when not at work. Weekly, onboard computers will awaken *ABE* so it can perform its duties. It will take pictures and store the images on the computer's hard disk, then return to its mooring and lie dormant, conserving energy until the following week. At the end of the year, the computer will release *ABE* from its mooring and it will float to the surface where a ship will retrieve it.

One of the first places that *ABE* is slated to explore is the area around the "black smokers." Black smokers are vents or holes in the floor of the ocean. Molten, volcanic rocks heat the water that is thrust from the holes. This water belches out at a temperature of 350 degrees centigrade—hot enough to melt lead. As the water gushes from these geyser like formations, minerals from within the earth are deposited outside the hole. These minerals, over time, form a cone of minerals through which the water flows.

Scientists are hoping that discoveries made at Yellowstone National Park can be repeated under the ocean. Microbes containing a DNA replication enzyme were found in the hot pool of the geysers at the park. Geysers in the park and black smokers in the oceans appear very similar in makeup. "It's incon-

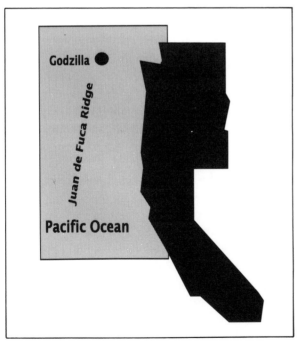

Juan de Fuca Ridge and the black smoker Godzilla are off the coast of the Pacific Northwest.

ceivable that there are not fundamental discoveries in microbiology to be made in the examination of that [black smoker] ecosystem," says Albert Bradley, an engineer and one of the three researchers who designed and built *ABE* at Woods Hole.

And while some of the underwater robots, like *Odyssey*, move like airplanes, *ABE* is more like a helicopter. It can hover over something, then move off and observe. *ABE* was built expressly for monitoring, while *Odyssey* was built for speed and distance.

Another use would be as "underwater police." There are approximately 75 toxic sites below the surface of the sea from nuclear warheads to submarine reactors. Should one of them start to leak, *ABE* could notify the scientists on land about the leaking radiation.

"Artificial lobsters" are being developed by several universities in the Northeast. And while such a vessel takes its name from a tasty treat from the sea, it has nothing to do with food. It, too, is an underwater robot that "would use chemical sensors like a lobster's antennae to follow a chemical trail," reported the *Globe*. It could either find the source of the pollution, or follow the pollution from its source to see if and how well it dissipates.

The Navy, also, is still in the business of designing and building underwater robots. Its version, called the *Advanced Unmanned Search System*, or *AUSS*, is 17 feet long and weighs 2,800 pounds.

The first *AUSS* prototype was built in 1984. It could descend only to a depth of 2,500 feet. Far too shallow to be of any scientific benefit in exploring the dark depths of the sea. But this ship, through a series of 89 dives, served as the tester for the more capable ship of today that can now dive to a depth of 20,000 feet, or 3.75 miles.

Because of the pressure exerted on underwater vessels by the sea, the construction of the ship's hull had to be made of material that could withstand the proposed depth of 20,000 feet. Deemed five times stronger than steel, a new carbon fiber was used to make the cylinder hull of the ship. The cylinder holds the ship's computers and batteries that power the ship. The batteries can run the ship for up to 20 hours before recharging is needed.

The scanning equipment called Side Looking Sonar (SLS) can scan from its cruising height of 100 feet off the ocean bottom, an area two-thirds of a mile wide. These images are continuously being transmitted back to the land base. Forward Looking Sonar (FLS) is used to hone in on interesting underwater objects, from the size of a basketball on up. *AUSS* does this while moving at a speed of up to five knots per hour. When objects are sighted, the land base can then command *AUSS* to go to the object of interest and take a picture of it from directly overhead with a 35mm camera. The image is then transmitted to the base in as little as 15 seconds.

International Competition

And while most of the science community is leaning toward the unmanned robot models, one man, marching to the beat of that different drummer, has built a fast, manned deep-diving ship that is keeping the United States in a dead heat with Japan in the race toward the bottom of Mariana Trench, near Guam. At 36,000 feet, it's the deepest spot in the Pacific Ocean.

Graham Hawkes, a baby boomer originally from England, now lives in the San Francisco area. He is still in the building stage of *Deep Flight,* his newest manned submarine he hopes will take him to Mariana Trench.

Hawkes began his career by designing and building diving suits that were used by the offshore oil-drilling companies. He designed a suit that let a diver descend 2,000 feet and still be able to function. By 1978, he had built his first submarine, named *Mantis*. It consisted of a small cylinder with a transparent dome. Mechanical controls operated two external mechanical arms, and it could go deeper than a man in a suit—over 2,300 feet.

In the early 1980s, Hawkes met Dr. Sylvia A. Earle, his soon-to-be wife, and present-day business partner. They worked together to devise a less-cumbersome diving suit and new designs of submarines, with off-shore oil companies in mind.

Eventually their designs turned more toward what the scientific community needed in their type of research. He designed a robot called *Phantom* that sold for as little as $20,000—a steal in the robot field. They sold well and were used in scientific research, police searches, retrieval of lost or hidden objects, and inspections of ships' hulls.

But their first love was the deep-diving submarine. "As you go down in a vehicle, the ocean goes from light blue, through dark blue, to indigo, to blackness. It's a beautiful transition. If you're really lucky, you get into a blackness that is really black and then cut out all the lights and fall through a bioluminescent cloud of plankton," remarked Hawkes in an August 3, 1993 *New York Times* article. "Sylvia calls it falling through stars," he added.

Deep Flight will soon be finished and a record depth of 4,000 feet for a solo dive is planned. If all goes well with the testing, the adventurers could soon realize their dream of seeing the bottom of Mariana Trench in *Deep Flight II.*

Deep Flight is unique in its concept and design. It is to be a buoyant submarine, which is a safety feature. Should mechanical problems ever occur, the sub would float to the surface instead of sinking to the bottom. It has wings like an airplane with flaps that are movable, and back wings that can also move. The pilot lies prone on a form-fitting fiberglass pouch. "Is this a coffin?" Mr. Hawkes was asked of his craft. "Possibly. But so is my car."

Competition's Not New in the Race for the Deep

In 1960, a submarine that resembled an underwater blimp actually won the race to the bottom of the world. In the U.S. bathyscaph *Trieste,* two Americans descended the nearly seven miles only to sit on the bottom for 20 minutes, unable to explore. The pilot of the *Trieste* was Don Walsh, now a consultant on the *Deep Flight* team. So Graham Hawkes and the scientists from the oceanographic institutes are vying for the title of second-place winner to the bottom. And their competition for the title is Japan, who also has entered the race.

The Japanese have built *Kaiko,* which means "trench." It is the pride and joy of the Japan Marine Science and Technology Center, or Jamstec for short, according to a July 5, 1993 *Newsweek* article. Hawkes is trying to beat them to the trench in the *Jules Verne Explorer,* which will be testing the special hull designed to be used on *Deep Flight II,* another vessel he hopes will take him seven miles under in early 1996.

Jamstec, with the help of Japan's five major corporations, has built a $50 million dollar robot that comes equipped with five cameras and a set of 6-foot arms. Beginning in the early 1980s, Japan built five underwater vehicles that have gone deeper with each dive. The last dive took place in 1989 with a three passenger submarine named *Shinkai* diving to a depth of 6,500 meters. Jamstec hopes to reach the sea's deepest point first with *Kaiko*. Japan will use the *Yokosuka,* their best research vessel available, to launch *Kaiko*.

Hawkes plans to launch his $300,000 *Explorer* from "the cheapest ship he can rent in Guam," reported *Newsweek*.

The Why and Wherefore

Hawkes envisions a fleet of *Deep Flight* vehicles, traveling between 15 and 20 knots as they explore the unknown frontier beneath the waves. The Japanese take a more pragmatic view. They want *Kaiko*, among other things, to position seismometers in the Japan Trench, which is the meeting place of the Eurasian plate and the Pacific plate, the two continental plates that are the source of Japan's constant tremors and earthquakes. While *Kaiko* is a robot, the Japanese government wants a manned submarine that can reach the 11,000 meters of the Challenger Deep in the Mariana Trench by the year 2000.

Scientists are split on why Japan and the United States are spending so much money on these projects. Robert Hessler, the first scientist to command *Alvin,* said, "[I]t will serve no purpose. Japan is a lot like the United States was in the 1960s. They have a lot of money to throw around, and they can afford to go on a fishing expedition," reports *Newsweek*. Robert Ballard, a pioneer in the field of underwater robots and submarines, said that robots can replace man in underwater research, "When we go to the sea floor, we don't get out, so are we really there?" Ballard said in the *Newsweek* story. He continued, saying that man going down in Challenger Deep is only "a stunt. There's nothing down there but mud."

And while the controversy continues as to the relevancy of this endeavor, Richard Lutz, a biologist at Rutgers University, said, "You're doubling the [water] pressure, which means you could find some really spectacular life forms down there, a winter-wonderland environment. Then again, you could find nothing—but you don't know until you look."

Gelatinous animals like jelly fish grow larger in deeper water, say scientists who study them. Jelly fish that are three feet in diameter, compared to a four-inch diameter jelly fish at the surface, have been found, in addition to 100-foot-long worm-like creatures. Some scientists say that such things are possible at depths below 6,000 meters. "All of us have questions about life in that extreme habitat that we'd love to investigate. What lives at those depths, and how do they do it? The enzyme system would be radically different. The biomolecular structure would be grossly distorted. How do they behave? Where does the food come from?" asked biologist Bruce Robison, science director at the Monterey Bay Aquarium Research Institute in California, in the *Newsweek* article.

One problem scientists anticipating is how they'll keep specimens alive. They know that just as the environment 11,000 meters down is harmful to humans unless precautions are taken, so is human environment to creatures that might be found below. Jamstec is spending $40 million on a pressurized chamber to "cultivate microorganisms retrieved from depths below 6,500 meters," *Newsweek* revealed. Deep Star, as it is called, will first analyze the gene and protein structure. A Jamstec spokesman said that the "research will become useful for medical or industrial use in the long haul."

With advances in space exploration, and continued exploration of ocean depths, the frontiers for humans may appear to be dwindling. But, as history has shown throughout modern civilization, once one frontier has been conquered, another lies just beyond reach.

Building the Information Superhighway

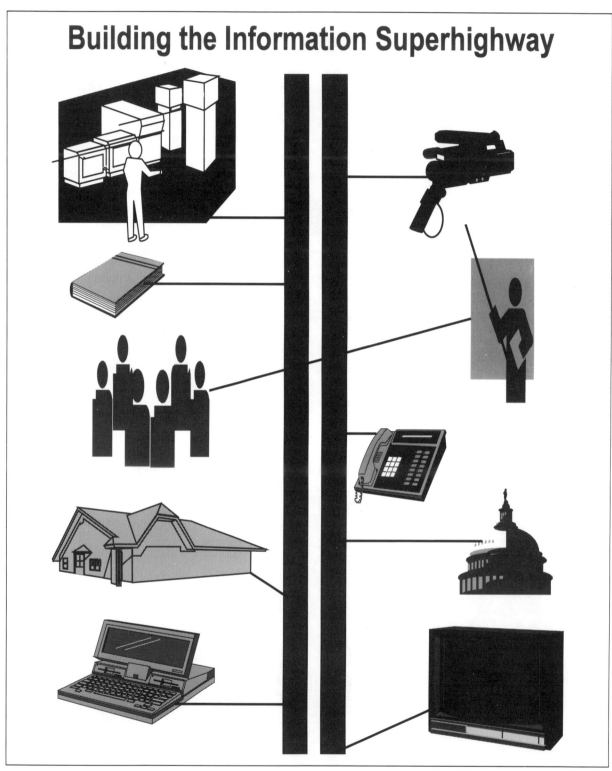

The information superhighway, as presently envisioned, will be a high-tech conduit for business, education, entertainment, and general enlightenment. It will connect homes to businesses, businesses to government, and teachers to distant classrooms. Huge supercomputer servers (top left) will be able to supply a variety of information quickly to an array of users.

15

A New President Promotes Science and Technology, and an "Information Superhighway" Gets Closer to Reality

In 1993 political squabbles immediately erupted between newly elected President Bill Clinton and the U.S. Congress, yet the president and the lawmakers agreed on at least one thing: technology needed a helping hand, and it was time for the government to provide it. The president placed Vice President Al Gore, who had been a champion of science, environmental and technological causes as a U.S. senator, in charge of the new administration's effort to boost high technology efforts in the United States.

On February 22, only one month after taking office, the president and vice president issued their plan: *Technology for America's Economic Growth, A New Direction to Build Economic Strength*. The 36-page report contained three main goals and steps to reach these ends. And it linked technological advancement firmly not only to economic prosperity, but economic survival as well.

The report envisions:

- Long-term economic growth that creates jobs and protects the environment.
- A more efficient, more responsive government.
- World leadership in basic science, mathematics, and engineering.

The initiatives included tax incentives for research and experimentation; investment in a national infor-

mation network; promotion of advanced manufacturing technology; helping private business develop a new generation of automobiles; and spurring improvement of technology for education and training. If carried to its full potential, the blueprint could be the catalyst for development of government-industry alliances in research and development.

Clinton and Gore want the government to spend $17 billion over four years to carry out this mission. Budgets, however, are subject to congressional approval, and during the president's first year in office, budgetary compromises had to be made. How much of the $17 billion will actually be spent on this effort will depend on the persuasive powers of the president and vice president over their four-year term.

While many of the basic elements of the Clinton-Gore plan were not new concepts, the effort represented a shift in focus for the government. In funding research and development, the government in the past has concentrated on military and defense needs. Under the Clinton plan, the emphasis would gradually shift more funding to economic priorities, focusing on the advancement of technology that can be applied in private industry, particularly small businesses that collectively are credited with creating a greater share of new jobs than the huge corporations.

Another change is toward applied research as opposed to basic research. Whereas basic research is simply the pursuit of knowledge, applied research has a defined goal in mind when it is initiated. While the latter depends to a great extent on knowledge generated by basic science, the issue was how resources should be allocated to these two different directions. For instance, researchers could theoretically invent a better mouse trap every day, but until that knowledge is applied to the practical world—that is, brought to market—it is elusive. Economic realities of recent years have caused a shift toward applied science.

Part of the reason for the new focus can be attributed to the change in political parties at the White House, but the shift also can be viewed as the administration's coming to grips with a post-Cold War world and an overall trend of the world becoming more of a single economic market rather than a collection of various, divergent economies. In a global economy, technological advancements can put one country ahead of another in the race for economic prosperity.

"To keep the United States on the cutting edge, my job as president is to adjust America so we can win in the 21st century," President Clinton said when he addressed an audience of computer executives in California in April.

"A New Direction . . ."

The president's goals already had been articulated in *Technology for America's Economic Growth*:

"We are moving in a new direction that recognizes the critical role technology must play in stimulating and sustaining the long-term economic growth that creates high-quality jobs and protects our environment. We are moving in a new direction to create an educational and training system that challenges American workers to match their skills to the demands of a fast-paced economy and challenges our students to reach for resources beyond their classrooms. We are moving in a new direction to dramatically improve our ability to transmit complicated information faster and further, to improve our transportation systems, our health care, our research efforts, and even the ability of our military to respond quickly and decisively to any threat to our nation's security."

The government's policy toward technology development since World War II has centered on promoting research to ensure that the military branches are well equipped and the national security is preserved. But with the demise of the Soviet Union, much of the threat that existed has diminished. Other government funding has financed space exploration. Private industry has benefited from the research mostly on a second-hand basis as the knowledge and techniques trickled down from the military and space applications.

"Although that approach to commercial technology may have made sense in an earlier era, when U.S. firms dominated world markets, it is no longer adequate," the president's report stated. "The nation urgently needs improved strategies for government/industry cooperation in the support of industrial technology. . . . This new policy will result in significantly more federal [research and development] resources going to projects of commercial relevance."

Specifically, the Clinton administration aims to:

- Increase the percentage of civilian/dual-use research and development (R&D) funding. In 1993, the civilian share of the federal R&D funding was 41%, or $27.9 billion. Under the Clinton plan, it would exceed 50%, or $36.6 billion, by 1998.
- Expand the U.S. Commerce Department's Advanced Technology Program (ATP). The ATP was established in 1990 to issue grants for research projects conducted by private industry.
- Rename the Defense Advanced Research Projects Agency to just the Advanced Research Projects Agency (ARPA), and expand of ARPA's role in dual-use R&D.
- Design new U.S. Department of Energy programs to increase the productivity of energy use in industry, transportation, and buildings. These programs would balance environmental protection with business objectives, and encourage industry alliances to reduce pollution and manufacturing waste.

Sharing the Resources

Two major elements of the administration's program are training people to use technology and giving them access to new developments.

To speed up the use of new technology in the manufacture and marketing of new products, the plan promotes regional technology alliances, where firms and research institutions within a particular geographic area

Malvin H. Kalos is director of the Cornell University Theory Center, where a virtual microcosm of the proposed "information superhighway" is being coordinated. NYNET will connect Cornell supercomputers with other educational institutions in New York.

would "exchange information, share and develop technology, and develop new products and markets."

To help private companies do this, the government would create a national network of manufacturing extension centers. Existing Department of Commerce extension centers would be the basis for expansion, "to give all businesses access to the technologies, testing facilities, and training programs they need." The plan also advocates expansion of the "Manufacturing Experts in the Classroom" program, in which labor and industry specialists offer their expertise to technical and community colleges.

Information Superhighway

The element of the plan that is receiving greatest attention from the public and businesses, however, is the concept of a national computer network that will provide access to unlimited information.

Writing in the October 1993 issue of *Discover* magazine, Vice President Gore emphasized a need to continue development of a national high-speed computer network, or the "information superhighway," to increase accessibility to what he called a "national information infrastructure."

He was referring to a high-performance computing program already under development as a result of the High-Performance Computing Act of 1991, which he promoted as a U.S. senator. Government officials use the term "infrastructure" to refer to the system of people and things that makes something possible. For instance, for people to be able to drive around the country, there have to be highways, people at toll booths, buildings, repair equipment, and so forth. In fact, many people have been comparing the importance of the high-speed data network to the development of the country's interstate highway system.

New "infrastructure" under development includes the National Research and Education Network (NREN), which Gore championed in the Senate. At five federally financed centers, industry and academic researchers are developing technologies for NREN, which is envisioned as a network that will have the capacity to carry data at a speed of 3 billion bits per second. That is equal to 300 copies of the book *Moby Dick*.

Computer users already are using a form of information superhighway, called Internet, but at a much slower pace. The U.S. Department of Defense financed the development of the network, which, over the past 25 years, has grown to include a collection of more than 11,000 interlocking networks and serve millions of users worldwide. Although the government still supervises its operation to a certain extent through the National Science Foundation, most of the services provided by Internet come from private enterprise.

Internet has traditionally linked mostly the government, universities, and research labs. Scientists and academicians worldwide are participating. The scientists need only a personal computer with a modem to trade electronic messages that can range from simple queries for information to lengthy discussions and reviews of new research results. Scientific journals are actively considering publishing electronic versions of their editions through Internet. And as the price of personal computers has dropped over the past two years, more people, not just professors, have signed onto Internet.

There also are other computer networks in place, such as CompuServe, America Online, and Prodigy. Anyone—again, with a personal computer and a modem—can sign up for these networks' services,

which include on-demand sports scores, electronic data bases of published magazine and newspaper articles, on-line encyclopedias, electronic shopping malls, and airline reservations.

Some envision the information superhighway, to be broader than any one of these present systems. Their goal is for access to computer information to be available to a broader base of users—from the president to the attendant at the corner fruit stand.

The information superhighway would "bring the advantages of high-performance computing to our schools, businesses, and health-care facilities," Gore wrote in *Discover*. "Just as innovation feeds technology, information feeds innovation. That's why the national information infrastructure is so critical to America's success in the technology revolution. Just as government played a key role in stimulating development of the railroads and highways, government has a key role to play in working with the private sector to develop this information infrastructure."

New Options in Education and Training

While the president's technology plan is part of an economic program, it addresses schools as a source of education and training. These include kindergarten through 12th grade (K–12) schools, community and technical schools, adult-education centers, and colleges and universities. And it is the goal for the information superhighway to be accessible to all these destinations.

"Computers can create an unprecedented opportunity for learning complex ideas, creating an environment that can closely approximate real work environments," the plan states. "Interconnected systems can help students work together as parts of a team even if the members of the team are separated geographically.

"Communication technologies can bring a rich education and training environment to people isolated because they live in remote areas or because of the demands of work and family responsibilities. Technology can reduce the burden of record-keeping and other paperwork that consumes so much teacher time in today's classrooms. It can also bring teachers and schools together in ways that facilitate the exchange of ideas and build a sense of community."

President Bill Clinton

Vice President Al Gore

Words of Caution

Plenty of issues remain to be decided about the information superhighway, such as data integrity and security, and the protection of intellectual rights, such as copyrights.

"Before the nation goes on-line, we must address issues such as security, property rights, and access controls," warns Eugene Spafford, a Purdue University computer scientist who has written and lectured extensively on computer security. Spafford is one of the pioneers of USENET, a global information network and bulletin board.

For example, emerging technologies make it easier to copy and distribute information, and as the use of electronic networks grows, ownership rights of people who create computer software and other products are endangered.

"Laws differ from country to country, and some countries have no laws governing intellectual property," Spafford explained, in a statement issued by Purdue University in November. "People don't respect copyrights now. We don't have the etiquette in place to make people think it's wrong to copy software and other products without paying for them."

Other issues to be resolved include methods to interpret the material placed on the network, and the validity of that material, he adds. "Trying to find something on such a large system with our current technology would be like going to a library with no card catalogs, no on-line resource, no librarians," he explains. "We need standard indexing systems and guidelines on how information should be presented. [Also,] there's no way of checking which information is authentic. Who should be allowed to put what information on the system is a major concern."

While such a network could be of value to all people who know how to use computers, security and privacy is a concern to Spafford: "Electronic access to commercial files, medical data bases, government files, and personal computers represents a tremendous opportunity to misuse or vandalize that information, and social conventions and regulations do not adequately address personal-privacy issues. We need to explore each of these areas, such as what defines property and theft, come to a consensus, and develop standards."

Recognizing the Potential

Even before the new president took office in 1993, private industry had recognized the potential of an information superhighway, and many companies already were scrambling to develop their own technology to meet this potential. Also, colleges and universities had formed consortia to pool their resources and develop networks based on their super-computers' capabilities.

The primary competition among private-industry firms to satisfy the market for an information superhighway is between regional telephone companies and cable television firms. Computer makers and computer software manufacturers also are vying for shares of the roadway. Entertainment companies are forging partnerships with telephone and cable television companies to anchor their positions.

Lofty Goals and Economic Realities

Ultimately, an ideal information superhighway would link just about everyone—in some capacity, either at work, school, or home—to the voluminous amount of information available today via computer. It also would open up to the home, business or classroom more than encyclopedias, published articles, electronic mail, and sports scores. It would carry first-run movies, up to 500 channels of television, video telephone service, multipoint video teleconferencing for businesses, and on-demand network television shows, where a viewer could watch his favorite show at any time without having to program the videocassette recorder to tape it for him. The vehicle for bringing all this to the home, office, or classroom would most likely be a combination of computer, telephone, and television, as opposed to just one product such as the computer.

But such a network would cost hundreds of billions of dollars and take possibly two decades to complete. What is likely to happen is a phase-in of that ideal type of superhighway, a gradual technological advancement based on affordable, cost-effective transmission methods. In other words, technologically, the information superhighway is set and waiting to be built, but as in the case of most infrastructures, economic reality will determine how fast.

Who will build such a network—the government, private enterprise, or a combination of both? Through the NREN, the government already is developing some of the technology. The next question is what physical form the network will take.

It will take a national system of fiber-optic cable to carry the data. Fiber-optic cable is made up of extremely thin strands of glass and is capable of transmitting information at the speed required by the superhighway. Already, long-distance telephone companies have installed their own fiber-optic systems, and they are poised to jump into the commercial computer network business. Whether a government-built fiber-optic network is on the horizon, or arrangements are worked out to use existing cables, remains to be seen.

Some forms of the information superhighway already are taking shape in various areas of the country, using the fiber-optic cable already installed. But just as drivers have to slow down when they exit the interstate highway and enter local city streets, the information superhighway is encountering traffic problems in localities and regions where fiber-optic cable has not replaced traditional copper wiring and coaxial cables.

A Microcosm

One example of a new regional venture is the New York Network (NYNET), which was gearing up for operation in 1993. NYNET is an "ultra-high-speed, fiber-optic network" that will eventually link several universities around the state of New York, according to a statement by Cornell University. NYNET will initially connect supercomputers and parallel computers at the Cornell Theory Center in Ithaca, N.Y., and Syracuse University's Northeast Parallel Architectures Center, the Museum of Science and Technology in Syracuse, and Rome Laboratory in Rome, N.Y.

Set for later connection to the network are Columbia University in the Manhattan borough of New York City, Polytechnic University in Brooklyn, and the NYNEX Science and Technology Center in White Plains, N.Y. Other universities will be added later through the New York Telephone system.

"The link will mean that scientists at workstations, doctors at hospitals, industrial researchers at their companies, and schoolchildren at the science museum all will be able to access the fastest computers available today for parallel processing and supercomputing," according to the Cornell statement.

The system will use a new technology called ATM to transmit information over fiber-optic cables. ATM, in this case, is not a bank teller machine. The initials stand for asynchronous transfer mode. It is a computer format for transmitting data and images over networks. ATM transfers digitized information asynchronously, or out of sequence, which allows multiple computer conversations to take place at the same time. The information is then reassembled in sequence at the receiving point. ATM can be used to transmit data over various types of wires, from office computer cables to fiber-optic lines. Over the latter, ATM can transmit at up to 2.5 billion bits per second, but it can also slow down to 56,000 bits per second over regular telephone lines.

In many ways, the New York project resembles what President Clinton and Vice President Gore say they have in mind for a national information superhighway. It is being launched by a consortium of research centers who separately could not finance such a venture. Industry also is collaborating with the universities. The network will eventually extend to most or all of the points mentioned in the president's plan: health centers, libraries, K–12 schools, businesses, and, of course, research laboratories. And as the researchers develop the technology, the network will eventually carry a combination of voice, video image, and data.

As this and other systems develop around the country, the image of a national information superhighway is taking shape. But that image is still comparable to "virtual reality," a state that computers can create on screen that simulates actual events and places. In the not-too-distant future, though, with the government, industry, and educational establishments scrambling to meet the potential, the image of a national information superhighway will simply be "reality."

PART TWO

AQUARIUMS, MUSEUMS, AND SCIENCE CENTERS

In no other setting is the science of today more accessible to the general population than in museums, aquariums, and science centers around the country. This chapter is a little different than earlier ones, in that it reviews not only some of the 1993 activities, but wherever possible, what exhibits are on display in 1994. What connects many exhibits are the themes "hands-on" and "high-tech." Hopefully, readers can take full advantage of this information by visiting nearby exhibits or other exhibits while on vacation. The museums, aquariums and science centers are arranged alphabetically by state and city.

ALABAMA

U.S. Space & Rocket Center
1 Tranquility Base, Huntsville, Ala. (205) 837-3400

The **U.S. Space & Rocket Center** is the largest space science center with the nation's only full-scale shuttle exhibit. There is also a Russian spacecraft display and the world's fastest plane, the SR-71 Blackbird, which flew coast to coast in 68 minutes. There are 1,500 artifacts at the center, including the Apollo 16 capsule that took three astronauts to the moon and the Saturn V rocket that is longer than a football field.

The U.S. Space & Rocket Center is the official visitor's center of the National Aeronautics and

International Space Camp trainees mingle with wildlife at Tennessee Aquarium, U.S. Space & Rocket Center, Huntsville, Ala.

Visitors to the U.S. Space & Rocket Center in Huntsville, Ala., can imaginatively hurl across deep space at greater-than-light speed aboard a futuristic shuttle in the Journey to Jupiter *exhibit A motion-based simulator creates the mood, and displays teach passengers about the evolution of science fiction to science fact.*

An articulated gorilla head in the Special Effects *exhibit at the California Museum of Science and Industry shows how lifelike movie characters can be.*

Space Administration, and Alabama's top tourist attraction. There are more than 60 hands-on displays at the space center. The Spacedome Theater has a 67-foot curved screen on which to view the OMNI-MAX movies "The Dream is Alive," "Blue Planet," and "Speed."

Visitors can experience a deep-space voyage with the motion-based simulator, "Journey to Jupiter." "This latest addition to the Space Center encompasses the most modern technology and symbolizes our commitment of presenting the past, present, and future of space exploration. The simulator was conceived and designed with the intentions of teaching and providing a hands-on experience that will stimulate both young and old to reach for the stars," said Director Edward O. Buckbee.

Motion-based simulators are routinely used by astronaut and pilot trainees, but "Journey to Jupiter" is the first of its kind in the country. The motion

system and a 70-mm film are synchronized to allow passengers to see, hear, and feel what it is like to lift off from Earth and maneuver around a space station. The simulator creates the feeling of freefall by shifting 20 degrees in a second, while a 15' 7" curved screen creates a "you are there" feeling.

CALIFORNIA

Davis

Explorit Science Center
3141 5th St., Davis, Calif. (916) 756-0191

Explorit Science Center offers *Discovery Days*, a drop-in exhibit program for the general public. There are hands-on displays and staff available to answer questions. On Saturdays, experts participate in special demonstrations, slide shows, and discussions on plants and animals. The following five programs are scheduled for 1994:

- *Energy—Forms and Transformations*, January 15–February 20, 1994
- *Boom! The Nature of Sudden Loud Noises*—Rapidly expanding gases, breaks in rigid structures, collisions of solids, February 26–April 3, 1994
- *Muscles and Movement—Muscles and How They Work*, April 9–May 15, 1994
- *Floating, Swimming, Sinking*—How different kinds of bodies behave in fluids, May 21–June 19, 1994
- *Science of Recreational Activities*—July 2–August 28, 1994

Los Angeles

California Museum of Science and Industry
700 State Drive, Los Angeles, Calif. (213) 744-2014

Several new exhibits are due to open at the **California Museum of Science and Industry** in 1994. A description of them follows:

- *Blue Planet*—Takes visitors aboard the space shuttle for a moving and informative simulated exploration of Earth.
- *Liquid Vision: Lasers, Holograms and Virtual Reality*, February–April, 1994
- *Behind the Seams: The Science in Fashion*, June–August, 1994

Fig 85 @ 50%

Fig 86 @ 44%

(Top) Latex masks converted earthly actors into the galactic terrorists Beastman and Skelator in "Masters of the Universe." They are part of the hundreds of artifacts in the California Museum of Science and Industry exhibit Special Effects, *which has returned home after a five-year national tour.*

(Above) The claymation California Raisins return from their five-yera national tour as part of the California Museum of Science and Industry's Special Effects *exhibit.*

Special Effects: The Science of Television and Movie Magic was on display through May 2, 1993, but was so popular that *Special Effects II*, a sequel, will debut in late 1994. The exhibits explain the "how" of special effects, and show that knowledge only goes so far. "It takes an artist to transform technical knowledge into dramatic reality. It's a combination of science and art," said museum Executive Director Jeffrey N. Rudolph.

Children's Museum
310 N. Main St., Los Angeles, Calif. (213) 687-8801

A new science exhibit called *H2O: The Story of Water* was scheduled to open at **The Children's Museum** in February 1994, featuring water experiments, water play areas, a giant Archimedes screw, a swirling vortex powered by bicycle riders, water videos and a child-operated system of locks and dams.

Griffith Observatory
2800 E. Observatory Road, Los Angeles, Calif. (213)664-1181

An interactive exhibit designed by the **Griffith Observatory** opened in the spring of 1993. It is called *Planet Odyssey*, a self-guided video tour of the solar system. Through the use of a computer and disc

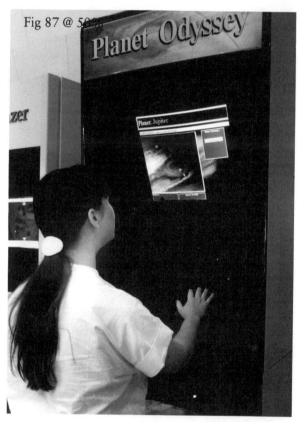

Fig 87 @ 50%

Planet Odyssey is one of the most popular exhibits at the Griffith Observatory. This visitor uses a trackball and button to navigate through a simple set of menus to view pictures and movies of the planets and moons.

Among the educational subjects at Monterey Bay Aquarium in La Jolla, Calif., are ocean-born eels, who live in rivers but migrate 2,500 miles into the Atlantic Ocean to reproduce.

player, a visitor can view 25 minutes worth of clips and still photographs. The visitor can see pictures and movies of the planets and their moons. They can receive a general overview of the planets, or very specific information on a particular topic of their choice. Although complicated in the amount of information available, the video tour is simple to operate and appeals to a broad range of ages, children through adult.

Monterey

Monterey Bay Aquarium
886 Cannery Row, Monterey, Calif. (408) 648-4800

An exhibit called *Mating Games: Reproduction and Survival in the Aquatic World* was due to open at **Monterey Bay Aquarium** December 18, 1993 and run through September 4, 1995. This is a 6,000-square-foot exhibit on the survival techniques of aquatic creatures. It shows how they meet at breeding grounds, types of sexual and asexual reproduction, courtship, eggs and babies, and family life. The exhibit offers games, videos, hands-on activities, and a view of more than three dozen species of live animals, from shore birds to sea turtles. Two featured species, the green sea turtles and a fish called the California grunion, live in the sea but come ashore to lay their eggs. There is also an "egg lab" with seasonally changing eggs to view under microscopes or with the naked eye.

Traditional American gender roles fade at the exhibit, where visitors can see fathers who act like mothers and care for the young, plus Amazon mollies—fish that are only females—and species with no sex at all that clone themselves.

San Diego

Stephen Birch Aquarium-Museum
2300 Expedition Way, La Jolla, Calif. (619) 534-4086

Stephen Birch Aquarium-Museum is offering a one-of-a-kind exhibit on oceanography called *Exploring the Blue Planet*. This exhibit offers visitors an overview of the ocean sciences and research projects. The exhibit is divided into seven areas:

- *Introduction*—The Blue Planet Theater gives an audiovisual presentation on the origin of the oceans and stresses the importance of water.
- *To Depths Unknown—The History of Oceanography* looks at how scientists study the oceans.
- *Water and Its Movements*—This demonstrates the properties of pure and sea water.
- *Air: Ocean and Atmosphere*—This demonstration shows the link between the oceans and the atmosphere. It explains how wind, ocean currents, hydrologic cycle, and land masses interact to create long-term climate and day-to-day weather.
- *Land: The Shifting Seafloor*—The study of plate tectonics and how their actions affect earthquakes and ocean basins.

Scripps Hall of Oceanography at the Stephen Birch Aquarium-Museum offers the exhibit Exploring the Blue Planet.

- *Life: The Living Ocean*—This shows how sea life survives in the depths of the ocean.
- *Future: Our Changing Planet*—This shows the interrelated world of water, air, land, and life, and how they coexist. This exhibit's seven areas surround a learning center that serves as a central point of orientation and rest. There are benches and reading material there.

Reuben H. Fleet Space Theater and Science Center
Balboa Park, San Diego, Calif. (619) 238-1233

Two traveling exhibits are planned for 1994 at the **Reuben H. Fleet Space Theater and Science Center.** Running through May 8 is *Harvesting the Sun.* Developed by the Science Museum in Richmond, Va., this exhibit traces the passage of the sun's energy through living systems. This unique exhibit is set up so that families can visit together with the adults reading the materials to their children. School classes with their teacher also can benefit from this exhibit.

The second traveling exhibit scheduled to open in 1994 is called About Faces. It will open May 27 with an undetermined closing date. This exhibit invites visitors to become active participants in the exploration of their faces. Playing and working with these exhibits, visitors using their own faces as the focus of study will discover distinctions and similarities. This exhibit allows two people to change faces at the

You and Me display; the "symulations" display allows visitors to see themselves symmetrically, that is, with either two left sides or two right sides of their faces instead of one of each. A muscle mirror show where the muscles in the visitor's face are located, and a mask corner, where the visitor can see different expressions of humans, also are featured.

San Francisco

California Academy of Sciences
Golden Gate Park, San Francisco, Calif. (415) 750-7145

California Academy of Sciences, is made up of the **Steinhart Aquarium** and the **Morrison Planetarium.**

Steinhart Aquarium houses more than 1,000 freshwater and saltwater fish, reptiles, amphibians, marine mammals, and penguins. There is a Fish Roundabout in which visitors stand in the middle of the tank and the fish swim around them.

Morrison Planetarium offers both educational and entertaining sky shows. There is also a Laserium, a laser light show several times a week; *Life Through Time*, a 3.5-billion-year journey through life on Earth; *Wild California*, an exhibit on California's history; *Wattis Hall of Human Cultures*, which shows how humans have adapted to their climate; *African Safari*, dioramas of African animals in their natural habitats; *The Far Side of Science Gallery* by Gary Larson, 159 original cartoons on science; *Hohfeld Earth* and

Two students enjoy the hands-on atmosphere at the California Academy of Sciences in San Francisco.

Space Hall, under a neon solar system, in which visitors learn about the forces that shape the Earth and the other planets; *Gem and Mineral Hall*, which contains 1,000 specimens from gold to granite; and *Discovery Room For Children*, hands-on everything for children in the elementary grades.

Three new exhibits will be featured in 1994:

Hands On Science will be open May 29, 1993 through Labor Day 1994. *Hands On Science* will be an interactive science center with displays from all the specialty departments in science. There will be Touchable Specimens, things known for their different textures; Discovery Drawers, fossils, minerals, and bones; Featured Creatures, live animals; Selections from the Collections, rare specimens, Opticals, working with lenses; and Microscopes, Scanning Electron Microscope (SEM), Mini-computers, and Computers in the Biodiversity Center.

Birds of a Feather opens June 19, 1993 and will run through the Labor Day 1994. Feathers first appeared on dinosaurs more than 140 million years ago. Birds are modern dinosaurs with characteristics from their huge relatives. Dioramas have been restored, and rarely seen eggs and nests, colorful graphics, hands-on displays, and a sound gallery treat visitors to the "secret life" of birds.

Star Trek: Federation Science runs February 5, 1994 through May 1, 1994. It was designed and built by the Oregon Museum of Science and Industry in Portland. It includes more than 40 modular displays and covers more than 6,000 square feet. The exhibit is divided into several different areas: "The Bridge" will be the central focus of the exhibit. It will include the communications and navigation work stations. "Engineering" and "Sickbay" also will be highlighted. A simulation of the "Transporter Room" will give the visitor the feeling of "beaming down." Visitors also will be able to navigate through an asteroid field, program a voice-activated computer, and command the ship. They will even be able to be turned into a Klingon.

There will be exhibits directly related to astronomy and planetology and will be located in a special science area. The exhibit designers relied heavily on basic science principles, incorporating particle physics, practical astronomy, and physiology with the hope of challenging the future scientists of America.

Also intertwined are the principles behind propulsion systems, medical science, and life support.

COLORADO

Denver Museum of Natural History
2001 Colorado Blvd., City Park, Denver, Colo.
(303) 370-6387

Denver Museum of Natural History hosted *Whales: Giants of the Deep*, a traveling exhibition featuring some of the largest denizens of the sea, October 15, 1993 through January 9, 1994. The exhibit featured lifesize, robotic whales, each in a simulated marine environment with the sperm whale, narwhal, and orca shown as they would appear from underwater. The gray whale and the humpback whale are partially exhibited, as would be visible from above the water. The whales have movable tails, flukes, fins, heads, eyes, and jaws, Some also "swim" while others spout water. This exhibit was developed by the Pacific Science Center in Seattle, Washington.

The Denver museum also houses an IMAX Theater and Gates Planetarium. The IMAX has a screen that is 4½ stories tall and 6½ stories wide. At the Gates Planetarium, visitors travel into the solar system with the star machine. The museum also has a number of permanent exhibits and offers an array of hands-on activities.

CONNECTICUT

New Haven

Peabody Museum of Natural History
170 Whitney Ave., New Haven, Conn. (203) 432-5050

The **Peabody Museum of Natural History** is located on the campus of Yale University but is open to the public. The museum is home to nearly 9 million specimens and is one of the oldest university-connected natural history museums in the country. Among several permanent exhibits is *The Great Hall of Dinosaurs*, which contains an extensive dinosaur collection, including some of the first North American skeletons to be collected.

Some of the dinosaurs available for viewing include the giant *Apatosaurus*, which was collected by O.C. Marsh, Peabody's first curator of vertebrate paleontology. He called the animal *Brontosaurus*.

The Great Hall of Dinosaurs *is at Peabody Museum of Natural History, Yale University, New Haven, Conn.*

Also included are the specimens of *Stegosaurus, Camptosaurus, Edomontosaurus* (duck-billed), skulls of *Torosaurus and Triceratops,* and a cast of *Tyrannosaurus rex.*

The Peabody also is home to two murals by Rudolph F. Zallinger. They are *The Age of Mammals,* located in the Hall of Mammals, and *The Age of Reptiles.* Zallinger was awarded a Pulitzer prize for *The Age of Reptiles* mural.

The *Hall of Human Cultures* includes extensive Meso-American and South American collections with artifacts from the Machu Picchu archaeological site.

Exhibits of both North America and Connecticut also are on display, and programs of special interest to school groups are given high priority from the staff.

A traveling exhibit, *Design and World View: The Politics of Hopi Ceramics,* was scheduled to run from October 16, 1993 to January 30, 1994, after which it was to be moved to the **Philbrook Museum of Art** in Tulsa, Okla., for display there from March 13 through June 5, 1994.

This exhibit explores the traditions, both cultural and spiritual, of the Hopi people and discusses the "whys" behind the two different types of Hopi pottery.

This exhibit is a result of the joint efforts of Yale's Peabody Museum, the Philbrook Museum of Art and the Harvard Peabody Museum of Archaeology and Ethnology. It contains more than 60 pieces of prehistoric, historic, and contemporary Hopi ceramics. Also on display will be photography, videotape, and text. Some of the oldest pieces have never been available to the public before.

West Hartford

The Science Center of Connecticut
950 Trout Brook Drive, West Hartford, Conn.
(203) 236-2961

The **Science Center of Connecticut** offers a range of exhibits and hands-on activities for the young and young-at-heart.

After Dark at the Science Center offers families the chance to play together. Whether it is solving a mystery or watching a show about dinosaurs (opening in February), the family can have a feeling of accomplishment through a cooperative effort.

The Science Center of Connecticut is sponsoring its first-ever International Robotics Contest. The goal is to build a robotic device that can move through a home, look for fire (a candle will be lit), and put it out. The model will be 8' x 8' with doors, rooms, and closets. The exact floor plan and official rules are available by writing to the Science Center. This contest is open to all, and the judging criteria will differ for different age and experience groups. The grand prize is $1,000. The judging takes place April 17, 1994.

The Garden of Hesperides is a mythological adventure highlighting the constellations of the spring and summer skies. This is a two-part program that tells of the titan Hercules as he attempts to recover the Three Golden Apples. A live presentation then follows that explains the origin of the story and points out the stars visible in the sky that evening that tell the story. The fall and winter sequel to this story begins in February of 1994.

A selection of rare Hopi ceramic pottery, such as this one illustrated, was on view through early 1994 at Yale's Peabody Museum.

DISTRICT OF COLUMBIA (WASHINGTON)

The **National Museum of Natural History** is one of the oldest museums in the Smithsonian Institution's complex of 16 museums and galleries. It is an 82-year-old green-domed building in Washington, D.C., and it draws 6 million visitors a year. Four traveling exhibits are planned for 1994:

- *Earthsense*, through July 24
- *Chiefly Feasts: The Enduring Kwakiutl Potlatch*, through March 6
- *Painting Wondrous Wings*, through October 1
- *Spiders*, from June 17, 1994 through January 2, 1995

Permanent exhibits cover nearly every subject imaginable. A partial listing of the exhibitions are: minerals and gems; dinosaurs and other fossil animals and plants; live insect zoo; living marine ecosystems; life in the ancient seas; Ice Age mammals and the emergence of humans; origins and traditions of Western culture; cultures of the native peoples of the Americas, the Pacific region and Asia; Earth, lunar, and meteoritic geology; reptiles and amphibians; mammals and birds of the world; and comparative skeletal structure.

Along with the permanent exhibits, the museum provides free programs for a wide audience. A free film and lecture series is offered each week and information can be mailed to interested parties with highlighting free programs and events for the whole museum. Exhibits pioneered by the Office of Education include: the Discovery Room, a touchable exhibits room for all, the "Living Marine Ecosystems" exhibition, and the Naturalist Center, designed to provide a quiet place for use by amateur naturalists of specimens, artifacts, and reference books.

The museum also houses one of the world's largest collections of our natural history heritage. The collections are divided into eight major research and curatorial units. They are the departments of anthropology, botany, entomology, invertebrate zoology, mineral sciences, paleobiology and vertebrate zoology, and the Laboratory of Molecular Systematics.

FLORIDA

The Museum of Science and History
1025 Museum Circle, Jacksonville, Fla. (904) 396-7062

The **Museum of Science and History** has gone "buggy" with its *Backyard Monsters* exhibit. Giant robotic insects—up to 96 times normal size—show visitors their environment and demonstrate the importance of their little corner of the world. "This is a world where insects tower over humans and blades of grass are the size of trees. While giant animatronic bugs and hands-on displays will amaze and entertain our visitors, *Backyard Monsters* is an educational exhibit, one that dramatically demonstrates the importance of insects in our lives," said Margo Dundon, executive director of the museum.

The Museum of Science and History in Jacksonville, Fla., has been host to the Backyard Monsters *exhibit, with hands-on activities such as "Assemble an Ant" and "Bug's Eye View," a close-up look through a bug's multilensed eyes.*

Praying mantis, scorpion, black widow spider, unicorn and carpenter ants are set in 12'-tall grass. Each monster is capable of 20 different movements from darting eyes, waving antennae, moving back and forth and creeping legs. There also is a dragon fly with a 10' foot wingspan that stands guard over the backyard.

"Each robotic insect has been re-created from a living specimen so that lifelike colors and movements could be captured," said Gene Bullard, founder of Creative Presentations, Inc., the company responsible for the creation of the "monsters."

There are also 14 hands-on play areas for children. They all are educational in concept. Bugs Eye View allows visitors to see the world through the complex eyes of insects. The Better to Eat You With shows how insects chew plants and drink nectar and blood. More than 1,000 insects and arachnids are on display. And the mating dance of the scorpion can be viewed along with the world's largest beetle.

Backyard Monsters opened in late 1993 and will close in early 1994.

Other exhibits at the Museum of Science and History are as follows:

- *Fort Mose: Colonial America's Black Fortress of Freedom* will focus on the African-Americans' life in colonial Spanish Florida from the time of Chris-

More than 1,000 exotic insects and arachnids from around the world, displayed in lifelike dioramas and detailed collections, are part of the Jacksonville museum's exhibit. Displays include beetles, butterflies and moths, arachnids, insect camouflage, and fossil insects.

topher Columbus to the American Revolution. This exhibit ends in early 1994.

- An exhibit called *Bats* is considered to be one of the best ever produced on the subject of bats. Their ecological importance is highlighted in their important task of insect control and reforestation. This exhibit ends in early 1994.

- *Americans With Disabilities* is a traveling exhibit that highlights the accomplishments of Americans with disabilities. The museum's pledge to make it accessible to all is becoming a reality with the installation of a Hearing Assistive System for the hearing impaired and Braille star domes for the visually impaired in the Planetarium. This exhibit closes in the Spring of 1994.

- *The Good, The Bad, and The Cuddly* exhibit deals with animals and the attitudes of people toward them. This will be open April–August 1994.

GEORGIA

Fernbank Museum of Natural History
767 Clifton Road NE, Atlanta, Ga. (404) 378-0127

Fernbank Science Center
156 Heaton Park Drive NE, Atlanta, Ga. (404) 378-4311

The **Fernbank Museum of Natural History** and **Fernbank Science Center** offer a wealth of opportunities to explore the world of science. Four traveling exhibits will be at the Fernbank Museum of Natural History in 1994. They are:

- *Happy Birthday, Smokey!*—February 4–March 14, 1994. This exhibit honors the 50th birthday of Smokey Bear. It was organized and designed by Fernbank and will travel nationally after its premiere in Atlanta. The exhibition includes a retrospective of Smokey's successful forest fire prevention campaigns, including early art and video; a look at forests and who lives in them, and the changing ideas on fire in the forest, including the fire cycle and managed fire.

- *The Great Southwest/Two Eagles/Dos Aguilas*— April 1–May 15, 1994. This Smithsonian Institution exhibit examines the unique wildlife and habitats found along the boundary between the United States and Mexico, featuring the land-

The Fernbank Museum of Natural History in Atlanta features a lively Dinosaur Hall, *with an 800-sq.-ft. Cretaceous mural behind re-creations of* Hadrosaurus, Talasaurus, *and* Albertasaurs.

scape, plants, and animals of the Rio Grande River. Special attention will be paid to spiders, scorpions, and snakes, and the Rio Grande's abundant birds.

- *Mind Games*—May 27–August 31. This is a collection of interactive displays, including a discovery space for kids, designed to explain the nature of perception, memory, language, stress, and other concepts of psychology and behavior.
- *Whales: Giants of the Deep*—October 8, 1994–January 8, 1995. This robotic whale exhibition features five lifesize whales, including a 32-ft. sperm whale, a 22-ft. orca, and a 21-ft. narwhal. This exhibit, developed by the **Pacific Science Center,** will also be at the **Denver Museum of Natural History.** *(See page 183.)*

The Museum of Natural History has an active volunteer program and encourages people to work as volunteers. The museum also has a Friends of Fernbank Travel Program, with trips planned to such places as the Gallapagos Islands, Portugal and Spain, Belize, and Costa Rica.

The Fernbank Science Center has the following exhibits and shows planned for 1994:

- *Other Moons*—March 1–June 5, 1994—tells of the other natural objects floating in space besides the planets.

- *The Hubble Space Telescope*—June 7–September 2, 1994. This exhibit gives the visitor a first-hand look at what the Hubble has revealed to scientists through the pictures of space that have been sent back to Earth.

Special seasonal programs are available year round in the Fernbank Planetarium at the science center.

HAWAII

University of Hawaii at Manoa—Harold L. Lyon Arboretum
3860 Manoa Road, Honolulu, Hawaii (808) 988-7378

At **Harold L. Lyon Arboretum,** visitors are invited to study and enjoy botanical and environmental splendors. The grounds are covered with assorted tropical plants. Classes and workshops are run year-round, offering the general public a hands-on experience with nature. Classes include Caring for Endangered Plants; Bonsai; Herb Gardens; and Medicinal Herbs.

Waikiki Aquarium
2777 Kalakaua Avenue, Honolulu, Hawaii (808) 923-9741

Waikiki Aquarium, closed for renovations in 1992, was scheduled to reopen January 15, 1994. Four main exhibit galleries will show marine life in Hawaii and the tropical Pacific. They are:

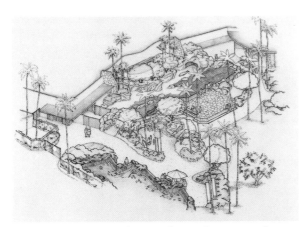

A rendering shows the new home for two endangered Hawaiian monk seals at the Waikiki
Aquarium in Honolulu, Hawaii. It is a re-creation
of the monk seal's rocky primary habitat in the
northwest Hawaiian Islands.

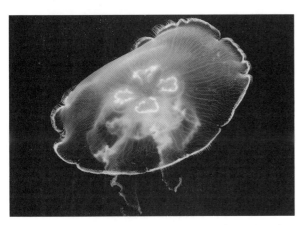

The Waikiki Aquarium's SeaVisions Theater and
Jellyfish Exhibit was to reopen in January 1994.
The moon jellyfish here is of the Aurelia aurita
species.

- Gallery I: *South Pacific Marine Communities*
- Gallery II: *Hawaiian Marine Communities*. This
  will include an interactive wall with a floor-to-
  ceiling map of the Pacific. Here the evolutionary
  journey of Hawaii's marine life can be tracked.
- Gallery III: *Diversity and Adaptations*. Unique
  and realistic marine displays
- Gallery IV: *Fisheries and Conservation*. State-of-
  the-art exhibits will explore this topic.

The aquarium also will offer outdoor exhibits.
Northwest Hawaiian Islands Monk Seal Habitat is a

Waikiki Aquarium's SeaVisions Director Bruce
Carlson weighs the oldest giant clam in the United
States. Weighing in at 121 pounds, the clam,
Tridacna gigas, *is by far the largest in the nation.
The clam is 16 years old and has been a resident of
the aquarium since 1982. He could live another 50
years and reach a maximum weight of 600 pounds.*

new exhibit. It is a representation of the primary
natural habitat of the monk seal, which is an endangered animal in the Northwestern Hawaiian Islands.
This endangered marine mammal lives only in Hawaii. Its population today numbers less than 2,000,
living and breeding on the coral shoals and atolls of
the Northwestern islands. These seals sleep during
the day and hunt for their food in the evening,

thereby conserving their energy. Dining on a diet of fish, octopus, and lobster they dive to depths of as much as 400 feet to find their dinner. Also featured will be the *Edge of the Reef* and *Mahimahi Hatchery* exhibits and the *Hawaiian Coastal Gardens*.

Waikiki Aquarium also has other exhibits, events, and programs planned.

The SeaVisions Theater will show two films on jellyfish to accompany an exhibit on jellyfish.

Hunter of the Reef, a shark and reef predator exhibit, will have a 5-ft. bubble to allow visitors an "inside" look at the exhibit. The reef houses algae, corals, invertebrates, and small fish. A reef is a hunting ground for the sharks. The sharks keep the food web balanced.

The largest and oldest clam in the nation is on display at the Waikiki Aquarium. The clam recently celebrated its 16th birthday. It stands 18 inches high and weighs 121 pounds. This clam, species *Tridacna gigas*, is from the Micronesian Mariculture Demonstration Center in the Republic of Palau. It was obtained in 1982. It is one of seven species of giant clams known to live in the coral reefs. They have been known to grow to a length of 3 feet and weigh as much as 660 pounds.

The Blue-Water Marine Lab Program is a seagoing learning experience designed for middle- and high-school students. Through hands-on activities students explore the sea, learning about the relation-

ship between their island home and the ocean that surrounds it. BML offers four programs:

- Semester Cruise Program (SCP). These are three-hour school class cruises. The students conduct lab tests on plankton, sediments, sea-floor life, seawater studies, and coastal navigation.

- Summer Ocean Studies Program. This is a six-week program for high school students only. There is an instructional classroom program with guest speakers. The subjects include ocean science, marine affairs, navigation, seamanship, teaching techniques, water safety, and first aid. Field trips are also incorporated into the program. Successful completion of the course earns the student Department of Education credit and an invitation to attend the cruise instructor program.

- Cruise Instructor Program. Students in this program work as instructors. The cruise instructors are responsible for not only the equipment and ship maintenance and teaching the students but also their regular studies that they are missing while away on the cruise. Students learn more in the field of marine science and add another credit in science for a school year's participation.

- Cruise Leader Program. Three or four college students in the University of Hawaii system are selected to serve as leaders. They learn skills in oceanographic research methods, seamanship, teaching, management, and program administration.

ILLINOIS

Museum of Science and Industry
57th Street and Lake Shore Drive, Chicago, Ill. (312) 684-1414

The **Museum of Science and Industry** in Chicago recently opened a new permanent exhibit called *Imaging: The Tools of Science*. It is a 7,000-square-foot exhibit that allows the visitor to examine and test the most advanced innovations in computer imaging. On entering the exhibit, the visitor is photographed from overhead and the image is transformed onto a video screen. Warm and cool spots on the visitor's body are noted. The visitor can bring his or her facial image up on a computer and see the distortions through color enhancement as it dissolves, changes colors, and becomes three-dimensional.

A young boy interacts with "Face Net," part of the Imaging: The Tools of Science *exhibit at the Chicago Museum of Science and Industry.*

Radiant sun beams, slow-moving clouds and towering mountains are part of the "Virtual Reality" experience at the Chicago Museum of Science and Industry.

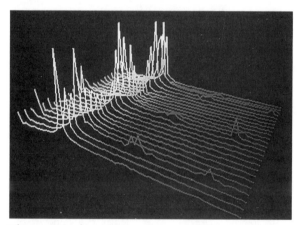

The sound of a voice is captured and numerically manipulated into a three-dimensional graphic terrain in "Seeing Sound," part of Imaging: The Tools of Science.

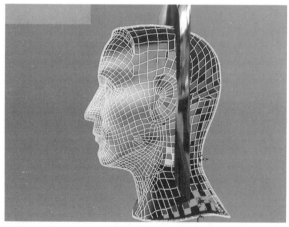

A three-dimensional facial image is created in "Metamorface," part of Imaging: The Tools of Science.

"This interactive exhibit is the only one of its kind in the world. Computer imaging allows you a peek into the work of the future as well as gain a fundamental understanding of practical applications in today's medical, science, investigative, climatology, and entertainment fields," said James S. Kahn, Museum president and chief executive officer. The exhibit has four areas:

- *Planet Sphere* takes the visitors above Earth to see environmental, weather, and seasonal changes, or to visit other planets.
- *Metamorface* allows visitors to create facial distortions using 3-D modeling and texture-mapping.
- *Be a Brain Surgeon* allows visitors to try radio surgery through 3-D imaging.
- *The Mystery Lab* challenges the visitor to solve mysteries by applying imaging to forensic science. The crime can be solved with the use of magnetic resonance imaging, fingerprint enhancement, microscopy, and face aging. This is a favorite of 10- to 15-year-olds.

An 8,000-square-foot permanent exhibit called *Communications*, that has been three years in the making, is now open. This exhibit shows the technological wonders that have changed the world since the days of Alexander Graham Bell. There are several components to this exhibit:

- *Dissolving Distances* highlights the communication pioneers such as Bell, Morse, and Marconi.
- *Making Connections* allows the visitor to learn about telecommunication highways from copper cables to fiber optics.
- *Going Digital* explores digital technology.
- *Home Connections* tells of futuristic technologies.
- *Superschool* shows the educational uses of telecommunications.
- *Timeline* shows the history of communication from pictographs to satellites.
- *The Electromagnetic Spectrum* graphically presents the frequency spectrum.
- *The World, Live! Theater* shows the world of today via satellites and cable.
- *Worldspeak* is the same greeting in 24 languages.

The newest permanent exhibit at Chicago's Museum of Science and Industry is a Boeing 727 airplane. The airplane will be the centerpiece of the Take Flight *exhibit opening in Fall 1994.* Take Flight *will provide scientific explanations of aerodynamic principles, air traffic control, radar, engine and wing construction, and weather.*

- *The Whispering Gallery,* a long-time favorite of visitors to the museum, is part of the communications exhibit.

Navy exhibit is scheduled to open in the summer of 1994. It will demonstrate how members of the U.S. Navy use modern science and technology in their everyday operation. The exhibit will include a simulated ride on an aircraft carrier.

Take Flight exhibit will open in the Fall of 1994. It is a chance to experience the world of flight with hands-on activities. A visitor will be able to learn about aerodynamic principles, air traffic control, radar, engine and wing construction, ticketing, and weather. The plane was donated by United Airlines. This will be a permanent exhibit.

MARYLAND

National Aquarium in Baltimore
Pier 3. 501 E. Pratt St., Baltimore, Md.
Information: (410) 576-3800; Out-of State Tickets:
(800) 551-SEAT

The **National Aquarium in Baltimore** is a uniquely designed aquarium. From the main entrance, the visitor is directed through a set path that assures viewing each and every exhibit, spending as much or as little time as desired along the way.

Connected by a footbridge to the aquarium is the Marine Mammal Pavilion. This new attraction boasts a variety of activities including a state-of-the-art dolphin habitat, hands-on exhibits, and changing marine and environmental programs. The major exhibits at the Marine Mammal Pavilion are:

- *The Dolphin Habitat.* Surrounding the pool are the world's largest acrylic windows that provide visitors with unprecedented underwater viewing of the marine mammals. There are several daily dolphin shows entitled "Dolphin Discoveries: Life Beneath the Waves."

- *Scylla* is a life-size replica of a humpback whale. Visitors can discover the most intricate details of this mammal through a series of specially designed viewscopes located around the perimeter of the second level. Scylla spans two levels of the pavilion.

- *Educational Arcade* contains a series of custom-designed hands-on exhibits where the visitor can learn about the behavior and characteristics of marine mammals.

- *Discovery Room* is a collection of marine artifacts from shark's teeth to baleen. The Resource Center is designed as an aquatic learning center for the aquarium's school visitors.

- *Animal Care and Research Complex* is an animal care center with a surgical facility, clinical/diagnostic laboratory, two-room research center, and rehabilitation pool. The complex enables staff to investigate, diagnose, and treat diseases of aquatic animals in and out of the wild.

National Aquarium in Baltimore houses 7,000 animals from around the world.

Other major exhibits include:

- *Seal Pool*—home to harbor and gray seals
- *Wings in the Water*—home of the largest ray collection in the country
- *Maryland: Mountains to the Sea*—depicting four Maryland water habitats.
- *Surviving through Adaptations Gallery*—depicting how adaptations have helped sea life survive
- *North Atlantic to Pacific Gallery*—exploring America's coasts
- *South American Rain Forest*—with tropical birds, piranhas, and giant plants.

Two new exhibits are to open in 1994.

Exploration Station is a one-of-a-kind hi-tech, hands-on exhibit. This innovative exhibit gives visitors an intimate view of the animals' lifestyles and habitats. Exhibits worth noting at the Exploration Station are:

- *Swim-Along*—The hologramlike illusion, created by Rufus Seder, will mystify visitors. Seals, otters, manatees, and other marine mammals swim and frolic, keeping pace with those strolling by. As the spectators stop and start, so do the animals.
- *Sounds From the Sea Theater*—Theatergoers experience, by feeling and hearing, underwater sounds from a whale's perspective.
- *A Whale's Eye View*—Viewers will discover in dramatic fashion why whales are targets for large ships. After viewing a picture of a ship on the ocean, visitors don "whale-vision" binoculars. The ship disappears. Visitors gain a new understanding of why whales are threatened.
- *Meals on the Move*—Visitors are jolted with the reality of the food chain in action. Predators who hunt to live, as well as vegetarian manatees chomping on seaweed, are among the high-impact, up-close feeding scenes portrayed. Visitors will witness natural feeding rituals that have rarely been observed by humans.
- *Can You Catch It?*—A fun exhibit of trying to catch your prey. Up-to-the-minute technology contributes to this whimsical attraction.

ImaginOcean is the aquarium's newest exhibit. It reveals a vast world of animated undersea creatures.

From a frolicking whale and her calf to a school of shimmering damsel fish, ImaginOcean's images will be created through a multi-media system that includes the most elaborate laser technology ever employed for entertainment purposes. "Fantasea" world will take visitors from the edge of the rain forest to the depths of the sea by creating a complex underwater environment teeming with fish and other sea creatures. This exhibit is scheduled to close in the Spring 1995.

MASSACHUSETTS

New England Science Center
222 Harrington Way, Worcester, Mass. (508) 791-9211

New England Science Center has a permanent exhibit entitled *Abiding Locally, Thinking Globally*. It opened October 18, 1993, and explores energy, how humans have harnessed it, and the ramifications of that on Earth.

The exhibit covers 3,000 square feet and takes a nontraditional approach that all life is energy, the exhibit shows a relationship between the visitor's bodily energy and the energy of the universe.

Exhibits include a 14' foot tower with living plants that represent Earth energy, the atmosphere, carbon

This image was created from 400 billion bytes of computer data and is part of the Abiding Locally, Thinking Globally *exhibit at the New England Science Center in Worcester, Mass.*

Abiding Locally, Thinking Globally explores the planetary forces that comprise energy, human control of these forces and the future consequences of energy consumption.

sources, deforestation, and global change. Another part includes a video microscope through which visitors can see microorganisms and the energy on that level. Here, the story of how ferns are changed into coal is explained.

Two dioramas are included. One is of a Northern forest in which wood turtles live; the other is of a desert with live lizards. A computer laser kiosk shows environmental issues on world maps with emphasis on fuel resources, ozone problems, toxins, pollution, and deforestation. Executive director Laura H. Myers said that, "*Abiding Locally, Thinking Globally* provides valuable information on a subject that is vital to the survival of our planet. The material is presented in upbeat and interactive ways that allow each visitor to access the amount of information and level of sophistication they choose. While a young child may play with our wave tank, a concerned adult will access data through one of the many interactive computers."

MICHIGAN

Cranbrook Institute of Science
1221 N. Woodward Ave., Bloomfield Hills, Mich.
(313) 645-3230

The **Cranbrook Institute of Science** will open *Sport* on June 11, 1994. It will run through Labor Day weekend. Not only is this exhibit hands-on, it is

body-on too, and it has been designed to appeal to all members of a family. This exhibit is from **Ontario Science Center** in Canada, which is loaning it to other science centers.

The exhibit covers 10,000 square feet and features dozens of hands-on and body-on athletics exhibits and activities. There is a balance beam; a bob-sledding video (with the visitor in the driver's seat) that shows why aerodynamics is so important; the baseball pitch exhibit that measures the speed and accuracy of a thrown pitch; and an exhibit on drugs in sports—what steroids are and what they can do to a body.

Land Like a Cat shows what parachutists and gymnasts know about the right and wrong way to land and the force exerted on the body during a landing. *Materials in Action* lets the visitor see what really makes up a golf ball or basketball and what relation there is between a hockey goalie today and a medieval knight of yesteryear. *A Rock Climbing, Rotating Arena* creates a real illusion, then a display discusses the physics of it all.

Other elements of the exhibit include: *Sports Injuries*, watch a knee surgery operation in progress; *Watch Yourself Walk*—it's not as easy as it looks; and *Wheelchair Race*, which lets the visitor learn the workings of a wheelchair that is used for racing and shows a new design for a prosthetic running leg. This exhibit also has a ball that can be used by the blind

The Sport *exhibit opens in June 1994 at Cranbrook Institute of Science in Bloomfield Hills, Mich.*

In the Sport *exhibit at Crambrook is a 10cm-wide competition balance beam, on which visitors can try the sport now practised primarily by young women but which originated as a military exercise.*

in a game. A *Women in Sports* display takes a look through history at famous female athletes and what they endured to make it in a world of male-oriented sports. *You Be the Judge* allows a visitor to judge an athletic performance and see how difficult it is. *Freeze-game Replay* will show what is and is not important in each athlete's routine.

MINNESOTA

Science Museum of Minnesota
30 E. 10th St., St. Paul, Minn. (612) 221-9488

Science Museum of Minnesota has a continual parade of traveling exhibits. In 1993, the museum hosted *Science in Toyland* and *Tropical Rainforests: A Disappearing Treasure.*

Whodunnit? The Science of Solving Crime runs through early 1994 and is a hands-on activity that gives visitors a chance to solve a crime through the use of crime stations.

Green Street opened in late 1993 and is a permanent exhibit about energy, water, air, solid waste, and urban ecology.

NEW JERSEY

Jersey City

Liberty Science Center in Liberty State Park
251 Phillips St., Jersey City, N.J. (201) 200-1000

Liberty Science Center (LSC) is the country's newest hands-on science center. Located in Liberty State Park, where visitors can view the Statue of Liberty, Ellis Island, and the skyline of New York City, LSC houses a 170-ft. observation tower and an 11-ton geodesic dome, which houses the Omni Theater. This is the world's largest OMNIMAX theater. It has an eight-story screen and seating for 400 visitors.

"Science equals fun" is the motto of LSC. One of the permanent exhibits, for example, is "Bug Lady," who casually walks through the exhibits carrying her "bug du jour" for all to see and pet. Sometimes it's a giant millipede—sometimes a tarantula. The other permanent exhibits are broken into three categories: environment, health, and invention.

"We want to provide activities that enable the guest to observe, investigate, question, share with others, and wonder about the world around them," said Arlene Jangaard, manager of the exhibit floor programs. There are five areas in the environment exhibits area. They are the Estuary, the MicroZoo, the Interactive Theater, the Atmosphere, and the Green Room (the discovery room).

"Our overall goal is to create a sense of celebration and wonder about what makes us human," said Janice Walker, manager of training and development. In the health exhibits there are five exhibit areas: Perception, which houses a 100-ft-long Touch Tunnel that must be crawled through in pitch-blackness with only the sense of touch as a guide; the Heart, Bodies in Motion; Choices, which deals with health issues; and the Living Room (the discovery room).

"The goal of these exhibits is to explore the process of invention—not just as an end product, but as a vital form of problem-solving and creativity," said Max Cameron, Manager of Design and Production. There are five focused areas in the invention exhibits. They are Buildings and Bridges, with the Hoberman Sphere, the first ever in a museum; Machines and Motion; Light and Optics; Sound and Music, Media; and the Workshop (the discovery room).

Stone Harbor

Wetlands Institute
1075 Stone Harbor Blvd., Stone Harbor, N.J. (609) 368-1211

The **Wetlands Institute,** dedicated to scientific research and public education concerning intertidal salt marshes and other coastal systems, is open year-

Children explore the challenge of sports-chair racing in the Bodies in Motion area at Liberty Science Center.

Children experiment with the principles of air pressure in the Atmosphere area of Liberty Science Center.

Liberty Science Center, in New Jersey, just across the river from New York City, is the nation's newest hands-on science center. It is located in Liberty State Park, directly across from lower Manhattan and within view of the Statue of Liberty. Note the World Trade Center towers in the background.

round. It features the *Secrets of the Saltmarsh*, an education center that houses a saltwater aquarium and shows life in the marsh; an observation tower for a panoramic view of the wetlands; and the Saltmarsh Trail for a first-hand look at the plants and animals that inhabit the marsh. Field trips are available for school-age children from pre-kindergarten through high school and cover basic marsh walks through the ecology of the wetlands and the barrier islands.

NEW MEXICO

Space Center
Alamagordo, N.M. (505) 437-2840

The **Space Center** runs a Shuttle Camp each summer. It teaches space sciences, aerodynamics, astronomy, and physics. The hands-on approach to learning is used with the students preparing and eating space food, building and launching model rockets, and going through underwater weightlessness training.

Programs are run throughout the year that involve the youth of the area in the world of science. There are rocket launches on Father's Day; night sky programs; Spaceweek, a celebration of science in space; hosts to the International Space Hall of Fame, with the "One Planet, One People" celebration day in its honor; Soapbox-type Spacerace; teacher workshops to instruct the teachers as to how they can use art to teach science and help them find unusual, yet easy-to-acquire materials for their projects; an egg-dropping contest called Humpty Dumpty's Revenge; and a science-fiction short-story writing contest.

NEW YORK

Buffalo

Buffalo Society of Natural Sciences
1020 Humboldt Parkway, Buffalo, N.Y. (716) 896-5200

The **Buffalo Society of Natural Sciences** has planned two travel tours for the students of Buffalo. During the first week in April 1994, there will be a Florida Outback Safari, where students interested in the coastal environment can see it first-hand. Students will be airboating in the Everglades and participating in an invertebrate study at the Loxahatchee Environmental Institute. Snorkeling, and the study of coral reefs also are part of the agenda. The students will

meet with a paleontologist at Bone Valley to go on a fossil hunt and river study.

During the summer of 1994, the students will be able to attend In-On-And-About Water: The San Juan River Ecosystem. They will be able to discover the cultural impacts and natural history of water. Using the San Juan River, they will look at the geology, biology, history, ethics. and impacts of water use and misuse by residents of the area.

Flushing Meadows Corona Park, Queens

New York Hall of Science
47-01 111th Street, Flushing Meadows Corona Park, Queens, N.Y. (718) 699-0005

The **New York Hall of Science** featured *What about Aids?* from October 1993 to January 1994. This exhibit, using hands-on displays, interactive videos, and personal stories of people with AIDS, sought to educate the public on the science of AIDS. The center especially hopes to reach the 10- to 17-year-olds. "Since a cure for AIDS is still not available, prevention is the only way we know to stop the spread of AIDS. Education is the only vaccine," said Alan J. Friedman, director of the Hall of Science.

Three topics were explored in the exhibit. They were:

"What is HIV and AIDS?" Through models, graphs, photos, and a special interactive computer, the concepts of virology and immunology were explored.

"Protect Yourself" explained how HIV is transmitted and methods of protection.

"What Can We Do About It?" examined the search for a cure and sought suggestions from individuals on how to stop the spread of AIDS.

This is a traveling exhibit. It also was scheduled to be viewed in Philadelphia, Pa., at the **Franklin Institute Science Museum** and in Richmond, Va., at the **Science Museum of Virginia.**

Manhattan

American Museum of Natural History
Central Park West at 79th St., New York, N.Y.
(212) 769-5100

The **American Museum of Natural History**, in its newest permanent exhibit, the *Hall of Human Biology and Evolution*, has given humans a stunning,

The American Museum of Natural History in New York features four lifesize dioramas in its newest permanent exhibit, the Hall of Human Biology and Evolution. In this setting, two members of the Australopithecus afarensis species are depicted as they may have left footprints in Laetoli, Tanzania some 3.5 million years ago. The species is best known for the skeleton called "Lucy," discovered in 1974 by Donald Johanson. The Beatles' song "Lucy in the Sky with Diamonds" was the inspiration for the name.

This American Museum of Natural History diorama shows a pair of Homo ergaster as they may have appeared about 1.6 million years ago. They are butchering a carcass while a vulture and jackal try to steal the kill.

A glacial period about 50,000 years ago is depicted in this diorama at the American Museum of Natural History. The Neanderthal family prepares animal hides and makes tools at a site in Le Moustier, France.

Huts constructed from mammoth bones and tusks are considered the earliest example of architecture. In this scene at the American Museum of Natural History, a Cro-Magnon residence is shown in what today would be the Ukraine.

spectacular look at themselves. Five years of painstaking research and exacting craftwork came to life in April 1993 when the $6.7 million Hall opened to the public. The Hall is organized into three sections: biology and anatomy, human evolution, and human creativity. Dynamic, lifelike dioramas and state-of-the-art technology combine to give visitors a three-dimensional view of how humans evolved, how humans are composed biologically today, and how creativity sets humans apart from other species.

A hologram of a DNA double helix greets visitors at the entrance to the Hall, and just around the corner is a life-size hologram of a modern-day woman. Visitors view the hologram from different angles to see different systems—circulatory, nervous, skeletal—and organs of the body. Then, a high-speed video tour of the human body, through computer animation, takes viewers on an exploration of the structures of the eye, lung, kidney, muscles, bones, heart, brain, digestive tract, and ear.

Also part of the exhibit is Biosystems, a 30-seat theater with surround-sound and the latest video technology. The theater serves as a high-tech classroom, capable of interactive presentations.

The Hall does not rely on fossils to tell the story of evolution; the dioramas display lively, life-size beings as they might have appeared in their own time and place. "The general public is not used to dealing with teeth and bones. They're used to dealing with flesh-and-blood individuals. We wanted to put some life into the past," said Ian Tattersall, chairman and curator of anthropology at the museum, in a May 1993 *Life* article entitled "Brought to Life." Tattersall also is author of a companion book to the exhibit, *The Human Odyssey: Four Million Years of Human Evolution.*

The first diorama takes visitors to a scene in Laetoli, Tanzania, where, it is believed, footprints from 3.5 million years ago are from upright walkers known as the species *Australopithecus afarensis.* The best-known skeleton from that era is named "Lucy."

Other dioramas show later species in their environments, from *Homo ergaster* on an African savanna 1.6 million years ago to Cro-Magnons in a glacial setting in the Ukraine 15,000 years ago.

The final section of the Hall has a ceiling replica of the 14,000-year-old decorated cave roof of Altamira in northern Spain, where researchers discovered evidence of a burst of human creativity. An Ice Age Art gallery explains the development of art and symbolism during the Upper Paleolithic, 34,000–10,000 years ago.

In the final section, visitors can go on their own anthropological digs through an interactive computer display or learn about new discoveries and theories in human evolution in the electronic newspaper.

PENNSYLVANIA

Academy of Natural Sciences
1900 Benjamin Franklin Parkway (located on Logan Circle)
Philadelphia, Pa. (215) 299-1000

The **Academy of Natural Sciences** will be presenting the major traveling exhibit called *Bears: Imagination and Reality*. Through displays and programs, the Bears exhibit explores the myths and realities of the North American grizzly and black bears. Not only will there be scientific information about the bears, but also human interest in the bears will be examined through art, mythology, folklore, literature, and history.

Using hands-on games and multimedia displays, visitors will see the history of peoples' love of bears from advertising vehicles to the lovable teddy bear. There will by an 8' x 9' teddy bear sofa in which the visitor may curl up to watch the many bear videos featuring Winnie the Pooh, Smokey the Bear, and parts of the horror movie "Grizzly." Naturally, visitors also will be serenaded by Elvis Presley singing, "I Want to be Your Teddy Bear."

The exhibit features 25 taxidermic specimens, real bear hides, teeth, and paws that the visitors can handle. A re-created black bear den complete with the mother bear and her cubs will be there for the viewing, and visitors can listen to recordings of stories about people/bear encounters.

Special programs are available for children throughout the bear exhibit. There will be comic puppet shows with bears, storytelling using unusual and traditional folk bear stories, a teddy bear fashion show, and a clinic where the children can bring their bears for a free checkup.

Bears: Imagination and Reality looks at the relationship between bears and humans and questions the habits of the humans that may lead to the extinction of the bears. They are threatened by poachers and settlement of humans in their territory. Only 1% of the grizzlies that once roamed the United States still exist today. There are more black bears but poachers are a serious threat to their survival. Dr. Christopher Servheen, a bear specialist with the U.S. Fish and Wildlife Service, said, "The fate of bears in many areas of the world will be decided in the next 10 or 20 years."

This exhibit runs from January 29, 1994 through May 8, 1994.

The Academy of Natural Sciences also houses many permanent exhibits and sponsors field trips for adults and children. Adult courses and workshops also are offered.

TENNESSEE

Knoxville

East Tennessee Discovery Center
516 N. Beaman St., Chilhowee Park, Knoxville, Tenn.
(615) 637-1121; 637-1192

The **East Tennessee Discovery Center** is a museum of science and world cultures. Permanent exhibits cover the interests of preschoolers through adult. A planetarium has a show every Saturday. Among the exhibits are: *Jurassic Plus*; *Tornadoes*; *The Cosmic Arcade* (a hands-on science gallery); *African-American Contributions to Science and Technology*; *Diversity Endangered*, which is a Smithsonian Institution environmental exhibit; *Rocks, Minerals, & Fossils*; *Kid Korner*, designed for ages 2–7; *Discoverer Spacecraft*; *Insect Zoo*; *Life Science Gallery*; and 11 aquariums.

Nashville

Cumberland Science Center
800 Ridley Blvd., Nashville, Tenn. (615) 862-5160

The **Cumberland Science Museum** is celebrating its 50th birthday in 1994, and some special exhibits have been planned.

Along with the permanent exhibits, several temporary, or touring exhibits are scheduled to be stopping in Nashville this year. *Mission to Mars* is scheduled to open in early February. It has an interest level of grades 3–12. *Mars Base I* is a high-tech science research base containing 33 crew stations. The visitor will be assigned to a specific station and given various duties. Crew stations are equipped with robotic arms, glove boxes, lasers, satellite transmitters, video equipment, and other equipment necessary to perform the tasks. Talking computers assist the visitor throughout the mission. The data the visitor collects is used to determine the possibility of establishing a colony on Mars. This exhibit closes May 8, 1994.

Backyard Monsters is an exhibit that also travels. Before coming to Nashville, this exhibit will be at the **Museum of Science and History** in Jacksonville, Fla. Turn to page 185 for a complete description and picture of what is in store for the people of Nashville. *Backyard Monsters* will be open in Nashville from May 21 to October 30, 1994.

There are several permanent exhibits at the Cumberland Science Center. The HCA Kinetic Coaster demonstrates the science of motion. Curiosity Corner, specifically designed for the children 10 and under, is a hands-on setting with a giant spider web on which to climb, an old country store with a cash register the children can operate, and a mock bedroom of a child from Japan. Health Hall lets the visitor see how his body works. The Science Game tests the visitor's observation skills in a scientifically unique way, and Deep Sea Adven-

Alexis Clarke and Jennings Taylor, 2nd graders at St. Ann's Catholic School, enjoy a sneak preview of Miller Medical Group's Breathe Easy, *a new permanent exhibit about lungs and respiration at the Cumberland Science Museum in Nashville, Tenn.*

ture, which features 12 experiment stations, each equipped with a Macintosh computer and hands-on activities, allows the visitor to conduct experiments at a simulated underwater research station. A Rainforest Adventure permanent exhibit is in the building phase and will open in 1994.

At Camp-In at the Cumberland, students from grades K through 12 can spend the night interacting with robotic dinosaurs, learning about the "living Fossils," or being a crew member on a simulated mission to the mysterious red planet of Mars. The adventures change every few months.

Oak Ridge

American Museum of Science and Energy
300 S. Tulane Ave., Oak Ridge, Tenn. (615) 576-3200

The **American Museum of Science and Energy** is one of the world's largest energy museums. It features more than 200 highly interactive exhibits, computer games, and audiovisuals that tell the most complete story on energy forms and their uses. Its educational encounters are reinforced with live demonstrations requiring audience participation.

The museum chronicles the birth of the nuclear age in its "Oak Ridge Story" room. An audiovisual called "The Secret City" presents the mission of the top-secret Manhattan Project, which created the 1940s city of Oak Ridge to help win World War II. The exhibit halls on the second level include the new "Exploration Station," where problem solving, light, sound, motors, and aerodynamics compete for visitor attention.

An array of traveling exhibits are featured at the museum. *Thunderstorm Detectives*, with special programs on Air Traffic Control and Basic Weather Forecasting will run through early 1994.

There is no admission charge. A quick call will alert prospective visitors as to the current temporary exhibit.

TEXAS

The Science Place
1318 Second Ave., in Fair Park, Dallas, Texas
(214) 428-5555

The Science Place has a continual menu of temporary exhibits ready for viewing throughout the year. *What Makes Music* shows the technology behind musical sounds, the universal language. This exhibit is on display through April 1994.

Jason 5: Expedition to Belize is a field trip, led by Dr. Bob Ballard, to Belize to explore the rain forest, ocean life, and conduct experiments about ecology, biology, and chemistry. This trip will take place in March.

World Cup Communications—This exhibit will help the visitor understand how the world seems to get smaller and smaller through the world of electronics. This exhibit is planned for the summer of 1994.

Science Circus, scheduled for the Summer and Fall of 1994, should bring fun back into learning. The visitor will be able to blow gigantic bubbles, float, and see themselves as a ghost. This exhibit has been touring the country and now is back home in Dallas.

Along with the permanent exhibits of Kids Place, The Cecil and Ida Green Medical and Health Sciences Exhibition, and The Erik Jonsson Physical Sciences Exhibition, the **Science Place** Planetarium, has an array of shows available throughout the year.

VERMONT

Montshire Museum of Science
Montshire Road, Norwich, Vt. (802) 649-2200

Montshire Museum of Science is a hands-on museum with changing exhibits on physical and natural sciences, ecology, and technology. It is located on 100

The Balance exhibit at Montshire uses this "one-legged" chair and other devices to show how balance can be achieved and how bodily "balance detectors" can be fooled.

A Science Soda Fountain is a hands-on activity at Montshire Museum of Science in Norwich, Vt.

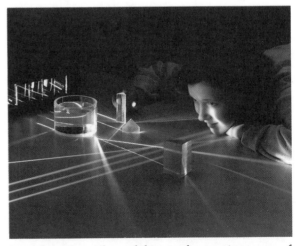

Montshire's Ray Play exhibit puts the amazing power of light in visitors' hands. Lenses and mirrors are used to illustrate how light can be reflected and refracted.

Discover Dolphins Off the Virginia Coast *is a popular attraction at the Virginia Marine Science Museum in Virginia Beach, Va.*

wooded acres across the Connecticut River from Hanover, N.H., and the Dartmouth College campus.

A special program is planned for Sunday, May 1, 1994, which will be the 23rd anniversary of Earth Day. The theme of Earth Day 1994 is Water. Participants in the planned treasure hunt will learn about water's importance to this planet and ways to use water wisely as part of their search for treasure.

The whole family will be able to explore the age-old wonders of flight alongside the latest advances in technology at the museum's celebration of Flight at Sky High Summer Day on July 10, 1994. World-class boomerang thrower Eric Darnell will give a demonstration with his polypropylene model that was praised by *Smithsonian* magazine for its innovative design. Hang-gliders and kites also will be there. Workshops of the day will include "Pizza Box Boomerangs" and "Pocket Kites." Pilots from Morning-side Flight Park in Claremont, N.H., and Post Mills Soaring Club in Post Mills, Vt., will be there to show off the latest in hang-gliders, parasails, and soarplanes.

There are permanent exhibits and trails, programs for families and teachers, and even Montshire Magic, an overnight camp-in for students aged 7–14. The campers will visit the Starlab, an inflatable planetarium; Kitchen Chemistry, where they will perform science experiments with a creative project to make and take home; an outdoor Night Walk on the museum's trails; and a Snake Visit to meet Stanley and Victoria, the boa constrictors of Montshire. The next day features a nature hunt.

VIRGINIA

Virginia Marine Science Museum
717 General Booth Blvd., Virginia Beach, Va.
(804) 437-4949

The **Virginia Marine Science Museum** is featuring a dolphin exhibit. By stepping into a model dolphin head, visitors will be able to hear how the dolphin echolocates (maneuvers by sound). A digital readout apparatus will then allow the visitor to test his own ability to use sound as a locating device. The exhibit is one of many hands-on activities in Discover Dolphins off the Virginia Coast. The exhibit explores dolphin behavior and biology and their survival off the coastline of Virginia.

The museum also sponsors "dolphin watch" boating trips to observe the dolphins in their natural habitat. A *Dial a Dolphin* exhibit allows visitors to make dolphin sounds and see them reproduced on a graph. A dolphin skeleton illustrates the similarities between the dolphin and human bodies. There is also a hands-on section for children.

The marine science museum has begun a whale-watching program. Humpback whales, an endangered species, were the victims of the whaling industry at the beginning of the 20th century. Not only are there whale-watching trips available through the museum, but there is a research project called Stranding Team to monitor the number of whales sighted in the area. Researchers are trying to find out why whale sightings seem to be on the rise off Virginia. Scientists believe that the whales like to migrate to the Chesapeake Bay area in the winter months, but they don't know if the same whales come back each year.

The scientists at VMSM have been cataloging each whale as sighted and taking pictures of them whenever possible. One whale, called Tattertail, was first seen in January 1992 in Virginia and again in 1993, had also been spotted in the Bay of Fundy and off the coast of New Jersey. Besides the land and water observations, the research team also has taken to the air to photograph the whales from above. They can cover a lot more territory that way and now have aerial shots from Virginia Beach to the Outer Banks of North Carolina.

WASHINGTON

Pacific Science Center
200 Second Ave. N., Seattle, Wash.
(206) 443-2001

The **Pacific Science Center** has a multitude of permanent and traveling exhibits that bring science and kids together. The U.S.'s first science center, it has more than 200 hands-on exhibits, an IMAX Theater, laser light shows and a planetarium. Some of the permanent exhibits include:

- *Body Works*, where visitors explore themselves.
- *Kids Works*, which offers hands-on fun making music in *Sound Sensations,* playing a TV reporter in *Video Vibrations,* spalashing in the bubble tub in *Just for Tots* and having a blast in the *Rocket Climb.*
- *Dinosaurs*, which is a journey back through time to meet five moving, roaring, robotic dinosaurs set in a semitropical Mesozoic environment.
- *Salt Water Tide Pool*, which answers questions such as: Do crabs swim? What do sea stars eat and how do they eat?
- *Water Works*, which shows a water arcade, a two-ton granite ball suspended on water, and a pelton wheel.
- *TechZone*, a permanent exhibit opening in March 1994, will explore virtual reality, robotics, and the latest in personal computers. Visitors can play virtual basketball, try tic-tac-toe against a 10-ft.-tall ball robot, and star in their own coffee commercial using multimedia software.

Two traveling exhibits are planned for 1994:

- *Lasers & Holograms: Discovering the Splendid Light*, February–May. Visitors can see how lasers and holograms are used in everyday life and create a laser show and see eye-to-eye with a huge hologram of a *Tyrannosaurus* skull.
- *Whales: Giants of the Deep*, June–September. This popular **Pacific Science Center** exhibit will be at the **Denver Museum of Natural History** before returning from its national tour. *(See page 183.)*

Besides the permanent and traveling exhibits, The **Pacific Science Center** also has special events that run only for a few days to a week. Some are:

- Couch Potato Science, April 8–10, 1994. Learn how potatoes generate electricity.
- Haunted Halloween, October 29–30, 1994.
- Model Railroad Show, November 25–27, 1994.
- Science Circus, December 26, 1994–January 1, 1995. A week of family-oriented science activities.

WISCONSIN

Discovery World Museum
818 W. Wisconsin Ave.,
Milwaukee, Wis.
(414) 765-9966

The **Discovery World Museum** has had the grand opening of its newest exhibit called *Fluid Power*, on the workings of hydraulics. Visitors can experience how fluid power can be fun and beneficial by oper- ating a working backhoe, controlling an elevator, or lifting a 100-pound anvil with one hand.

"Most people have never thought of air and water as tools. Yet some of the most powerful tools rely on these natural forces," said Discovery World Executive Director, William P. Chapman.

The exhibit explores how Blaise Pascal's Law became the foundation for modern hydraulics. The 300-year-old law states that pressure in a liquid acts equally in all directions.

Fig 121 @ 85%

At Discovery World in Milwaukee, Wis., students work at the Fluid Power *exhibit, featuring hydraulic-operated displays.*

PART THREE

TIMELINE

Science news never ends. Full chapters could not be devoted to all the important stories of 1993, so here is a compendium of more events and trends that shaped the course of the year.

January

Starting with a Bang—In a presentation at the American Astronomical Society meeting in Phoenix, Ariz., an official with the National Aeronautics and Space Administration (NASA) revealed four images captured by NASA's pioneering satellite Cosmic Background Explorer, or COBE. The images, NASA scientists maintained, confirmed a long-held theory that the universe began some 15 billion years ago with a Big Bang. The images, essentially maps, incorporated much data captured by COBE's far infrared absolute spectrophotometer, one of three instruments on the satellite that takes measurements far into space.

February

Left Is Fine—Scientists at the National Institutes of Health and Harvard University had some good news for left-handed people: A new study disputes an older study that claimed left-handers are at risk of dying 14 years sooner than right-handers In a six-year study of 3,774 people aged 65 or older, 32.2 percent of the deaths were right-handers and 33.8 percent were left-handers, "not a statistically significant difference."

March

Women's Health Initiative—The National Institutes of Health announced a $625 million program aimed at correcting a deficiency in research on women's health issues. Sixteen medical centers around the country were chosen to begin one of the largest clinical research projects ever in the United States. The project, scheduled to spread to possibly 19 more research centers, is officially part of the Women's Health Initiative, a program conceived in 1991 that combines several studies into one major effort. The research will deal with a broad range of health issues as they relate specifically to women, including low-fat diets, hormone therapy, and vitamin supplements.

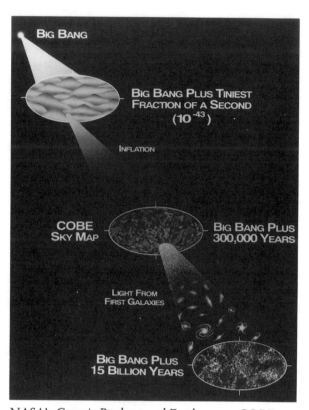

NASA's Cosmic Background Explorer, or COBE, has captured images that confirm the theory that the universe began with a Big Bang, the space agency says. In this artist's concept, crucial periods in the development of the universe are shown at three times. The first oval represents the universe just after the bang. The universe then rapidly expanded. The second oval, comprised of images captured by COBE over a year's time, represents the universe as it was at 300,000 years old. The bottom oval represents the universe today, 15 billion years old, full of galaxies and stars.

Spinning Star—Astronomers announced that they have discovered an ultra-dense neutron star—which leaves a guitar-shaped wake—flying faster than any star ever seen before in this galaxy. Astronomers James Cordes and Scott Lundren of Cornell University and Roger Romani of Stanford University, said the star may have originated in a supernova explosion a million years ago. It apparently is about 6,000 light-years away and is traveling about 600 miles a second.

April

Don't Drink the Water—Tiny waterborne parasites—cryptosporidia—caused a gigantic outbreak in illness in Milwaukee, Wis., contaminating the city's drinking-water supply and sickening at least 183,000 people. Discovered in 1907, the parasite has been linked to human disease only since 1976. Since then, it has been mentioned in a number of water-supply illnesses. The parasites, resistant to chlorination procedures standard in many public water systems, are only detected through a complicated, time-consuming water-sampling procedure that many public officials say is impractical. Meanwhile, a report issued by the General Accounting Office, an investigative agency that answers to the U.S. Congress, severely criticized the general conditions of the nation's water supplies overall. "Consumers may be getting their drinking water from systems that have not been inspected in 10 or more years or that may have significant undetected deficiencies," the report states.

No April Fool's Joke—Environmentalists praised manufacturers who in April stopped encasing compact discs in the familiar CD long boxes. The boxes, designed to help shield against shoplifting, added an estimated 25 million pounds of extra waste annually to landfills.

May

Mystery Illness—Medical researchers focused on the region of the United States known as Four Corners, where the states of Arizona, New Mexico, Colorado, and Utah converge at a common point. The researchers' goal was to find the cause of a mysterious disease that had quickly and surprisingly killed a number of otherwise healthy people. In the illness, victims suddenly contracted respiratory problems and died within hours. Within a few weeks, researchers had narrowed the source of the disease to a type of hantavirus, a virus carried by wild deer mice. Researchers surmised that victims contracted the disease by simply breathing in air that contained the dust of the deer mice feces. By November, the quick medical research and a public education campaign had reduced the death rate from the disease from 60% of its victims to 35% of its victims, and the disorder had become known as "Four Corners disease."

June

How're We Doing?—For the first time, a major scientific committee recommended a procedure for rating ongoing science projects so that the government can decide which fields are getting enough money—and which may be getting too much. A report from a committee of the National Academy of Sciences, the Institute of Medicine, and the National Academy of Engineers, concluded that American scientists can maintain their status at the forefront of science without a major increase in funding. Rather than ask for such increases, "we need to talk about doing a better job of spending what we have," said Dr. Phillip A. Griffiths, committee chairman. The committee proposed that panels, composed of U.S. scientists and some from other countries, be established to rate American scientists based on objective measures (how many in a particular field, the number of citations, level of funding compared to other countries, how many students entering a field, etc.). Based

Meanwhile, at the South Pole, scientists at the Center for Astrophysical Research in Antarctica (CARA), were studying the universe from the ground up. Researchers announced some of their findings in June: Using two specially designed radio telescopes, they detected small temperature fluctuations in microwave radiation left over from just 1 million years after the Big Bang. The fluctuations, the researchers say, appear to explain how some parts of the universe started out denser than other parts. In this photo, graduate student Hien Nguyen stands near one of CARA's 1-meter telescopes, shielded by a structure that protects it from the sun's radiation and blowing snow.

on the ratings, the government may see a need to shift resources from one field to another so that the country's competitive edge remains in the desired fields. "What is new about this is that previously we have not thought through the question: how much science do we need?" Dr. Griffiths said.

July

Find of the (16th) Century—Archaeologists excavating a site in St. Augustine, Fla., discovered evidence they say confirms the location of the first permanent European settlement in what became the United States. Unearthed were part of a moat and other artifacts that appear to be connected with a fort built in 1565 by Spanish explorer Pedro Menendez de Aviles, who along with 1,500 soldiers founded St. Augustine long before the English landed at Jamestown (1607) in Virginia and the Pilgrims landed at Plymouth Rock (1620) in Massachusetts. The site of the fort, which may not be the only one in the area, is near the Castillo de San Marcos, a 17th-century Spanish fort that still stands today as a national monument. "We feel confident that we have now finally located the original settlement and associated fort complex of St. Augustine," said Kathleen Deagan, an archaeologist and excavation director, in an article published in the July 27 *New York Times*. Researchers had been searching for the site for more than 60 years.

What Did that Whale Say?—One peace dividend from the collapse of the former Soviet Union and the end of the Cold War has been a little spare time for the U.S. Navy's submarines. That time, beginning in November 1992, has been consumed in part by research—eavesdropping, some say—on whales in their natural environments below the ocean surface. "The results have been nothing short of incredible," wrote Christopher W. Clark, a whale researcher and director of the Cornell University Bioacoustics Research Program, in a report to the Animal Behavior Society. "We recorded more than 35,000 whale detections during the first three months of the study. We're finding that blue and finback whales are vocally active throughout the year—not just in the winter and spring—and that their infrasonic sounds are detectable over hundreds of miles." The subma-

rines use "passive" underwater microphones that listen but produce no sound of their own. Navy analysts have mastered the technique to the point of being able to identify different whale species and regional differences in whale vocalizations. They've also been able to pick up voices of individual whales, such as one known as Old Blue.

August

Mars Mission Mum—What was to have been the country's first mission to Mars in 17 years dissipated when National Aeronautics and Space Administration controllers lost contact with the spacecraft *Mars Observer*. The craft was intended to extract data from the planet's surface for a full Martian year (about two years on Earth). The *Observer* was launched from Cape Canaveral in September 1992.

Christopher W. Clark, a whale researcher and director of the Cornell University Bioacoustics Research Program, is working with the U.S. Navy to conduct underwater sound research on whales.

NASA's goal was for the craft to be an interim explorer between the first reconnaissance mission 17 years ago and a possible human trip to Mars next century.

Oldest of Clues—University of Nebraska-Lincoln researchers were examining new evidence that humans and mammoths may have co-existed in the Great Plains of the United States more than 18,000 years ago. Archaeologist Steve Holen was investigating whether mammoth bones discovered on a farm near Cozad, Neb., where a road crew was excavating for a bridge, may have been left there after humans butchered the creature. Since 1989, Holen has been excavating a site in Nebraska where he recovered unbroken rib bones and a vertebrae section in 1992. That site is about 60 miles from the 1993 discovery. Radiocarbon dating has placed the earlier bones to be 18,500 years old.

September

This Is the Big One—Geologists unearthed new evidence to suggest that a Gulf of Mexico crater discovered in 1981 more than 1,000 feet under the north coast of Mexico's Yucatan peninsula may be the largest crater on any known planet—at least of those created in the past 4 billion years or so. Originally thought to be 110 miles wide, new measurements put the crater at 185 miles wide and 15 miles deep. The news was published in the September 17 issue of *Science*. The crater was blasted out of Earth's surface 65 million years ago, and scientists think this may have been the big slam that killed 60–80% of the species—especially dinosaurs—at that time, making way for evolutionary diversification of mammals.

Top to Bottom—Purdue University civil engineering students used high-flying satellite technology from newly acquired equipment to get down-to-earth details in their classes on land surveying. The university purchased four satellite receivers—three mobile and one stationary—that pick up signals from satellites orbiting Earth. One of the main benefits of the receivers is that they provide the capability for measurement of property lines, or the distance between two points, without the necessity of two people going out to a site, peering at each other from a distance, then

This excavation site at Medicine Creek Reservoir in Nebraska has yielded mammoth bones that are 18,500 years old.

Steve Holen, archaeologist at the University of Nebraska-Lincoln, is investigating whether humans co-existed with mammoths on the Great Plains.

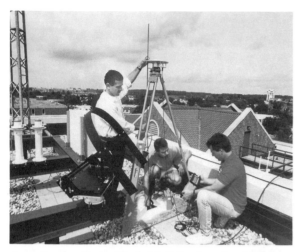

Atop Purdue University's Civil Engineering Building, graduate students (from left) Hazem Barakat, Peter Doucette, and Jeff Walker set up a satellite receiver to be used in land surveying.

writing down their measurements. "You don't need a tape measure to measure the distance between two points anymore," says Professor Boudewijn H.W. van Gelder. The receivers, which are in use by about 100 companies nationally, allow surveyors to avoid navigating around buildings, urban traffic, and natural barriers such as rivers and dense forests.

October

Not Lost in Space—Space science and space science fiction are not lost on today's young people. In a survey conducted by Purdue University over two years, more than 30,000 students in Indiana and around the Chicago, Ill., area, revealed who most influenced their science interests. At the top of the list were characters from "Star Trek: The Next Generation" and the original "Star Trek." However, also among the top 10 choices were real-life astronauts and the National Aeronautics and Space Administration.

November

Top Killer: Tobacco—Tobacco use led to an estimated 400,000 deaths in the United States in 1990, topping the list of causes of death, according to a study published in the *Journal of the American Medical Association.* Tobacco use was deadlier than alcohol, firearms, motor vehicles, and illegal drugs combined, the study revealed. Meanwhile, at the annual meeting of the American Heart Association, a 10-year study of more than 22,000 healthy male doctors was revealed, showing that smokers were twice as likely as nonsmokers to have strokes. The two studies preceded another study that was released in December, showing that more American teenagers are taking up smoking while adults are not.

December

A Tide to Stem—December 1 was World AIDS day, and countries around the globe mounted campaigns to bring attention to the disease. The World Health Organization believes that possibly 13 million people worldwide are infected by the human immunodeficiency virus, or HIV, that causes AIDS. The disease kills an average of 92 Americans a day. In the same week as World AIDS day, researchers announced two new developments, one good and one bad. First, a panel at the National Institutes of Health had approved a human genetic experiment to use a vaccine designed to boost victims' resistance. The vaccine, to be derived from a mouse virus altered to contain harmless HIV genes, is intended to help the immune system's "killer cells" to seek out and destroy cells that contain infectious HIV. The second announcement dealt what researchers feared would be a blow to the public's perception of AIDS. Doctors in Piscataway, N.J., revealed that the AIDS virus had been passed from one child to another apparently through use of a toothbrush or via a nosebleed. Doctors said this apparently was the first documented case where the virus was spread through external blood contact. Up to the point, children have contracted AIDS only through childbirth, sexual contact, or exchange of blood or blood products through abuse or transfusions. But doctors warned against public overreaction to this rare case, saying it was no reason to restrict HIV-infected children from schools. The case in point occurred between two unrelated children living in the same foster home.

1993 Science Awards

Nobel Prize in Chemistry

Kary B. Mullis, United States
Michael Smith, Canada

Mullis and Smith were recognized for separately discovering ways to speed genetic research. Mullis, of Xytronyx Inc. of San Diego, Calif., invented the polymerase chain reaction, a chemical process that allows researchers to mass produce copies of a strand of DNA. Smith, of the University of British Columbia in Vancouver, developed a technique called site-directed mutagenesis, which allows researchers to change, or reprogram, a piece of the genetic code. Both techniques allow researchers to conduct experiments that otherwise would be impossible.

Nobel Prize in Medicine

Richard A. Roberts, Great Britain
Phillip A. Sharp, United States

Roberts and Sharp were recognized for their discovery of "split genes" and for advancing research on cancer and hereditary diseases. Both working in the United States, but independently, Roberts, working a Massachusetts Institute of Technology, and Sharp, working then at Cold Spring Harbor Laboratory in New York, discovered in 1977 that genes are not necessarily continuous in a strand of DNA. Genes can be spread well-separated DNA segments. Their discovery led to the finding of the natural process of splicing, or the reassembly of the discontinuous segments. Errors in splicing can lead to hereditary diseases.

Nobel Prize in Physics

Russell A. Hulse, United States
Joseph J. Taylor, Jr., United States

Hulse and Taylor were recognized for discovering a a binary pulsar, a celestial object that provides an important test relating to Albert Einstein's theory of relativity. The pulsar is composed of a pair of unique dense, whirling objects. They discovered the pulsar while using the 300-meter radio telescope at Arecibo, Puerto Rico in 1974, while Taylor was a professor and Hulse was a student at the University of Massachusetts at Amherst. They both are now at Princeton University in New Jersey.

Albert Lasker Medical Research Award

Nancy Wexler, United States
Gunter Blobel, United States
Donald Metcalf, Australia
Paul G. Rogers, United States

Wexler, of Columbia University in New York, was recognized for leadership in research for the cause of Huntington's disease. Blobel, of Rockefeller University in New York, was recognized for his identifying codes that allow certain proteins to be recognized and pass through cells. Metcalf, of the Walter and Eliza Hall Institute of Medical Research in Melbourne, Australia, was recognized for discovering hormone-like substances, called colony-stimulating factors, which have wide use in drugs. Rogers was recognized for sponsoring and encouraging passage of health and environmental legislation during his 24 years as a U.S. congressman from Florida.

Glossary

allele alternative form of a gene that determines such characteristics as eye and hair color. Typically referred to in pairs, with one being dominant and the other recessive. One allele is inherited from each parent.

anorexia nervosa disorder in eating behavior, prevalent among females in their teens and early 20s, in which a pathological fear of gaining weight can lead to excessive weight loss and malnutrition.

base pair two nitrogenous bases, either adenine and thymine or guanine and cytosine, held together by hydrogen bonds. Bonds between base pairs unite the two strands of DNA in the form of a double helix.

big bang theory concept that all matter and energy in the universe was created when an explosion of enormous density and temperature occurred.

binge drinking unrestrained, often excessive consumption of alcoholic beverages.

bulimia disorder in eating behavior, prevalent among females, characterized by compulsive overeating followed by self-induced vomiting or diuretic abuse.

carbon dioxide colorless, odorless gas occurring in the atmosphere, consumed by plants but produced by respiration and combustion.

chlorofluorocarbon (CFC) chemical compound used as aerosol propellant, refrigerant, solvent, and in manufacturing of rigid packaging foam. In the upper atmosphere, CFCs react with ozone.

chromosome self-replicating, threadlike structure in the nucleus of cells. Each chromosome bears the genetic makeup of an organism.

clone group of cells or DNA molecules asexually produced from a single ancestor and genetically identical to that ancestor.

coaxial cable cable made of a central conductor that is surrounded by an insulator, primarily used to transmit high-frequency electronic signals.

depression in weather, an area of low atmospheric pressure, which form the main source of precipitation in mid-latitude lowland areas.

DNA deoxyribonucleic acid, the chemical molecule that encodes hereditary information in organisms.

DNA sequence the order of base pairs in a fragment of DNA, a gene, a chromosome, or a genome.

ecosystem an entire biological community and its associated environment.

eugenics practice of using genetic principles to improve the quality of human populations

extended family concept that more people, usually relatives, than just a nuclear family live in a particular household.

gene unit of heredity composed of DNA, in an ordered sequence of base pairs in a particular position on a particular chromosome. Each gene determines a particular characteristic.

genetic engineering altering the characteristics of an organism by inserting genes from another organism into its DNA.

genome sum total of genetic material in a particular organism, expressed usually in terms of the number of base pairs.

habitat place where an organism lives, characterized by physical features and plant types.

jet stream narrow, easterly flowing wind current in earth's atmosphere.

lymphocyte a white blood cell with a large nucleus, important to the function of the body's immune system.

magma hot molten material produced in earth's crust or mantle, discharged as lava during a volcanic eruption. When cooled and solidified, magma becomes igneous rock.

methane colorless, odorless gas, the main constituent of natural gas

molecule smallest unit of a chemical compound that can participate in a chemical reaction.

mutation sudden change in DNA base pair sequence that can cause an organism to differ in characteristics from ancestors or lead to susceptibility to hereditary diseases.

nucleus central core of an atom.

ozone colorless gas, produced naturally in the stratosphere, that acts as earth's screen for ultraviolet radiation

peat dark brown or black fibrous debris from plant disintegration in wetlands.

polymorphism a genetic variation occurring in a group of individuals, as opposed to a mutation, which is a genetic variation in an individual.

sex chromosomes chromosomes X and Y, that determine the sex of an individual. Human females have two X chromosomes, and human males have one X and one Y. An offspring will be female if an X chromosome is inherited from each parent; it will be male if an X chromosome is inherited from the mother and a Y chromosome is inherited from the father.

Index